Chapter

Chapter 10, # 17-23

AN INTRODUCTION TO
ASTRONOMY

THE AURORA BOREALIS

From a painting by Howard Russell Butler at Ogunquit, Maine. (*Courtesy of the American Museum of Natural History, New York*)

AN INTRODUCTION TO
ASTRONOMY

by

ROBERT H. BAKER
Author of *Astronomy*

SIXTH EDITION

D. VAN NOSTRAND COMPANY, INC.
PRINCETON, NEW JERSEY

TORONTO   LONDON
NEW YORK

D. VAN NOSTRAND COMPANY, INC.
120 Alexander St., Princeton, New Jersey (*Principal office*)
24 West 40 Street, New York 18, New York

D. VAN NOSTRAND COMPANY, LTD.
358, Kensington High Street, London, W.14, England

D. VAN NOSTRAND COMPANY (Canada), LTD.
25 Hollinger Road, Toronto 16, Canada

First Published January 1961

Reprinted August 1961, June 1962, August 1963

PREFACE TO THE SIXTH EDITION

The considerable revision of *An Introduction to Astronomy* in the new edition is intended to keep the book up to the times. The general plan and level remain as before; it is a textbook for an introductory course in astronomy without special prerequisites.

Among the developments in this active science since the preparation of the previous edition are accomplishments of the International Geophysical Year. These include prominently the launching of artificial earth-satellites and other space probes, which brought the discovery of the radiation belt around the earth, the first recording of features of the far side of the moon, and the effective photography of the extreme ultraviolet solar spectrum. Other developments have been promoted by the continuing remarkable activity in radio astronomy. The present renewed interest in problems of stellar evolution has seemed to justify the assembling of these matters in a separate new chapter.

Dr. Frank K. Edmondson has critically read the manuscript of the new edition.

ROBERT H. BAKER

Claremont, California,
December, 1960

CONTENTS

1

THE EARTH AND THE SKY

THE GLOBULAR EARTH – THE CONVENTIONAL GLOBE OF THE SKY – EFFECTS OF THE ATMOSPHERE

A relatively small planet attending the sun, which itself is one of the multitude of stars, the earth owes its importance to the fact that we live here. Here we view the celestial scene around us. In order to interpret the scene aright, we first consider the earth that looms large in the foreground. Our study of astronomy begins with the globe of the earth at the center of the apparent globe of the heavens and encompassed by the atmosphere through which we look out at the celestial bodies.

THE GLOBULAR EARTH

1·1. The Planet Earth. The earth revolves around the sun once in a year and rotates on its axis meanwhile once in a day. A dark globe illuminated by the sunlight, the earth has nearly the form of an oblate spheroid, flattened at the poles and bulged at the equator. Its diameter is about 7900 miles, and is 27 miles greater at the equator than from pole to pole. If its actual form is represented by a globe 18 inches in diameter, the equatorial diameter of the globe would be a sixteenth of an inch greater than the polar diameter and the highest mountain would rise an eightieth of an inch above sea level. The irregular surface of the earth is partly covered by water and is enveloped by an atmosphere to a height of several hundred miles.

The earth is the only planet known to have large water areas. It is likewise unique among the planets of the sun's family in having an abundance of free oxygen in its atmosphere. With these features and also with its sufficiently moderate range in surface temperature, the earth is the only planet known to us that seems inviting to life and particularly to human life. Planets attending other stars could not be detected with present means of observation. Such planets might indeed be very numerous; many of them might be abodes

1

of life and perhaps of intelligent beings who can observe and interpret the celestial scene. The opinion that life may be a widespread
and important feature of the universe is frequently heard.

1·2. The Texture of the Earth. Aside from its water areas and
atmosphere, the earth is a globe of rock that consists essentially of
two parts: the *mantle,* extending 1800 miles below the surface, and
the *core.* The *crust* is the outermost 3 to 25 miles of the mantle,
being thinner under the oceans than under the continents; its upper
levels are composed of igneous rocks, such as granite and basalt,
generally overlain with sedimentary rocks such as sandstone and
limestone, all together about 3 times as dense as water. The rest
of the mantle is composed of heavier silicates of magnesium and iron.
Knowledge of the earth's interior is obtained almost entirely from
the way it transmits earthquake waves at different depths to distant
seismographs.

The core of the earth begins about 2100 miles from the center.
Here the material behaves like a liquid in not transmitting trans-
verse earthquake waves, of the type resembling light waves. The
inner core, within 1000 miles from the center, is 18 times as dense
as water and is presumably very hot. Its composition may be mainly
nickel-iron, like the material in many meteorites; or in another view
it may be similar to the composition at higher levels but under pressure here that is high enough to collapse the molecules. The
marked difference in chemical composition between the earth and
the sun, which is composed mainly of hydrogen and helium, will
be noted in a later chapter.

1·3. The Earth as a Celestial Body. The photographs of a region
of the earth from a rocket at an altitude of 101 miles (Fig. 1·3) give
an idea of how the earth would appear from the moon with a telescope magnifying 2400 times. It would appear as a globe on which
the surface features would be visible. As indicated by the Gulf of
California at the upper left in the figure, the water areas would
contrast clearly with the land. Bright areas of snowfields and drifting clouds would add variety to the scene. The works of man would
be less clearly revealed. Observed from the moon with the unaided
eye, as the artist imagined in Fig. 1·3A, the earth would appear
among the constellations in the lunar sky as a faintly marked disk
having 4 times the apparent diameter of the moon in our skies and

going through the whole cycle of phases from new to full and back to new again.

From the nearest planets the earth would appear to the unaided eye as a bright star. From Mars it would be a fine evening and

Fig. 1·3. The Earth from the Altitude of 101 Miles. A mosaic of 4 photographs from a rocket. A large area of southwestern United States and northern Mexico is shown. (*Courtesy of Naval Research Laboratory, Washington*)

morning star accompanied by the moon as a fainter star, and both showing cycles of similar phases with the aid of a telescope. From the outermost planets the earth would be lost in the glare of the sun. From the nearest star the earth and all the other planets would be invisible with the largest telescope, and the sun would appear only as one of the stars.

1·4. Recording Apparatus Above the Earth. The initial stage in the probing of space around the earth was the launching of single-

Fig. 1·3A.   Artist's Conception of the Earth as Seen from a Crater on the Moon.   (*Courtesy of the American Museum of Natural History, New York*)

stage rockets in the late 1940's. The purpose was to investigate the atmosphere at heights not previously attained and to obtain clearer views of celestial bodies from above the most troublesome levels of the atmosphere. Among the records recovered after the rockets crashed to the ground were photographs of the earth from heights up to more than 100 miles.

The second step was a spectacular feature of the International Geophysical Year, which began in 1957 and extended through 1958. This was the launching by multistage rocket assemblies of instrument vehicles that attained nearly horizontal speeds of about 5 miles a second at heights of several hundred miles. The vehicles were thereby placed in elliptical orbits around the earth as temporary

Fig. 1·4.   Trail of 3rd-Stage Rocket of Artificial Satellite 1957-Alpha.   A
3-second exposure with a 4-inch camera on October 19, 1957.   The camera
vibrated slightly at the beginning of the exposure.   (*Photograph by
Kenneth M. Yoss, Louisiana State University*)

artificial satellites, until they spiraled down into denser atmosphere
and were burned up.   The purpose was to record conditions at the
higher altitudes and to transmit the information to stations on the
ground.   Another purpose was to obtain information about the
earth from its gravitational disturbance of the satellite orbits.

Eight successful launchings were accomplished during the period.
The most enduring of these satellites is Vanguard I (1958-Beta),
launched from Cape Canaveral, Florida, on March 17, 1958.   The
distance of the original elliptical orbit from the earth's surface
ranged from 400 to 2500 miles, and the expected lifetime is 200 years.

The third step in the program was the launching of artificial
planets; these must attain speeds of nearly 7 miles a second in order
to escape from the earth's gravitational field and to orbit the sun

as independent planets. The first of these was the Soviets' Lunik I, launched on January 2, 1959. The second was the Americans' Pioneer IV, launched on March 3, 1959; it passed the moon's orbit, and was last heard at a distance of 410,000 miles from the earth. Its path around the sun is slightly larger than the earth's orbit. The probe Lunik II, launched in September, 1959, crash-landed on the moon. Lunik III, launched on October 4, 1959, curved part way around the moon on October 7 at the distance of about 40,000 miles from it and accomplished the spectacular mission of photographing its far side.

1·5. The Earth's Magnetic Field resembles the field of a bar magnet thrust through the earth's center and inclined at a considerable angle to the axis of rotation. The north *geomagnetic pole*, where the axis of the field intersects the earth's surface, is in the vicinity of northwest Greenland 1200 miles from the north pole of rotation. The corresponding south pole is in Antarctica. These poles drift westward slowly around the earth. At any particular place the direction of the compass needle oscillates, and becomes especially unsteady during a *geomagnetic storm*.

Among the significant achievements of the International Geophysical Year was the discovery of the *Van Allen radiation belt,* a region of unexpectedly high density of electrically charged particles trapped by the magnetic field and girdling the earth. This effect was first reported by J. A. Van Allen of the State University of Iowa from studies with his associates of Geiger counts gathered by artificial satellites.

More detailed information about the radiation region was obtained by these scientists from the space probe Pioneer III, launched in December, 1958, both on its outward flight to the distance of 65,000 miles and during its return. Continuous data are being gathered by the "paddle-wheel" satellite 1959-Delta, Explorer VI. Launched on August 7, 1959, its original highly elongated orbit ranged between 26,000 and 150 miles from the earth's surface. The satellite passed through the most intense regions of the radiation belt twice in each revolution period of half a day, and should continue to do so during a considerable part of its expected lifetime of about two years.

The radiation belt has its greatest intensity in two zones at heights of 2000 and 10,000 miles above the earth's surface; it disappears almost completely at the height of 40,000 miles. The belt comes

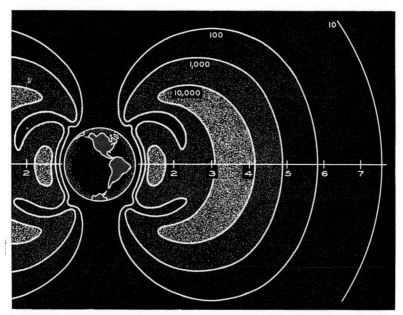

FIG. 1·5. The Van Allen Radiation Belt. Distances are given in earth-radii. Radiation intensities, represented by the contours, are in Geiger counts per second. This diagram appeared in *Sky and Telescope* for June, 1959.

closer to the earth in the high latitudes north and south where auroral displays are observed most frequently.

1·6. Positions on the Earth. One way of denoting positions on the earth's surface is with reference to natural or conventional areas. It is often satisfactory to the inquirer if we say, for example, that Havana is in Cuba or that Cleveland is in Ohio. A second way, especially where positions are required more accurately, is with reference to circles imagined on the earth and represented on globes and maps. These familiar circles are mentioned here so that the resemblance to systems of circles imagined in the sky may be noted later.

The earth's *equator* is the great circle halfway between its north and south poles. *Parallels of latitude* are small circles parallel to the equator. *Meridians* pass from pole to pole and are accordingly at right angles to the equator; they are slightly elliptical but are considered as half-circles for some purposes. The *meridian of Green-*

wich, or *prime meridian,* passes through the original site of the Royal Observatory at Greenwich, England. It crosses the equator in the Gulf of Guinea at the point where the longitude and latitude are zero.

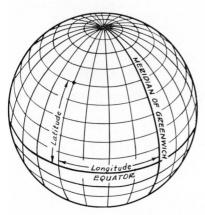

FIG. 1·6. Circles of the Terrestrial Sphere. The position of a point on the earth is denoted by its longitude and latitude.

The *longitude* of a place is its angular distance east or west from the Greenwich meridian, from 0° to 180° either way. If the longitude is 60° W, the place is somewhere on the meridian 60° west of the Greenwich meridian. The *latitude* of a place is its angular distance in degrees north or south from the equator, from 0° to 90° either way. If the latitude is 50° N, the place is somewhere on the parallel of latitude 50° north of the equator. Where the longitude and latitude are given, the position of the place is uniquely defined. As an example, the longitude of Yerkes Observatory at Williams Bay, Wisconsin, is 88° 33′ W, and the latitude is 42° 34′ N.

THE CONVENTIONAL GLOBE OF THE SKY

A very early picture of the earth and sky represents the appearance so well that it is often employed in diagrams, as in Fig. 1·11. Here the earth is imagined as a circular plane on which the sky rests like an inverted bowl. A somewhat later picture, proposed by Greek scholars in the 5th century B.C., is useful in other diagrams, as in Fig. 2·10. It shows the sky as a spherical shell surrounding a spherical earth at its center. The earth is relatively so small that it may be only a point in the diagrams at the center of the celestial sphere.

1·7. The Celestial Sphere. Although the stars are scattered through space at various distances from the earth, the difference in their distances is not perceptible to ordinary observation. All the stars seem equally remote. As we view the evening sky, we may imagine that the celestial bodies are set like jewels on the inner surface of a vast spherical shell. This *celestial sphere,* long regarded as a tangible surface, survives only as a convenient means of representing the heavens for many purposes. By this convention the stars can be shown on the surface of a globe or in projection on a plane map. Their positions are then denoted in the same ways that places are located on the globe of the earth.

The center of the celestial sphere may be the center of the earth, the observer's place on the earth's surface, the sun, or anywhere else we choose. The size of the sphere is as great as we care to imagine it. Parallel lines, regardless of their distance apart, are directed toward the same point of the remote sphere, just as the parallel rails of a track seem to converge in the distance.

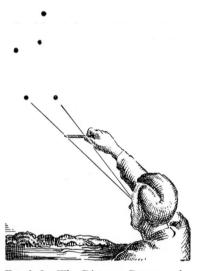

FIG. 1·8. The Distance Between the Dipper's Pointers is About 5°.

1·8. The Apparent Place of a Star is its position on the celestial sphere. It denotes the star's direction, and nothing else about its position in space. Where two stars have nearly the same direction, although one may be more remote than the other, they have nearly the same apparent place. Similarly, the apparent places of the sun, moon, and planets refer to their positions among the stars on the celestial sphere, as though all were at the same distance from us. We say that the sun is entering the constellation Leo and remark on the nearness of the moon to a bright star.

The *apparent distance* between two celestial bodies is accordingly their difference in direction; it is often called the *distance* between them, where there is no chance for ambiguity. Such distances are expressed in degrees. The distance between the Pointers of the Great Dipper is somewhat more than 5°; it is a convenient measuring stick for estimating other distances in the sky.

How may the place of a star be described so that other people will know where to look for it? One way is to specify the constellation in which the star appears. If the star is in the constellation Perseus, anyone who can recognize the different constellations knows about where this star is situated. It is like saying that New Haven is in Connecticut. A second way of denoting the apparent place of a star is with reference to circles of the celestial sphere, such as the horizon.

1·9. The Horizon. Sight along a vertical line. A cord by which a weight is suspended provides such a line when the weight comes to rest. This line leads upward to the *zenith,* the point directly overhead in the sky, and it leads downward through the earth to the *nadir,* the point directly underfoot.

The *celestial horizon,* or simply the *horizon,* is the great circle of the celestial sphere that is halfway between the zenith and nadir, and therefore 90° from each. The direction of the horizon is observed by sighting along a level surface, perhaps a table top. Evidently the positions of the zenith, nadir, and horizon among the stars are different at the same time in different parts of the world.

The *visible horizon,* the line where the earth and sky seem to meet, is rarely the same as the horizon of astronomy. On land it is usually irregular and above the celestial horizon. At sea in calm weather it is a circle that lies below the celestial horizon; this *dip* of the sea horizon increases with increasing height of the observer's eye above the level of the sea.

1·10. The Celestial Meridian. *Vertical circles* are great circles of the celestial sphere that pass through the zenith and nadir, and accordingly cross the horizon vertically. The most useful of these circles is the observer's *celestial meridian,* the vertical circle passing through the north and south poles of the heavens (2·8). The meridian determines the positions of the four *cardinal points* of the horizon: north, east, south, and west.

North and *south* are the opposite points where the celestial meridian crosses the horizon. The *east* and *west* points are midway between them; as we face north, east is to the right and west is to the left. When the cardinal points are already located, it is proper to define the celestial meridian as the vertical circle that passes through the north and south points of the horizon.

1·11. Azimuth and Altitude. The *azimuth* of a star may be measured in degrees along the horizon from the north point toward the right to the foot of the vertical circle through the star. Thus the azimuth of a star is 0° if the star is directly in the north, 90° in the east, 180° in the south, and 270° in the west. This coordinate is often reckoned around from the south point instead.

The *altitude* of a star is its distance in degrees from the horizon, measured along the vertical circle of the star. The altitude is 0° if the star is rising or setting, 45° if it is halfway from the horizon to the zenith, and 90° if it is in the zenith. The *zenith distance,* or the star's distance in degrees from the zenith, is the complement of the altitude.

This is one way of denoting positions on the celestial sphere. If, for example, a star is in azimuth 90° and altitude 45°, the star is directly east and halfway from the horizon to the ze-nith; and if it is in azi-muth 180° and altitude 30°, the star is directly south and a third of the way from the horizon to the zenith. Certain instruments operate in this system based on the horizon. The engineer's transit is an azimuth-altitude instrument. The navigator's sextant is em-ployed mainly for measuring the altitudes of celestial bod-ies.

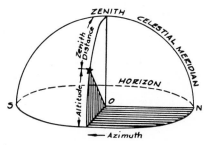

Fig. 1·11. Azimuth and Altitude of a Star. Azimuth is measured along the horizon from the north point around toward the east. Altitude is angular distance vertically above (or below) the horizon. Zenith distance is the com-plement of altitude.

Positions of stars denoted in this way are only for a particular instant and place on the earth. The azimuths and altitudes of the celestial bodies are always chang-ing with the daily motion of the heavens, and they are different at the same time in different parts of the world. More nearly perma-nent positions relative to the celestial equator rather than the hori-zon are defined in the following chapter. Meanwhile, we turn the attention to the earth's atmosphere and note particularly how it affects the view of the sky.

EFFECTS OF THE ATMOSPHERE

1·12. The Region of Clouds. The earth's atmosphere is a mixture of gases surrounding the earth. From its pressure of 15 pounds to the square inch at sea level, the mass of the entire atmosphere is calcu-lated to be 6×10^{15} tons, or somewhat less than a millionth of the

FIG. 1·12. Cirrus Clouds. (*Mount Wilson Observatory photograph*)

mass of the earth itself. The air becomes rarefied so rapidly with
increasing elevation that half of it by weight is within 3½ miles from
sea level.   The lower atmosphere is divided into two layers, the
troposphere and the stratosphere.

The *troposphere* extends to heights ranging from 10 miles at the
equator to 5 miles at the poles. It consists mainly of nitrogen and
oxygen molecules in the proportion of 4 parts to 1 by volume; it also
contains water vapor, carbon dioxide, and other gases in relatively
small amounts, as well as dust in variable quantity. The water
vapor and carbon dioxide are serviceable as a blanket to conserve
the surface heat at night. Like the glass roof of the greenhouse, they
let the sunlight through to warm the ground and then by strong
absorption in the infrared prevent rapid loss of the heat by reradia-
tion.

The troposphere is a region of turbulent air and of clouds. Fog-
like stratus clouds begin to form at an average elevation of half a
mile. Cumulus clouds rise from flat bases a mile aloft. The cirro-
cumulus clouds of the "mackerel sky" have an average height of 4
miles. Finally, the filmy cirrus clouds of ice crystals may be as high
as 7 miles or more.

1·13. The Stratosphere extends from the troposphere to a height of 45 miles. Its constituents are in about the same proportions as in the region below, except that there is less water vapor and more ozone. Ozone, having its molecules composed of three atoms of oxygen instead of two, is formed mainly by action of the sun's ultraviolet radiations on ordinary oxygen molecules.

Ozone is the most abundant at elevations of from 10 to 20 miles. It helps to protect us from the extreme ultraviolet rays of the sun, which would be injurious to life of all kinds if it could penetrate to the earth's surface. These rays are being studied in photographs of the solar spectrum taken from above the ozone levels to determine what additional information they bring about the sun itself.

The stratosphere contains one fifth of the entire air mass. Even at its upper limit it is still dense enough to make some contribution to twilight, as is known from the duration of this light. Twilight (2·19) is sunlight diffused by the air onto a region of the earth's surface where the sun has already set or has not yet risen.

1·14. The Upper Atmosphere reaches from the altitude of 45 miles to more than 500 miles. Here the rarefied gases are most exposed to impacts of high-frequency radiations and high-speed particles from outside. The molecules are largely reduced to separate atoms, and the atoms themselves are shattered into electrically charged components. The *ionosphere*, the region up to an altitude of 200 miles, contains at least four fluctuating layers where the ionized gas is concentrated. By successive reflections between these layers and the ground, radio waves can travel long distances before they are dissipated. When the layers are disrupted during a geomagnetic storm, communication by radio in the higher frequencies is disturbed.

The impacts of particles from outside on the gases of the upper atmosphere make these gases luminous in the varied colors of the aurora and in the airglow. In the lower ionosphere the resistance of the denser air to the swift flights of meteors heats these intruders to incandescence, so that they produce bright trails across the sky.

1·15. The Daytime Sky. The stars are invisible to the unaided eye in the daytime, because the atmosphere diffuses the more intense sunlight down to us from all parts of the sky. The sunlit air also conceals most of the other celestial bodies by outshining them. In addition to the sun, only the moon is conspicuous ordinarily in the daytime. The planet Venus near the times of its greatest brilliancy can be seen without a telescope as a star in the blue sky. The bright planets and stars, however, are easily visible in the daytime sky with a telescope, and with special devices they can be photographed even near the edge of the sun (Fig. 1·15).

Why is the clear sky of the daytime blue, whereas the sunlight itself is yellow? Sunlight is composed of many colors, as we observe when the light passes through a prism, or through raindrops or the spray of a waterfall; it contains all the colors of the rainbow. As sunlight comes through the atmosphere, the violet and blue light is most scattered by the air molecules, and the red light is least affected. Hence on a clear day the sky takes on the blue color of the light that is scattered down to us most profusely.

Fig. 1·15. The Star Regulus Near the Uneclipsed Sun. (*Photograph by M. Waldmeier, Arosa, Switzerland*)

When the sun is near the horizon, most of the blue of its direct light is scattered away before it can reach us through the greater thickness of air that then intervenes. Thus the sun appears reddened at its rising and setting.

1·16. Apparent Flattening of the Sun. Another aspect of the sun near the horizon is as familiar as its reddened color. There the sun sometimes appears so noticeably flattened at the top and bottom (Fig. 1·16) that it resembles a football. This appearance is caused by refraction of the sunlight in the atmosphere. Refraction of light is the change in the direction of a ray of light when it passes from one medium into another, as from rarer into denser air. The effect is described in Chapter 5 in connection with the operation of the refracting telescope.

As the light of a celestial body comes through the air, the rays are bent downward by refraction (Fig. 1·16A), so that the object appears higher in the sky than its true direction. The amount of the apparent elevation increases with the zenith distance of the object, but so gradually at first that for more than halfway to the horizon

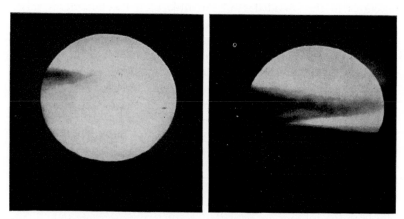

FIG. 1·16. Apparent Flattening of the Setting Sun by Refraction. (*Yerkes Observatory photographs*)

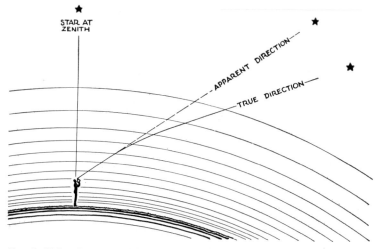

FIG. 1·16A. Apparent Elevation of a Star by Atmospheric Refraction.

the difference is not enough to be detected without a telescope. Near the horizon the increase is rapid, until the effect becomes conspicuous to the unaided eye. An object on the horizon is raised above its true place more than half a degree, or more than the apparent diameter of the sun or full moon. Because of the rapid increase in the amount of refraction as the horizon is approached, the circular disk of the sun appears elliptical; the lower edge is raised considerably more than the upper edge.

In addition to its flattened appearance the sun's disk seems to be larger near the horizon than when it is higher in the sky. This is an illusion having nothing to do with refraction. By the same illusion, the moon and the star figures, such as the Great Dipper, seem magnified near the horizon.

1·17. Twinkling of the Stars. A familiar feature of the clear night sky is the twinkling, or *scintillation,* of the stars; their light is unsteady, and the fluctuations in apparent brightness are especially noticeable near the horizon. The lower air is often turbulent; warmer currents are rising, cooler currents are descending, and horizontal movements of layers of different densities add to the confusion. Viewed through this turmoil the stars twinkle because of variable refraction and interference of their light, just as the landscape seems to be affected by the "heat waves" over the highway on a summer day.

The bright planets usually do not twinkle. They are disks instead of point sources of light, as a telescope shows. Each point of the disk may twinkle like a star, but the different parts do not do so in unison because their rays take slightly different paths through the disturbed air. Similarly, the moon shines with a steady light.

Viewed with a telescope, the stars appear blurred when the air is especially turbulent. The rays in each beam of starlight that enters the telescope have been diverted from perfect parallelism, so that they are not brought to the same focus by the lens. Features of the moon and planets also appear blurred in these conditions. The *astronomical seeing* is bad, and there is not much to be done about it except to wait for better seeing.

1·18. Lunar and Solar Halos. Bright rings that sometimes appear around the moon and sun have no special astronomical significance; but they are noticed and commented on by watchers of the skies and are fine examples of refraction effects in the atmosphere. The rings are produced by ice needles and snowflakes in the cirrus and cirro-

Fig. 1·18. A Solar Halo. (*Photograph by F. Quénisset*)

stratus clouds. These 6-sided crystals refract the moonlight and sunlight, concentrating it in certain directions. Although many effects are possible, the most common one is a single ring having a radius of 22° around the moon or sun. The ring often shows rainbow colors, with the red on the inner, sharper edge the most prominent.

"Moon dogs" and "sun dogs" are two enlargements of the ring on opposite sides of the moon or sun. These appear when many snowflakes in the clouds float with their bases horizontal. A second ring having a radius of 46° and parts of other rings are seen less frequently. The impression that the appearance of a ring around the moon or sun gives warning of an approaching storm has some basis in the fact that the filmy clouds which form the halos are likely to fly ahead of storm clouds.

1·19. The Aurora and the Airglow. Two natural illuminations of the night sky in addition to the light of the celestial bodies are the aurora and the airglow. The *aurora* is characterized in middle northern latitudes by a luminous arch across the northern sky, its apex in the direction of the magnetic pole. Rays like searchlight beams rise above the arch, drifting, dissolving, and reforming, and draperies may appear in other parts of the sky. Green is the usual color, but red and yellow are often seen as well. Especially in latitudes farther north, ribbons spread across the sky (Fig. 1·19). The aurora also appears in the southern hemisphere.

Auroral displays are manifestations of geomagnetic storms. They are produced in the ionosphere primarily by the influx of electrified particles from the sun, which are trapped in the earth's magnetic field. The displays are most intense in two zones centered around 23° from those poles. South of latitude 35° in our hemisphere, or south of about a line through San Francisco, Memphis, and Atlanta, they appear only during geomagnetic storms of considerable intensity.

FIG. 1·19. The Aurora in Alaska. *(Photograph by the Geophysical Institute, University of Alaska)*

The *airglow* is an illumination suffused over the sky. Its light is also caused by energy coming originally from the sun. It is faintest overhead and brightest not far from the horizon, which shows that the glow is from the atmosphere. Undetected by the eye, it is effectively studied with the photoelectric cell and color filters. Because it is always present, it is the greater menace to celestial photography. The airglow fogs the astronomers' photographs, placing a severe limit to the faintest objects that can be reached by increasing the exposure times.

QUESTIONS ON CHAPTER 1

1. If the form of the 7900-mile earth is represented correctly by an 18-inch globe, explain that the equatorial diameter of the globe would be $\frac{1}{16}$ inch greater than the polar diameter and that the highest mountain would rise $\frac{1}{80}$ inch.

2. Account for the bright trail of the artificial satellite in the photograph (Fig. 1·4). Why must the space probes be tracked more often by radio reception rather than by photography?

3. State the longitude and latitude of: (a) the earth's north pole; (b) a point on the equator; (c) the place where you are.

4. The moon's distance from us is much less than the distances of stars. What is meant by the statement that the moon is in the constellation Taurus?

5. Compare the celestial horizons as seen from an airplane and from the ground below it; the visible horizons.

6. Describe two characteristics of: (a) the troposphere; (b) the stratosphere; (c) the ionosphere.

7. What is the true altitude of a star: (a) when it appears on the horizon? (b) when it appears directly overhead? How is the daily duration of sunshine affected by atmospheric refraction?

8. Account for the apparent reddening, flattening, and enlargement of the sun near the horizon.

9. The bright planets generally shine with a steady light while the stars around them are twinkling. Explain.

10. Distinguish between the aurora and the airglow.

REFERENCES

Jeffries, Harold, *The Earth*. Its origin, history, and physical constitution. Third edition. Cambridge University Press, 1952.

Kuiper, Gerard P., editor. *The Earth as a Planet*. University of Chicago Press, 1955.

Sky and Telescope has had monthly articles on *Observing the Satellites,* which give news about artificial satellites and other space probes.

2

THE EARTH'S DAILY ROTATION

EFFECTS ON THE EARTH — APPARENT ROTATION OF THE HEAVENS

The distinction between rotation and revolution is more definite in astronomy than in some other sciences. _Rotation is turning on an axis, whereas revolution is motion in an orbit._ Thus the earth rotates daily and revolves yearly around the sun. In this chapter we consider the earth's rotation and some of its effects.

The earth rotates from west to east on an axis joining its north and south poles. Among the effects of the rotation are the directions of prevailing winds and cyclones, the behavior of the Foucault pendulum, the bulge of the equator, and the apparent rotation of the heavens.

EFFECTS ON THE EARTH

2·1. The Coriolis Effect. The speed of the earth's rotation becomes less with increasing distance from the equator. The speed exceeds 1000 miles an hour at the equator; it is reduced to 800 miles an hour in the latitude of New York, 500 miles an hour in southern Alaska, and so on, until at the pole there is no turning at all.

Consider an air current moving north in the northern hemisphere and carried eastward all the while by the earth's rotation. Because it is going from a latitude of faster rotation to one of slower rotation, the current forges ahead and is accordingly deflected to the right. If the current is moving south instead, it is going from a place of slower to one of faster rotation, and is again deflected to the right. Consider next a current moving either north or south in the southern hemisphere, and we see that it is deflected to the left. Thus we have the following rule which applies to all these horizontal motions.

The earth's rotation deflects moving objects to the right in the northern hemisphere and to the left in the southern hemisphere.

This deflection is known as the *Coriolis acceleration* after the French scientist who demonstrated it more than a century ago.

2·2. Deflection of Surface Winds. The global circulation of the atmosphere is generated by energy in the sunshine which heats the

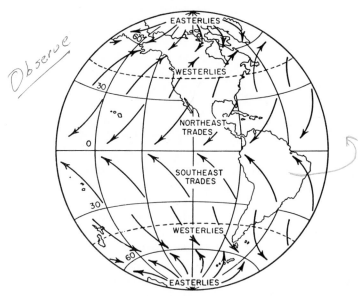

Fig. 2·2. Prevailing Surface Winds. The moving air is deflected to the right in the northern hemisphere and to the left in the southern hemisphere.

air most intensely in the tropics. The warmed air rises there and flows toward the poles. Cooled at high elevations the air descends, notably at latitudes 30° where it flows north and south over the surface. By our rule these surface winds are deflected to the right in the northern hemisphere and to the left in the southern hemisphere (Fig. 2·2). Thus we have the easterly trade winds of the tropics and the prevailing westerly winds of the temperate zones. The easterly winds of the frigid zones are an associated effect.

Ocean currents follow the prevailing winds in a general way, but are complicated by the land barriers. We see the effect of our rule clearly in the Gulf Stream, which flows initially from the southwest.

2·3. Eddies in the Air Circulation, such as cyclones and hurricanes, show the effect of the rule in the directions of their whirling. Consider a cyclone in the northern hemisphere, where the air is locally

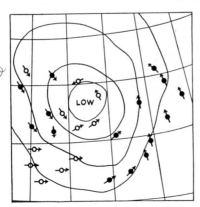

rising. The surface currents flowing into this area of low pressure are deflected to the right and reach its center indirectly. Thus the whole area, perhaps 1500 miles in diameter, is set whirling in the counterclockwise direction, or contrary to the direction taken by the hands of a clock. In the anticyclones, or "highs" of our hemisphere, the air is descending and flowing out over the surface; these accordingly whirl in the clockwise direction. The directions of cyclones in the southern hemisphere are clockwise, and those of anticyclones are counterclockwise.

FIG. 2·3. Cyclones in the Northern Hemisphere Whirl Counterclockwise.

The importance of the Coriolis effect extends beyond its meteorological consequences. Correction for the effect is required in long-range artillery fire control and to the altitudes of celestial objects as observed with the bubble octant by the air navigator.

2·4. The Foucault Pendulum. A convincing proof of the earth's rotation was first demonstrated to the public by the French physicist Foucault, in 1851. Under the dome of the Panthéon in Paris, Foucault freely suspended a heavy iron ball by a wire more than 200 feet long and started it swinging. Those who watched the demonstration saw the plane of the oscillation slowly turn in the clockwise direction. They were observing in fact the changing direction of the meridian caused by the earth's rotation relative to the direction of the swing of the pendulum. This celebrated demonstration is often repeated in some of the planetariums and elsewhere.

The rate of change in the direction of the swing of this pendulum depends on the latitude. At the equator, where the direction of the meridian in space is not altered by the earth's rotation, there is no change at all in the direction of the pendulum. In the latitude of Chicago the rate of change is 10° an hour. At the pole it is 15° an hour, so that the plane of the oscillation turns completely around in a day.

Another effect of the earth's rotation is seen in the behavior of the gyrocompass, where the rotor automatically brings its axis into

FIG. 2·4. The Foucault Pendulum.

the plane of the geographical meridian, and thus shows the direction of true north. This valuable aid to the navigator would not operate if the earth did not rotate. Still another effect is the bulging of the earth's equator.

2·5. Centrifugal Effect of the Earth's Rotation.

The equator is more than 13 miles farther from the earth's center than are the poles; in this sense it is downhill toward the poles. Why then does not all the water of the oceans assemble in these lowest regions around the poles? Why does the Mississippi River flow "uphill" toward the equator? The reason is found in the earth's rotation.

All parts of the rotating earth have a tendency to move away from the axis. It is the same centrifugal effect that urges a stone to fly away when it is whirled around at the end of a cord. Part of the effect of the earth's rotation on an object at its surface is to slide the object toward the equator (Fig. 2·5). The earth has adjusted its form accordingly, so that the upslope toward the equator offsets the tendency to slide toward it.

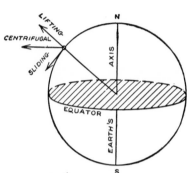

FIG. 2·5. The Earth's Rotation Tends to Propel an Object Toward the Equator and to Diminish Its Weight.

The second component of the centrifugal effect of the earth's rotation lifts the object, so that its weight is diminished. An object weighing 190 pounds at the pole, where there is no centrifugal effect, becomes a pound lighter at the equator, where this effect is greatest, although part of the decrease in weight here is due to the greater distance of the equator from the earth's center. If the period of the rotation should decrease to 1 hour and 24 minutes by our present clocks, an object at the equator would weigh nothing at all. At this excessive rate of rotation the earth would be unstable and liable to disruption.

2·6. Wanderings of the Poles. When the positions of places on the earth are determined repeatedly with high accuracy, it is found that their latitudes do not remain the same. This *variation of latitude* has been observed for many years at a number of international latitude stations distributed over the world, and these results tell us how the equator and therefore the poles have been wandering.

The wanderings of the poles are caused by shiftings of the earth relative to its axis, so that the poles change slightly on the surface. One variation is seasonal, having a period of a year; the other is an oscillation in a period of 14 months. The resulting motion of the poles is irregular and limited. Neither pole is withdrawing much more than 40 feet from its average place; all its wanderings are now confined to an area smaller than that of a baseball diamond. Some scientists suggest the possibility of wider migrations in the past, which might have caused the marked changes in the climates in geological times.

2·7. Changing Period of the Earth's Rotation. The earth's rotation has long set the standard for our timekeeping. The consequent daily rotation of the heavens has provided the master clock by which all other clocks have been corrected. The earth-clock was formerly considered entirely reliable; the period of the earth's rotation was supposed to be uniform, until it finally proved to be otherwise.

Suppose that someone begins with the idea that his watch is always right. As the days go by he is surprised to find that everything is getting ahead of time by his watch. He misses trains that seem to depart too early; the sun rises before it should; the town clock runs faster and faster. Presently he decides that his watch must be running slow. It is so with the earth's rotation. Periodic occurrences, such as the revolution of the moon around the earth, are forging ahead of regular schedules timed by the earth-clock. We conclude that the period of the earth's rotation is increasing, and also that the increase is not perfectly regular.

By comparing the recorded times of early eclipses with the calculated times when they would have occurred if the earth had been rotating uniformly all the while, astronomers have concluded that the length of the day is increasing at the rate of $0^s.0016$ in a century. This would mean that the earth-clock has run slow $3\frac{1}{4}$ hours during the past 20 centuries. The tides in the oceans have been regarded as the brakes that are so reducing the speed of the rotation. They are caused chiefly by the moon's attraction; and they follow the moon around the earth once in a month, while the earth itself rotates under the tide figure once in a day. Much uncertainty, however, remains in the amount of the increase of the period, which should be improved with the present more precise means of observing the moon's motion (6·8).

There are also sudden and not as yet accurately predictable variations in the length of the day. The earth's rotation has run off schedule both fast and slow as much as half a minute, after allowance for the tidal retardation is made. Small periodic variations mainly annual and semiannual, are detected by the best clocks; these are ascribed to winds and tides, and are reliably repeated.

APPARENT ROTATION OF THE HEAVENS

2·8. The Celestial Poles. The stars rise and set, circling westward daily and keeping precisely in step as they go around. The patterns of stars, such as the Great Dipper, look the same night after night and year after year. It is as though the stars were set on the inner surface of a rotating hollow globe. This celestial sphere seems to turn daily from east to west around an axis which is the axis of the earth's rotation prolonged to the sky.

The *celestial poles* are the two opposite points on the celestial sphere toward which the earth's axis is directed, and around which the stars circle. The north celestial pole is directly in the north, from a third of the way to halfway up in the sky for observers in different parts of the United States. The south celestial pole is similarly depressed below the south horizons of these places.

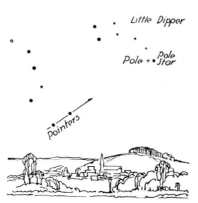

FIG. 2·8. The Great Dipper's Pointers Show the Way to the Celestial Pole.

The Pointers of the Great Dipper (Fig. 2·8) direct the eye to Polaris, the *pole star,* at the end of the Little Dipper's handle. This moderately bright star is within 1°, or about two moon-breadths, of the pole itself. It is also the *north star* which shows nearly the direction of north. The south celestial pole is not similarly marked by any bright star in its vicinity.

2·9. The Celestial Equator. Just as the earth's equator is halfway between the terrestrial poles, so the *celestial equator* is halfway between the north and south celestial poles. This circle crosses the horizon at its east and west points at an angle which is the complement of the latitude. Thus in latitude 40° N, or the latitude of Philadelphia, the celestial equator is inclined 50° to the horizon and has an altitude of 50° at its highest point in the south.

Hour circles in the sky are like meridians on the earth. They are half circles which connect the celestial poles and are therefore perpendicular to the equator. Unlike the circles of the horizon system which are stationary relative to the observer, these circles are generally considered as sharing in the rotation of the celestial sphere. Where 24 hour circles are imagined equally spaced, they coincide successively with the observer's celestial meridian at intervals of an hour. With reference to the celestial equator and its associated circles, the position of a celestial body is given by its right ascension and declination, which resemble terrestrial longitude and latitude.

2·10. Right Ascension and Declination. The *right ascension* of a star is its angular distance measured eastward along the celestial equator from the vernal equinox to the hour circle through the

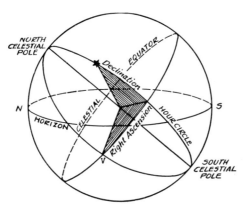

FIG. 2·10. Right Ascension and Declination. Right ascension is measured eastward from the vernal equinox along the celestial equator. Declination is measured north or south from the equator.

star. (The vernal equinox is the point where the sun's center crosses the celestial equator at the beginning of spring.) Right ascension is expressed in time more often than in angular units. Because a complete rotation of the heavens, through 360°, is made in 24 hours, 15° is equivalent to 1 hour, and 1° to 4 minutes of time. Thus a star's right ascension may be given as 60° or 4 hours.

The *declination* of a star is the star's distance in degrees north or south from the celestial equator, measured along an hour circle through the star. The declination is marked either N or with a plus sign if the star is north of the equator, and S or with a minus sign if it is south.

As an example, the right ascension of the star Arcturus is 14^h 14^m and its declination is 19° 23′ N. The star is accordingly 213° 30′ east of the vernal equinox and 19° 23′ north of the celestial equator. Notice that right ascension is measured only eastward, whereas terrestrial longitude is measured both east and west. The approximate right ascensions and declinations of the brighter stars can be read from the star maps in Chapter 11.

2·11. Hour Angle is often employed in the equator system instead of right ascension. The local *hour angle* of a star is reckoned westward along the equator from the observer's celestial meridian through 360° or 24 hours. Unlike right ascension, which remains nearly unchanged during the day, the hour angle of a star increases at the rate of 15° an hour and, at the same instant, has different values in different longitudes.

Hour angle is frequently used in directing a telescope to a celestial object by means of a graduated circle; the hour angle of the object is found by subtracting its right ascension from the sidereal time (4·2). Hour angle also has much use in celestial navigation. The Greenwich hour angles of celestial bodies are tabulated for this purpose at convenient intervals of the day throughout the year in nautical and air almanacs.

2·12. Latitude Equals Altitude of Celestial Pole. The latitude of a place on the earth is its distance in degrees from the equator. For our present purpose it is more conveniently defined as the number of degrees the vertical line at the place is inclined to the plane of the equator, or to the plane of the celestial equator. This vertical line is directed toward the observer's zenith.

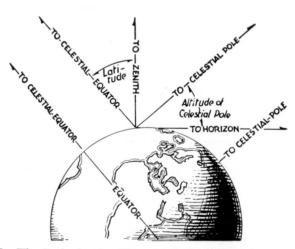

Fig. 2·12. The Latitude of a Place on the Earth Equals the Altitude of the Celestial Pole at That Place. Astronomical latitude is defined as the angle between the vertical line and the equator plane. This angle equals the altitude of the celestial pole because both are complements of the angle between the pole and the zenith.

In Fig. 2·12 we see that the observer's latitude is the same as the declination of his zenith. This angle equals the altitude of the north celestial pole, because both are complements of the same angle between the directions of the zenith and pole. Thus, *the latitude of a place equals the altitude of the celestial pole at that place.* In examining the figure we recall that parallel lines are directed toward the same point of the heavens.

The rule determines the *astronomical latitude*. This observed latitude depends on the vertical line and is affected by anything that alters the vertical. A mountain near the place of observation would cause the plumb line to incline a little in its direction. Such "station errors" may make a difference of nearly a minute of arc in the latitude, although they are usually much smaller. *Geographical latitude* is the observed latitude corrected for station error; it is the latitude that would be observed if the earth were perfectly smooth and uniform.

2·13. The Latitude of a Place on the earth is determined by the rule of the preceding section. If there were a bright star precisely

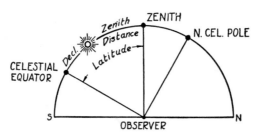

Fig. 2·13. The Latitude of a Place Equals the Zenith Distance of a Celestial Body at Its Upper Transit (4·1) of the Meridian of the Place Plus Its Declination at That Time.

at the celestial pole, the latitude could be found simply by measuring the altitude of that star. The pole star itself may be employed if correction is made for its distance from the pole. More often the observations are made to determine the declination of the zenith, which we have seen is the same as the latitude. A simple calculation gives the required value when the altitude of a celestial body is observed at its upper transit of the celestial meridian.

Suppose that a navigator sights the sun at its crossing of the meridian south of the zenith and determines its true altitude as

51° 10', so that its zenith distance is 38° 50'. Suppose that the sun's declination obtained from an almanac for the time of the sight is 22° 0' N. The latitude equals the sun's zenith distance plus its declination (Fig. 2·13); it is accordingly 38° 50' + 22° 0' = 60° 50' N. If the sun had crossed the meridian the same distance north of the zenith, the zenith distance would receive the minus sign, and the latitude would have been 16° 50' S. In operations of the Coast and Geodetic Survey and in some observatories the latitude is obtained very accurately by observing stars with a special instrument, the zenith telescope.

Let us now turn the latitude rule around. When the latitude of a place is given, we know the altitude of the north celestial pole at that place and how the daily courses of the stars are related to the horizon.

2·14. At the Pole the Stars Never Set. At the north pole, latitude 90°, the north celestial pole is in the zenith, and the stars go around it daily in circles parallel to the horizon. Stars north of the celestial equator never set, while those south of the equator never come into view. In this statement and some others we avoid confusion by referring to the true positions of the stars and not as they are elevated by atmospheric refraction (1·16). The sun, moon, and planets rise and set at the north pole whenever they cross the celestial equator. The sun rises about March 21 and sets about September 23. The moon rises and sets about once a month.

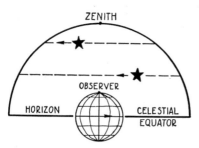

Fig. 2·14. At the Pole the Stars Circle Parallel to the Horizon.

At the south pole everything is reversed. There the south celestial pole stands in the zenith, and the stars of the south celestial hemisphere never set. The long period of sunshine begins with the rising of the sun about September 23.

2·15. At the Equator All Stars Rise and Set. Here, where the latitude is zero, the altitude of the celestial pole is zero by our rule. The north celestial pole is situated at the north point of the horizon, and even the pole star now rises and sets as it circles near this

pole. The south celestial pole is at the south point. The celestial
equator passes directly overhead from east to west.

At the equator, all parts of
the heavens are brought into
view by the apparent daily rotation. All stars rise and set.
Their courses cross the horizon
at right angles and are bisected
by it, so that every star is above
the horizon 12 hours daily if
we neglect refraction. This applies to the sun as well; the
duration of sunshine is 12 hours
at the equator throughout the
year.

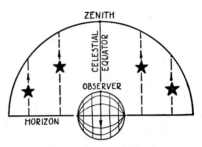

FIG. 2·15. At the Equator the
Daily Courses of the Stars Are Perpendicular to the Horizon.

2·16. The Heavens Turn Obliquely for Us who live between the
pole and equator. Suppose that we are observing from latitude
40° north. Here the north celestial pole is 40° above the north
point of the horizon, and the south pole is the same distance below
the south point. The celestial equator arches across from the east
point to the west, inclined so that its highest point is 40° south of

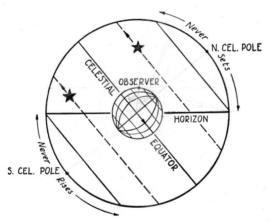

FIG. 2·16. For Observers Between the Pole and the Equator the Daily
Courses of the Stars Cross the Horizon Obliquely.

the zenith. The daily courses of the stars are likewise inclined toward the south. Half the celestial equator is above the horizon.

Northward from the equator the daily courses of the stars come up more and more above the horizon until they are entirely above it. Southward from the celestial equator they are depressed more and more until they disappear completely.

In this oblique arrangement the celestial sphere is divided into three parts: (1) a circular area around the elevated celestial pole contains the stars that never set; (2) a similar area around the depressed pole contains the stars that never rise; (3) the remaining band of the heavens symmetrical with the celestial equator contains the stars that rise and set. Hence, in latitude 40° N the area of the heavens which is always above the horizon is within a radius of 40° around the north celestial pole, and the area which never comes into view is within a radius of 40° around the south celestial pole. The remainder of the heavens, a band extending 50° on either side of the celestial equator, rises and sets.

If we travel north, the celestial poles move farther from the horizon. The polar areas grow larger until they come together when the pole is reached; there as we have seen no stars rise and set. If we travel south, the celestial poles approach the horizon. The polar areas grow smaller until they disappear when the equator is reached, where all stars rise and set.

2·17. Circumpolar Stars go around the celestial poles without crossing the horizon. These stars either never set or never rise, because they are closer to one of the celestial poles than the distance of that pole from the horizon, a distance that is equal to the observer's latitude. We accordingly make this rule about them for observers in the northern hemisphere:

A star having a distance from the north celestial pole (90° minus the star's declination) less than the latitude of a place never sets at that place. A star having a distance from the south celestial pole less than the latitude never rises.

Suppose that the observer is in latitude 40° N, and consider as an example the bowl of the Great Dipper, declination about 58° N. It never sets here because its north polar distance of 32° is less than the latitude. As a second example, consider the star Canopus, declination 53° S. This brilliant star is not visible in latitude 40° N because its south polar distance of 37° is less than the latitude.

2·18. The Midnight Sun. Consider the sun on June 22; on this date when the sun is farthest north of the equator, the declination

FIG. 2·17. The Heavens Turn Obliquely for Us. Trails of stars approaching their setting. The sky is illuminated with zodiacal light (9·10).

FIG. 2·17A. Circumpolar Star Trails. The exposure time was one hour. The bright trail a little below the pole is that of Polaris.

(Yerkes Observatory photographs)

FIG. 2·18. The Midnight Sun. The exposures were made at intervals of 20 minutes. *(Photographed at Etah, Greenland, by Donald B. MacMillan)*

of its center is $23\frac{1}{2}°$ N, so that its north polar distance is $66\frac{1}{2}°$. How far north must we go on June 22 to see the sun circle around the pole without setting? According to our rule we must go beyond latitude $66\frac{1}{2}°$. When we take into account the refraction effect and the size of the sun's disk, however, we expect to see the sun at midnight on this date as far south as $65\frac{3}{4}°$ N.

The *midnight sun* is seen wherever the sun becomes circumpolar. In far northern latitudes the sun in summer enters the area of the heavens that is always above the horizon; and it becomes circumpolar in far southern latitudes at the opposite season.

2·19. The Duration of Twilight. The gradual transition between daylight and the darkness of night, which we call *twilight,* occurs during the time that the sun, after its setting and before its rising for us, can shine on the atmosphere above us. What is said here about the evening twilight applies in reverse to the morning twilight.

Civil twilight ends when the sun's center has sunk 6° below the horizon. Then it is no longer possible without artificial illumination to continue outdoor operations that require good light. *Nautical twilight* ends when the sun's center is 12° below the horizon. Then the sea horizon is likely to be too dim for the navigator's sextant sights. *Astronomical twilight* ends when the sun's center is 18° below the horizon; by that time the fainter stars have come out overhead. The times of sunset and sunrise and the duration of twilight can be found in some of the almanacs for any date and latitude.

The duration of twilight varies with the time of year and the latitude. Twilight is shortest at the equator where the sun descends vertically and so reaches the limiting distance below the horizon in the shortest time. Astronomical twilight lasts about an hour at the equator, and an hour and a half or more in the latitude of New York. On June 22 it does not end at all north of 48° N, about the latitude of Victoria. Civil twilight persists from sunset to sunrise on this date from latitude 60°, or the latitude of Oslo, Norway, to nearly 66°, where the midnight sun is seen.

QUESTIONS ON CHAPTER 2

1. Explain the deflection of moving objects to the right in the northern hemisphere and to the left in the southern hemisphere. State 3 familiar examples.

2. Show that the behavior of the Foucault pendulum demonstrates the earth's rotation.

3. Why does an object weigh less at the equator than at the poles?

4. How is it possible to determine that the earth's rotation is not quite uniform?

5. Name the celestial circle or coordinate that corresponds to each of the following definitions:

(a) The circle halfway between the celestial poles.
(b) Any circle passing through both celestial poles.
(c) Angular distance north or south from the celestial equator.
(d) Angular distance measured eastward from the vernal equinox along the celestial equator.

6. In what respect does right ascension differ from terrestrial longitude?

7. From what places on the earth would the following situations be true in the absence of atmospheric refraction?

(a) The celestial equator coincides with the horizon.
(b) All parts of the celestial sphere rise and set.
(c) The south celestial pole is in the zenith.
(d) The daily duration of sunshine is 12 hours throughout the year.
(e) The daily circles of the stars are parallel to the horizon.

8. Which of the situations in Question 7 are modified by atmospheric refraction?

9. An observer sights a star at its crossing of the celestial meridian south of the zenith and finds that its altitude is 62° 20′. The star's declination is +12° 10′. Explain that the observer's latitude is 39° 50′ N.

10. In latitude 30° S, what part of the celestial sphere: (a) never sets? (b) never rises?

11. Which of the following stars never set, rise and set, or never rise for an observer in latitude 40° N: Arcturus, declination +19°; Canopus, −53°; Dubhe, +62°; Alpha Crucis, −63°?

12. (a) Distinguish between civil and astronomical twilight. (b) Why is the duration of twilight shortest at the equator?

3

THE EARTH'S ANNUAL REVOLUTION

THE EARTH REVOLVES – THE EARTH'S PRECESSION – THE SEASONS

While the stars are circling westward around us as though they were set on the rotating celestial sphere, the sun gradually lags behind. The sun shifts slowly toward the east against the turning background of the heavens. If we could readily view the stars in the daytime sky, we would then see that the sun moves eastward about twice its breadth in a day, and that it circles completely around the heavens in this direction in the course of a year. Although it is not easily possible to observe the sun's progress directly, this movement was recognized and charted by early watchers of the skies, for it is clearly revealed by the steady procession of the constellations toward the west from night to night at the same hour through the year.

3·1. Annual March of the Constellations. At the same hour from night to night as the seasons go around, the constellations march

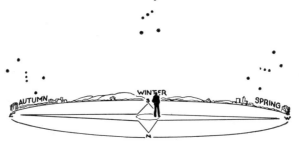

Fig. 3·1. Orion in the Evening at Different Seasons.

slowly across the evening sky and down past the sun's place below the horizon. If we look at a particular group of stars at the same time night after night, we eventually observe this westward movement. We notice, for example, Orion's part in the unending parade; it is the brightest and among the most familiar of the constellations.

Orion comes up over the east horizon early in the evening in the late autumn, a tilted oblong figure with three stars in line near its center. At the approach of spring this constellation appears up-ended in the south. As spring advances, Orion comes out in the twilight farther and farther west, its oblong now inclined the other way, until it follows the sun too closely to be visible. Then at dawn in midsummer Orion appears in the east again, on the other side of the sun.

This westward procession of Orion and other constellations past the sun's place shows that the sun is moving toward the east among the stars. Its motion is a consequence but not a proof of the earth's annual revolution around the sun. The same effect would occur if the sun revolved around the earth, as most people before the time of Copernicus supposed that it did.

THE EARTH REVOLVES

Everyone knows today that the earth revolves around the sun. We learn this fact at an early age and accept it as an item of common knowledge. We are told, too, that the sun is something like 93 million miles away, so that the earth must be speeding along at the average rate of 18½ miles a second to go all the way around in a year. There is nothing in our everyday experiences, however, to convince us that the earth is moving in this way. Displacements of the stars that prove the earth's revolution beyond reasonable doubt are too minute to be detected without a telescope. The aberration of starlight is an example.

3·2. Aberration of Starlight. Raindrops fall vertically when there is no wind. Yet they seem to come down slanting to one who walks rapidly through the rain, and still more slanting if he runs instead. As the observer's speed increases, the place from which the raindrops seem to fall shifts farther in the direction he is going. This is the aberration of raindrops.

There is a similar effect on the rays of light from a star. The *aberration of starlight* is the apparent displacement of the star in the direction toward which the observer is moving. It is a much smaller displacement, to be sure; starlight comes down so much faster than the rain that its direction is not appreciably altered by ordinary speeds. Even the earth's swift flight around the sun displaces the stars only 20½″ at the most, an amount too slight to be detected by the unaided eye. This displacement of the stars from their true positions is readily observed with the telescope; and here we have convincing evidence of the earth's revolution.

FIG. 3·2. Aberration of Raindrops and Starlight. Just as raindrops come down slanting to one who is running, so the stars are apparently displaced always ahead of us as we go around the sun. Each star seems to describe a small orbit around its true position.

If the earth is taking us around the sun, the direction of the revolution must change continuously. The direction of the star's aberration displacement must also change continuously, for it is always in the direction of the observer's motion. If the earth revolves once in a year, the stars must seem to move in small annual orbits around their true places. This is what they seem to be doing, as the telescope shows.

The aberration of starlight was first observed by the English astronomer Bradley who explained its important meaning in 1727, nearly two centuries after the death of Copernicus. Henceforth, there could be no reasonable doubt that the earth revolves around the sun. In a later chapter (12·1) we consider the parallax effect of the earth's revolution.

3·3. The Earth's Distance from the Sun Varies.

If the earth's orbit around the sun were a circle with the sun at its center, the earth's distance from the sun would remain the same throughout the year, so that the sun would always appear to be of the same size. Although the difference is not noticeable to the unaided eye, the sun's apparent diameter does vary during the year. It is greatest early in January and least early in July; the difference between the two is one thirtieth of the average diameter./Thus the earth is nearest the sun about the first of January and farthest from the sun about the first of July, which might seem surprising to anyone who had forgotten that the seasons are not caused by the earth's varying distance from the sun./

The earth's distance from the sun averages 92,900,000 miles; it varies from 91,300,000 to 94,500,000 miles.

3·4. The Earth's Orbit Is an Ellipse of small eccentricity with the sun at one focus. The terms used in this statement are defined as follows:

The *ellipse* is a plane curve such that the sum of the distances from any point on its circumference to two points within, called

FIG. 3·4. How the Ellipse Can Be Drawn.

the *foci*, is constant and equal to the longest diameter, or *major axis*, of the ellipse. The definition suggests a way to draw an ellipse (Fig. 3·4); and the drawing of several ellipses in this way makes clear the significance of the eccentricity.

The *eccentricity* of the ellipse denotes its degree of flattening. It is represented by the fraction of the major axis that lies between the two foci. If the eccentricity is zero, the foci are together at the center and the curve is a circle. The ellipse flattens more and more as the eccentricity increases, until at eccentricity 1 the figure becomes a straight line. The earth's orbit is nearly a circle; its eccentricity is .017, or $\frac{1}{60}$. If Fig. 3·4A were drawn to scale, the sun's center would be $\frac{1}{50}$ inch from the center of the ellipse, and the ellipse itself could be scarcely distinguished from a circle.

Perihelion and *aphelion* are the points on the earth's orbit which are respectively nearest and farthest from the sun; they are at opposite ends of the major axis. The earth arrives at perihelion about January 1 and at aphelion about July 1, as we have noticed before. These times move back and forth a little in the calendar and also

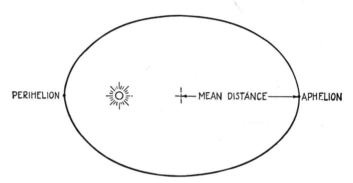

Fig. 3·4A. The Earth's Orbit. It is an ellipse of small eccentricity (much exaggerated in the diagram) having the sun at one focus.

advance an average of 25 minutes a year, because the major axis of the earth's orbit moves slowly around the sun in the direction of the earth's revolution. The earth's *mean distance,* 92,900,000 miles, from the sun is half the length of the major axis, or the average of the perihelion and aphelion distances. The earth is at this distance from the sun in early April and again in early October.

3·5. The Ecliptic. Thus the earth revolves eastward around the sun once in a year and rotates meanwhile on its axis in the same direction once in a day. The earth's axis is inclined $23\frac{1}{2}°$ from the perpendicular to the plane of its orbit, or we may say that the earth's equator is inclined $23\frac{1}{2}°$ to the plane of the orbit. This determines the relation (Fig. 3·5) between the celestial equator and the path the sun seems to describe eastward around the heavens as we revolve around the sun.

The *ecliptic* is the sun's apparent annual path around the celestial sphere; it is a great circle inclined $23\frac{1}{2}°$ to the celestial equator.

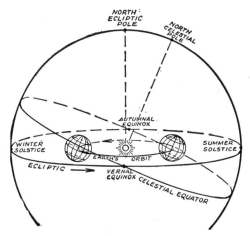

FIG. 3·5. The Celestial Equator Is Inclined to the Ecliptic. It is inclined by the same amount that the earth's equator is inclined to the plane of its orbit around the sun.

The ecliptic is in the plane of the earth's orbit, and the celestial equator is in the plane of the earth's equator. The *north and south ecliptic poles* are 90° from the ecliptic, and are respectively 23½° from the north and south celestial poles. The north ecliptic pole (R.A. 18ʰ, Decl. 66½° N) is in the constellation Draco (Map 1, Chapter 11).

3·6. The Equinoxes and Solstices. The *equinoxes* are the two opposite points of the celestial sphere where the ecliptic crosses the celestial equator. They are so named because days and nights are said to be equal in length when the sun arrives at an equinox, although atmospheric refraction makes the duration of sunlight slightly the longer on such occasions. The *solstices* are the two opposite points midway between the equinoxes, where the ecliptic is farthest north or south from the celestial equator. Here the "sun stands," so far as its north and south motion is concerned, as it turns back toward the equator.

The equinoxes and solstices are points on the celestial sphere; their positions in the constellations are shown in the star maps of Chapter 11. The *vernal equinox* (R.A. 0ʰ, Decl. 0°) is the point where the sun crosses the celestial equator on its way north, about March 21. The *summer solstice* (R.A. 6ʰ, Decl. 23½° N) is the northernmost point of the ecliptic; the sun arrives here about June

22. The *autumnal equinox* (R.A. 12ʰ, Decl. 0°) is the point where the sun crosses the celestial equator on its way south, about September 23. The *winter solstice* (R.A. 18ʰ, Decl. 23½° S) is the southernmost point of the ecliptic; the sun arrives here about December 22. These dates vary a little from year to year owing to the plan of leap years. The positions of the sun refer in each case to the sun's center.

3·7. The Ecliptic in the Evening Sky. The celestial equator keeps the same position in the sky through the year. It is inclined to the horizon at an angle which is the complement of the latitude. Thus

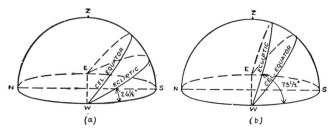

Fɪɢ. 3·7. Relation Between Ecliptic and Horizon. (*a*) The ecliptic is least inclined to the horizon in our latitudes at sunset at the beginning of autumn. (*b*) It is most inclined at sunset at the beginning of spring.

in latitude 40° N the equator crosses the horizon at the east and west points at an angle of 50°, and is 50° above the horizon in the south. The ecliptic, however, takes different positions in the evening sky during the year.

Because the ecliptic is inclined 23½° to the celestial equator, its inclination to the horizon can differ as much as 23½° either way from that of the equator. At sunset at the beginning of autumn (Fig. 3·7) in middle northern latitudes the ecliptic is least inclined to the horizon; the moon and bright planets that may be visible at the time are seen rather low in the south. At sunset at the beginning of spring the ecliptic is most inclined to the horizon; the moon and planets are then crossing more nearly overhead.

The varying angle between the ecliptic and horizon enters in the explanations of a number of features familiar to watchers of the skies. Among these are the harvest moon, the direction of the horns of the crescent moon, the favorable times for seeing the planet Mercury as evening or morning star, and the favorable seasons for viewing the zodiacal light.

3·8. Celestial Longitude and Latitude. The moon and bright planets never depart far from the sun's path around the heavens. For this reason, astronomers of early times, who were especially interested in the motions of the sun, moon, and planets, referred the places of these and other celestial bodies to the ecliptic, and they named the coordinates celestial longitude and latitude. _Celestial longitude_ is measured in degrees eastward from the vernal equinox along the ecliptic. _Celestial latitude_ is measured north or south from the ecliptic along a circle at right angles to it.

The ecliptic coordinates have only limited use today. The position of a celestial body is now referred more conveniently for most purposes to circles based on the celestial equator by means of right ascension and declination, which closely resemble terrestrial longitude and latitude. These newer coordinates themselves would doubtless have been called celestial longitude and latitude if the terms had not already been appropriated.

THE EARTH'S PRECESSION

3·9. The Earth Resembles a Spinning Top. If a top is spinning with its axis inclined to the vertical, the axis moves around the vertical line in the direction of the spin. The rotation of the top resists the effort of gravity to tip it over; and the conical motion of the axis results, until the spin is so reduced that the top falls over.

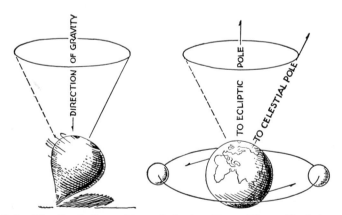

Fig. 3·9. The Earth Resembles a Spinning Top. The pull of the moon on the bulging equator of the rotating earth is the chief cause of the precessional motion.

The earth is rotating similarly on an inclined axis, inclined to the ecliptic plane which is not far from the plane of the moon's motion around us. The attractions of the moon and sun on the earth's bulging equator tend to bring it into the plane with themselves, and thus to straighten up the earth's axis relative to its orbit.

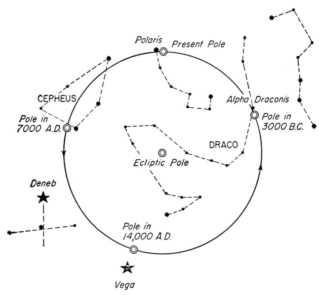

FIG. 3·10. Precessional Path of the North Celestial Pole. The celestial pole describes a circle of 23½° radius around the ecliptic pole.

Their efforts are resisted by the rotation, so that the earth's axis moves slowly instead around the line joining the ecliptic poles in the direction opposite to that of the rotation, once around in 26,000 years at the present rate. This is the *earth's precession.*

3·10. Paths of the Celestial Poles. As the earth's axis goes around in the precessional motion, the celestial poles, toward which the axis is directed, move among the constellations. The poles describe circles 23½° in radius around the ecliptic poles (Fig. 3·10), bringing successively to bright stars along their paths the distinction of being the pole star for a time. Thus Alpha Draconis was the pole star in the north 5000 years ago, the predecessor of our present pole star.

The north celestial pole is now approaching Polaris and will pass nearest it about the year 2100 at half its present distance. There-after, Polaris will describe larger and larger daily circles around the pole, and its important place will at length be taken by stars of Cepheus in succession. In the year 7000, Alpha Cephei will mark the north pole closely. In 14,000, Vega in Lyra will be a brilliant, although not very close, marker.

In our skies the constellations are slowly shifted by precession relative to the circumpolar areas, while the poles remain in the same places at the distance from the horizon equal to the observer's latitude. Six thousand years ago the Southern Cross rose and set everywhere in the United States. Now it is invisible from here except in the southernmost parts of the country.

3·11. Precession of the Equinoxes. The earth's precession, as we have seen, causes the line joining the celestial poles to describe the surface of a right cone around the line joining the ecliptic

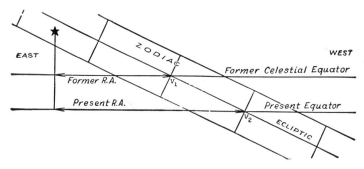

Fig. 3·11. Precession of the Equinoxes. The westward motion of the vernal equinox, from V_1 to V_2, causes the signs of the zodiac (the 12 equal divisions marked off from the equinox) to slide westward away from the corresponding constellations. The right ascensions and declinations of the stars are altered by the precession.

poles. This motion is counterclockwise as we face north. Mean-while the celestial equator slides westward along the ecliptic, keep-ing about the same angle between them. The equinoxes, where the two inclined circles intersect, slide westward along the ecliptic. This is the *precession of the equinoxes*. Their motion, including smaller effects of planetary attractions of the earth, is at the rate of 50″ a year.

The precession of the vernal equinox (Fig. 3·11) causes continu-ous variations in the right ascensions and declinations of the stars.

It is accountable for the lack of agreement between the constellations and signs of the zodiac, and it makes the year of the seasons shorter than the period of the earth's revolution around the sun (3·13).

3·12. The Zodiac; Its Constellations and Signs. The *zodiac* is the band of the heavens 16° wide, through which the ecliptic runs centrally. It contains the sun, moon, and bright planets at all times, with the occasional exception of the planet Venus. This is the reason for the special importance of the zodiac in the astronomy of early times and in the ancient and now discredited pseudoscience of astrology, in which the places of the planetary bodies had great significance.

Twelve *constellations of the zodiac* lie along this band of the heavens. Because these constellations are of unequal size, the *signs of the zodiac* were introduced in early times in the interest of uniformity; these are 12 equal divisions of the zodiac, each 30° long, marked off eastward from the vernal equinox. Each block, or sign, of the zodiac has the name of the constellation it contained 20 centuries ago.

The names of the 12 constellations and signs of the zodiac are: Aries, Taurus, Gemini, Cancer, Leo, Virgo, Libra, Scorpius, Sagittarius, Capricornus, Aquarius, and Pisces.

In the meantime, the vernal equinox has moved westward among the stars of the zodiac, and the whole train of signs has followed along, because the signs are counted from the equinox. Each sign has shifted out of the constellation for which the sign was named and into the adjoining figure to the west. Thus, when the sun arrives on March 21 at the vernal equinox, or "first of Aries," the sun is entering the zodiacal sign Aries. The sun is then in the constellation Pisces, however, and will not enter the constellation Aries itself for another month.

3·13. The Year of the Seasons is about 20 minutes shorter than the true period of the earth's revolution. The difference is caused by the precession of the equinox.

The *sidereal year* is the interval of time in which the sun appears to perform a complete revolution around the heavens with respect to the stars. This is the true period of the earth's revolution. The length of the sidereal year is 365^d 6^h 9^m 10^s of mean solar time.

The *tropical year* is the interval between two successive arrivals of the sun's center at the vernal equinox. Because the equinox is shifting westward to meet the sun, this *year of the seasons,* from the beginning of spring to the beginning of spring again, is short-ened. The length of the tropical year is $365^d\ 5^h\ 48^m\ 46^s$. This is nearly the average length of the present calendar year.

THE SEASONS

3·14. Cause of the Seasons. Why is the weather warmer in summer than in winter? It is not because we are nearer the sun in summer; for we have seen that the earth is more than 3 million miles farther

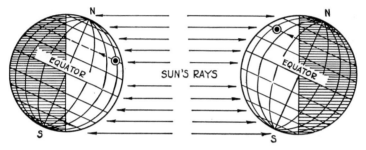

F<small>IG</small>. 3·14. Summer and Winter in the Northern Hemisphere. The weather is warmer in summer because the daily duration of sunshine is greater and the sun's rays are more nearly direct.

from the sun in summer than in winter. The cause of the seasons is found in the inclination of the earth's equator to the plane of its orbit.

In summer the northern end of the earth's axis is inclined toward the sun. Not only is the daily duration of sunshine longer at any place in our northern latitudes than it is in winter, but the sun also climbs higher, so that its rays are more nearly vertical and more concentrated on our part of the world. In winter the northern end of the axis is inclined away from the sun. The daily duration of sunshine is then shorter for us and the sun is lower at noon. The sun's rays come down more slanting in the winter, so that they are more spread out over the ground and are also obstructed more by the greater thickness of the intervening air. Thus the weather is warmer in summer than in winter because the sun shines for a longer time each day and reaches a greater height in the sky.

3·15. The Lag of the Seasons. Summer in our northern latitudes begins about June 22, when the sun arrives at the summer solstice and turns back toward the south. The duration of sunshine is longest on that day, and the sun climbs highest in the sky. Yet the hottest part of the summer is likely to be delayed several weeks

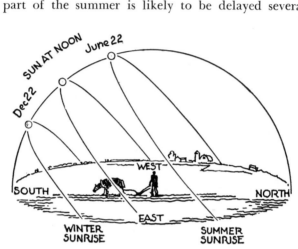

FIG. 3·15. Daily Circles of the Sun in Summer and Winter.

until the sun is well on its way south. Why does the peak of the summer come after the time of the solstice?

As the sun goes south, its rays bring less and less heat to our part of the world from day to day. For some time, however, the diminishing receipts still exceed the amounts of heat we are losing by the earth's radiation into space. Summer does not reach its peak until the rate of heating is reduced to the rate of cooling. Similarly our winter weather is likely to be more severe several weeks after the time of the winter solstice. After the sun turns north, about December 22, the temperature continues to fall generally until the amount of heat we receive from the sun becomes as great as the daily loss.

3·16. The Seasons in the Two Hemispheres. Although the seasons are not caused by the earth's varying distance from the sun, the earth is farther from the sun in our summer and nearer the sun in our winter than at similar seasons in the southern hemisphere. Summers in the northern hemisphere might well be a little cooler than southern summers, and northern winters might be milder than

southern winters. Thus the northern hemisphere might seem to
have the more agreeable climates. Yet the variation in the earth's
distance from the sun is only 3 per cent of the distance itself, and
there is more water in the southern hemisphere to modify extremes
of temperature.

It would be unsafe to make a general comparison of the weather
in corresponding latitudes north and south of the equator. Dif-

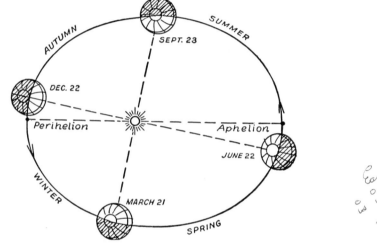

Fig. 3·16. The Seasons in the Northern Hemisphere. The earth arrives
at perihelion soon after the time of the winter solstice.

ferences in elevation and in the effects of air and ocean currents
would have to be taken into account. Consider, for example, the
climates near the two poles. There is mainly water around the
north pole; on the other hand, a great expanse of land surrounds
the south pole, and high land too, so that the winter there is the
more severe.

3·17. The Climatic Zones. The positions and widths of the climatic zones are determined by the inclination of the earth's equator
to the plane of its orbit. Because this inclination is $23\frac{1}{2}°$, the
torrid zone extends $23\frac{1}{2}°$ north and south from the equator; everywhere in this region the sun is directly overhead on some days of
the year. The *tropic of Cancer*, $23\frac{1}{2}°$ north of the equator, forms
the northern boundary of the torrid zone. Here the sun is overhead at noon on June 22, when it arrives at the summer solstice

and enters the sign Cancer of the zodiac. The *tropic of Capricorn,* 23½° south of the equator, is the southern boundary of the torrid zone. Here the sun is overhead at noon on December 22, when it enters the sign Capricornus.

Similarly, the north and south *frigid zones* extend 23½° from the poles and are bounded by the arctic and antarctic circles, respectively. Although they are modified a little by the effect of refraction near their borders, the frigid zones are the regions where the sun may become visible at midnight during part of the year, and may not appear even at noon at the opposite time of the year. The extreme conditions obtain at the poles themselves, where the sun shines continuously for 6 months and remains out of sight for the following 6 months.

The north and south *temperate zones* lie between the torrid and frigid zones. Here the sun never reaches the point overhead, nor does it ever fail to appear above the horizon at noon.

QUESTIONS ON CHAPTER 3

1. Explain that the sun's annual eastward motion becomes evident when we observe the westward march of the constellations in the south at the same hour of the evening during the year.

2. How do the annual aberration orbits of the stars demonstrate the earth's revolution around the sun?

3. What information about the earth's revolution is given by the statement that the orbit is an ellipse of small eccentricity having the sun at one focus?

4. Explain that the ecliptic unlike the celestial equator does not keep the same position in the sky of a particular place. Show that it passes nearest the zenith in middle northern latitudes at sunset at the beginning of spring.

5. Name the celestial points or coordinates which are defined as follows:

(a) The northernmost point of the ecliptic.
(b) The intersection of ecliptic and celestial equator where the sun is going north.
(c) The two points 90° from the ecliptic.
(d) Angular distance along the ecliptic measured eastward from the vernal equinox.

6. The precession of a top is in the direction of its rotation, whereas that of the earth is in the opposite direction. Explain this difference as a consequence of the difference in one of the factors producing the precessions.

7. Explain the effect of the earth's precession on the celestial poles. Show that when Vega becomes the pole star (Fig. 3·10) our present pole star will rise and set in latitude 40° N.

8. Explain the effect of the precession on the vernal equinox; on the right ascensions of the stars.

9. Distinguish between the signs and constellations of the zodiac. Explain the displacement of the signs caused by precession.

10. State and explain the difference in length between the tropical and the sidereal year.

11. Why is the weather warmer in summer? Why are the warmest days in middle northern latitudes likely to come considerably later than June 22?

12. Show that the boundaries of the climatic zones are determined by the inclination of the ecliptic to the celestial equator.

Mount Wilson Observatory, California.

4

TIMEKEEPING

THE TIME OF DAY – THE CALENDAR

Our watches are likely to be more reliable timepieces if they are compared frequently with clocks or time signals that are regulated by a clock in an observatory. The observatory clock may be regulated by comparisons with the master clock in the sky, which itself is operated by the daily rotation of the earth. The time of day in ordinary use will be more clearly explained after we have considered the kinds of time that astronomers read from the celestial clock in order to derive the correct standard time.

THE TIME OF DAY

4·1. The Clock in the Sky. Any one of the stars or any other point on the celestial sphere might be chosen as the time reckoner at the end of an hour hand of the clock in the sky. The hour hand would be that part of an hour circle connecting the time reckoner and the celestial pole. This hour hand would go around once in a day, telling the time of day to those who can read it. The following definitions hold for whatever point is selected as the time reckoner.

A *day* is the interval between two successive transits of the time reckoner over the same branch of the celestial meridian. A star *transits* when it crosses the meridian. Because a star does so twice a day, the distinction is made between *upper transit,* over the half of the circle through the celestial poles that includes the observer's zenith, and *lower transit,* over the other half that includes the nadir. It is *noon* when the time reckoner is at upper transit. Local *time of day* is the hour angle (2·11) of the time reckoner if the day begins at noon, or it is 12 hours plus the hour angle if the day begins at midnight.

4·2. Sidereal Time. Instead of selecting one of the stars as the time reckoner for sidereal time, or star time, astronomers choose the vernal equinox. The *sidereal day* is accordingly the interval between two successive upper transits of the vernal equinox; this interval is 0ˢ.008 shorter than the period of the earth's rotation, because of the precession of the equinox. *Sidereal time* is the hour angle of the vernal equinox, and might have been more correctly called equinoctial time. It is reckoned from local sidereal noon through 24 hours to the next noon.

Sidereal time is kept by special clocks in the observatories, which may be set directly from the clock in the sky. The principle, illus-

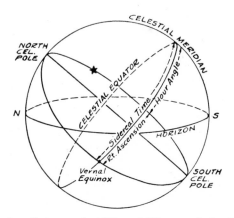

FIG. 4·2. Relation Between the Sidereal Time and the Right Ascension and Hour Angle of a Star. Sidereal time equals the right ascension of a star plus its hour angle. When the star is at upper transit (hour angle zero), the sidereal time equals the star's right ascension.

trated in Fig. 4·2, is as follows. The sidereal time at any instant is the same as the right ascension of a star that is at upper transit at that instant. Evidently what is needed is something to show the place of the celestial meridian precisely, so that the instant of the star's crossing can be correctly observed. The astronomical transit instrument will serve to explain how the observation may be made.

4·3. Determining the Sidereal Time. The astronomical transit instrument is a small telescope that can be rotated on a single axis set horizontally in the east and west direction. As the telescope is turned, it points always toward the celestial meridian, which is represented by a vertical thread in front of the eyepiece. When the observer directs the telescope to the place where a star is about to transit, he can watch the star move across the field of view until it reaches the meridian line.

FIG. 4·3.   The 8-inch Photographic Zenith Tube at the U.S. Naval Observatory.   (*Official U.S. Navy photograph*)

Suppose that the sidereal clock reads $3^h 42^m 22^s.7$ at the instant the star is at upper transit and that the star's right ascension as given in a catalog is $3^h 42^m 26^s.2$, which by the rule is the correct sidereal time at that instant.   The sidereal clock is therefore 3.5 seconds slow.   By comparison of clocks and a simple calculation the error of a standard time clock can be found as well.

Recording devices are employed to time the transits of stars more accurately than direct visual observations can do. The *photographic zenith tube* has replaced the simple transit instrument at the Naval Observatory and elsewhere. This is a fixed vertical telescope for photographing stars as they cross the meridian nearly overhead. The converging beam of starlight formed by its lens is reflected by a mercury surface before coming to focus on a small photographic plate below the lens. With this device an error of only 0ˢ.003 is expected in a time determination from a set of 18 stars.

4·4. The Solar Day Is Longer than the Sidereal Day. Suppose that the sun's center is just now at the vernal equinox and that the two are at upper transit on the celestial meridian of the observer at *O*

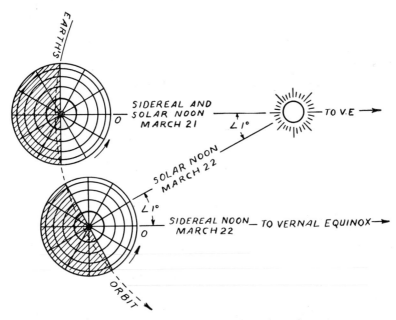

FIG. 4·4. The Solar Day Is Longer than the Sidereal Day.

(Fig. 4·4). It is sidereal noon and also solar noon—noon by the sun. The sidereal day will end when the earth has made a complete rotation relative to the vernal equinox, bringing the equinox again to upper transit. Meanwhile, the earth has advanced in its orbit around the sun an average of 360°/365.25, or a little less than 1°, so that after the end of the sidereal day it must rotate through this additional angle to bring the sun again on the meridian. Because the earth rotates at the rate of 1° in 4 minutes, the solar day is longer than the sidereal day by a little less than 4 minutes. The difference is more nearly 3ᵐ 56ˢ.

Because the apparent rotation of the celestial sphere is completed in slightly more than a sidereal day, a star rises at nearly the same sidereal time throughout the year. <u>On solar time, however, it rises about 4 minutes earlier from night to night</u>, or 2 hours earlier from month to month; so that at the same time on successive nights the star appears a little farther west than on the previous night. Thus at the same hour by our watches the stars march slowly westward across the sky as the year advances (3·1). Each season brings its own display of constellations.

4·5. Apparent Solar Time. Because our activities are regulated by the sun and not by the stars, we prefer to keep solar time rather than sidereal time; sidereal noon, for example, comes at night dur-

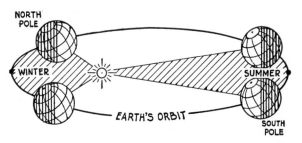

FIG. 4·5.   The Earth's Variable Revolution.   The earth revolves faster in the northern winter, because it is then nearer the sun.

ing part of the year. *Apparent solar time* is time by the *apparent sun, that is, the sun we see; it is reckoned from local apparent midnight through 24 hours to the next midnight.* The apparent sun, however, is not a uniform timekeeper. The apparent solar day, measured by the sundial, varies in length for two principal reasons:

1. The earth's revolution around the sun is not at a uniform rate. The earth revolves in its elliptical orbit in accordance with the *law of equal areas:* the line joining the earth to the sun sweeps over equal areas in equal times. The shorter line joining the earth and sun in winter in the northern hemisphere must go around farther than the longer line in summer to sweep over the same area (Fig. 4·5). Accordingly, the earth revolves farther in a day in winter and must rotate farther after the ending of the sidereal day to bring

the sun again to the observer's meridian. For this reason the apparent solar day is longer in winter than in summer.

2. The ecliptic is inclined to the celestial equator. When the sun is near a solstice, where the ecliptic is parallel to the equator, its daily eastward displacement by the earth's revolution has the full effect in delaying the sun's return to the observer's meridian. When it is near an equinox, however, part of the sun's daily displacement is north or south, and this part does not delay the return. For this reason the apparent solar day is longer in summer and winter than in spring and fall. Both effects conspire to make the day by the apparent sun longer in winter in the northern hemisphere.

4·6. Mean Solar Time is time by the mean sun; it is reckoned from local mean midnight through 24 hours to the next midnight. The *mean sun* may be regarded as a point moving eastward along the celestial equator at a rate equal to the average rate of the apparent sun's motion along the ecliptic. This conventional sun would be a smooth-running timekeeper if the earth's rotation were precisely uniform. Its day, which is the average of all apparent solar days through the year, would then have constant length.

The *equation of time* is the difference at any instant between apparent and mean solar time; its value can be found from tables in astronomical almanacs. Table 4·I shows how much the appar-

TABLE 4·I EQUATION OF TIME

(Apparent time faster or slower than mean solar time)

Jan. 1	3^m 8^s	slow	July 1	3^m 30^s	slow
Feb. 1	13 32	slow	Aug. 1	6 18	slow
Mar. 1	12 40	slow	Sept. 1	0 20	slow
Apr. 1	4 16	slow	Oct. 1	9 57	fast
May 1	2 48	fast	Nov. 1	16 20	fast
June 1	2 28	fast	Dec. 1	11 21	fast

ent time is fast or slow with respect to mean solar time on the first of each month. The values are for midnight at the Greenwich meridian during 1955, and are correct within a few seconds for any other place or year.

The rapid change in the equation of time near the beginning of the year has an effect that is noticed by everyone. At this time of year the earth is nearest the sun and is accordingly revolving fastest.

The apparent sun is then moving eastward fastest along the ecliptic, delaying its rising and setting as timed by the mean sun. For this reason the sun does not begin to rise earlier in the morning by our watches, which keep mean time, until about 2 weeks after the date of the winter solstice, although it begins to set later in the evening about 2 weeks before that date.

4·7. Universal Time and Ephemeris Time. *Universal time* is the local mean solar time at the meridian of Greenwich. It is the basis of all ordinary timekeeping and is likely to continue to be, because observatories that transmit mean solar time signals keep their clocks corrected by frequent sights on meridian transits of the stars. For the foretelling of astronomical events, however, the irregularities in the earth's rotation make it hazardous to predict precisely what the universal times of the events will be. Beginning with the year 1960, the *American Ephemeris and Nautical Almanac* and the British *Astronomical Ephemeris,* which now conform in other respects as well, have tabulated the fundamental ephemerides of the sun, moon, and planets for intervals of ephemeris time.

Ephemeris time goes on uniformly without regard for irregularities in the earth's rotation. Its constant arbitrary unit equals the length of the tropical year at the beginning of the year 1900 divided by 31,556,925.9747, which was the number of mean solar seconds and fraction in the year at that epoch.

Ephemeris time has run increasingly fast with respect to universal time during the present century; the difference between the two was 35 seconds in 1960. The difference, which can be known approximately by extrapolation for a future event predicted in the almanac, awaits precise determination nearer the time of the event. For this purpose the observed universal time of a particular position of the moon among the stars (6·8) is compared frequently with the predicted ephemeris time of that position.

Unlike sidereal time and apparent solar time, which are always local times, mean solar time is most often employed in the conventional forms of zone time and standard time now to be considered.

4·8. The Difference Between the Local Times of Two Places at the same instant is the difference between their longitudes expressed in time. This is true because the earth makes a complete rotation with respect to a celestial time reckoner in 24 hours of its kind of time; and there are 360° or 24 hours of longitude around the world. The rule applies to any kind of local time, whether it is sidereal, apparent solar, or mean solar, where the same kind of time is denoted at the two places. When the local time at one place is given and the corresponding local time at another place is required, add the difference between their longitudes if the second place is east of the first; subtract if the second place is west.

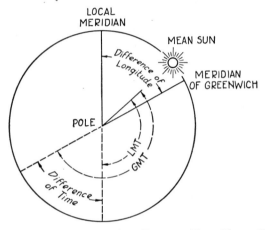

LOCAL
MERIDIAN

MEAN SUN

Difference of Longitude

MERIDIAN
OF GREENWICH

POLE

LMT

GMT

Difference of Time

Fig. 4·8.   Difference of Local Time Between Two Places Equals Their Difference in Longitude.

In the time diagram of Fig. 4·8 we are looking at the earth from above its south pole and are projecting the sun onto the equator in the longitude where the sun is overhead; the east to west direction is counterclockwise. The observer on the earth is in longitude 60° W, or 4ʰ W. The local mean time (LMT) there is 9ʰ, and the Greenwich mean time (GMT), or universal time, is 13ʰ, so that the difference of 4ʰ in the local times of the two places is the difference of their longitudes. In this case the time of day is counted through 24 hours continuously; 9ʰ is 9 A.M. and 13ʰ is 1 P.M.

Conversely, the difference between the longitudes of two places is the difference between the local times of the places at the same instant. This is the basic rule for determining longitudes.

4·9. The Time Zones. The local mean solar times at a particular instant are the same only for places on the same meridian. The time becomes progressively later toward the east and earlier toward the west; the rate of change in latitude 40° is 1 minute of time for a distance of a little more than 13 miles. The confusion that would ensue if every place kept its own local time is avoided by use of time zones. In its simplest form the plan is as follows.

Standard meridians are marked off around the world 15° or 1 hour apart both east and west from the meridian of Greenwich. The local times on these meridians accordingly differ successively by whole hours. The time to be kept at any other place is the local

Fɪɢ. 4·9. Time Zone Diagram. The earth is viewed from above the south pole. The numbers outside the circle are the longitudes of the standard meridians. The numbers inside are corrections in hours to universal time.

mean time of the standard meridian nearest the place. Thus the world is divided by boundary meridians into 24 equal time zones, each 15° wide and having one of the standard meridians running centrally through it. The time is the same throughout each zone; it is 1 hour earlier than the time in the adjacent zone to the east and 1 hour later than the time in the zone to the west. The rule to be followed when crossing a boundary between two zones on an eastward voyage is to set the watch ahead 1 hour, the minutes and seconds remaining the same as before; and on a westward voyage to set the watch back 1 hour.

Zone time is employed in the operation of ships at sea and of many aircraft over the sea. This uniform plan is occasionally modified near land so that the ship's clock may agree with the standard time kept ashore.

4·10. Standard Time divisions on land follow in a general way the pattern of the time zones at sea. Their boundaries are often irregular; they are affected by local preference and are subject to change.

FIG. 4·10.   Time Zone Chart of North America.   The large numbers at the top are corrections in hours to universal time.   (*Adapted from H. O. 5192, U.S. Navy Hydrographic Office*)

In some areas the legal time differs from the times in adjacent belts by a fraction of an hour. There is also the arbitrary and nonuniform practice of setting the clocks ahead of the accepted standard time for part of the year.

Four standard times are employed in the greater parts of the continental United States and Canada, namely, Eastern, Central, Mountain, and Pacific standard times; they are respectively the local mean times of the meridians 75°, 90°, 105°, and 120° west of the Greenwich meridian and are therefore 5, 6, 7, and 8 hours slow as compared with universal time. The standard time in Newfoundland and Labrador is $3\frac{1}{2}$ hours instead of 4 hours slow, and in Alaska is mainly 10 hours slow of universal time. Certain changes for Canada are shown in the Dominion Observatories Operations Map of 1958. Apart from Quebec, Ontario, and the Northwest Territories, each province of Canada has adopted a single standard time.

4·11. The International Date Line. Suppose that an airplane leaves San Francisco at noon on Monday and proceeds due west around the world with the speed of the earth's rotation relative to the sun in that latitude. The sun accordingly remains practically stationary in the sky during the voyage, and the watches aboard are set back to noon whenever a boundary between the time divisions is crossed. When the plane comes around again to San Francisco, the crew might be surprised to find that it is now Tuesday noon if they had forgotten the rule for the change of date.

The rule is to change the date generally at the 180° meridian. When this meridian is crossed on a westward voyage, as in going from San Francisco to Manila, the date is advanced; if the line is crossed on Monday noon, it is then Tuesday noon. At the eastward crossing the date is set back. Where the 180° meridian traverses land areas, the international date line may depart from the meridian to avoid populated areas and so as not to divide a politically associated region; thus it bends to the east around Siberia and to the west around the Aleutian Islands.

4·12. Radio Time Service. The seconds beats of a standard time clock at the U.S. Naval Observatory are transmitted from 4 naval radio stations and 2 stations of the National Bureau of Standards. This crystal-controlled clock is kept accurate by frequent observations of meridian transits of stars, and is also corrected for certain predictable variations in the earth's rotation.

The naval radio station NSS at Annapolis transmits the time signals on a variety of frequencies during the last 5 minutes of scheduled hours. They are on continuous waves and can be heard only with receivers suited to code reception. These dash signals are omitted at specified seconds (Fig. 4·12) so that the listener can readily identify the minute and second of each signal. A long dash following the longest break announces the beginning of the hour.

The standard frequency station WWV of the National Bureau of Standards at Beltsville, Maryland, transmits the seconds signals

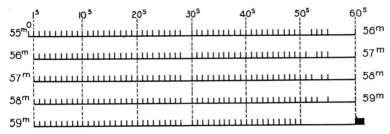

Fig. 4·12.   Plan of Time Signals from U.S. Naval Radio Station NSS. The short lines represent the seconds signals; these are omitted at the 29th second and before the beginning of each minute, where the number of signals immediately preceding the long break denotes the number of minutes before the beginning of the hour.

continuously day and night on frequencies of 2.5, 5, 10, 15, 20, and 25 Mc/sec. The signals are clicks superposed for part of the time on standard audio frequencies; they employ modulated waves and may therefore be heard with ordinary radiophone receivers. The seconds clicks are interrupted at the 59th second of each minute. These are examples of the distribution of the correct time by observatories in various parts of the world.

4·13. Conversion of Time. When the time at one place is given, it is frequently desired to know the corresponding time at another place. The conversion is often to or from universal time, for which almanacs tabulate a considerable part of their data. In passing from zone time to universal time, the correction is found by dividing the longitude of the place in degrees by 15 and taking the nearest whole number of hours. In passing from the standard time of a place to universal time, the correction may not be the same as from zone time in the same longitude, because of irregularities in the standard time zones and the possible use of daylight saving time at the place. The following examples illustrate some conversions.

1. The zone time is $21^h 22^m$, May 25, at a place in longitude 103° W. Required the corresponding universal time and date.
Answer: The UT is $4^h 22^m$, May 26.

2. The Diary of the *American Ephemeris and Nautical Almanac* gives the time of the beginning of autumn in 1960 as September 23^d 1^h, universal time. Required the corresponding Central standard time and date.

Answer: The CST was September 22^d 19^h (7 P.M.).

3. The daylight saving time in San Francisco is 7:30 P.M. Required the corresponding time at Galveston, Texas, which remains on Central standard time.

Answer: The CST is 8:30 P.M.

THE CALENDAR

Calendars have been in use since the beginnings of civilizations. They have tried to combine natural measures of time, the solar day, the lunar month, and the year of the seasons, in the most convenient ways, and have encountered difficulties because these measures do not fit evenly one into another. Calendars have been of three types: the lunar, the lunisolar, and the solar calendar.

4·14. Calendars of Three Types. (1) *The lunar calendar* is the simplest of the three types, and it was the earliest to be used by almost all nations. Each month began originally with the "new moon," the first appearance for the month of the crescent moon after sunset. Long controlled only by observation of the crescent, this calendar was eventually operated by fixed rules. In the fixed lunar calendar the 12 months of the common lunar year are alternately 30 and 29 days long, making 354 days in all. The Mohammedan calendar is a survivor of this type.

(2) *The lunisolar calendar* tries to keep in step with both the moon's phases and the seasons, and is the most complex of the three types. It began by occasionally adding a 13th month to the short lunar year to round out the year of the seasons. The extra month was later inserted by fixed rules. The Jewish calendar is the principal survivor of the lunisolar type.

(3) *The solar calendar* makes the year conform as nearly as possible to the year of the seasons, and neglects the moon's phases; its 12 months are generally longer than the lunar month. Only a few early nations, notably the Egyptians and eventually the Romans, adopted this simple type.

4·15. The Early Roman Calendar dates formally from the founding of Rome in 753 B.C. It was originally a lunar calendar of a sort, beginning in the spring and having 10 months. The names of the months, if we use mainly our own style instead of the Latin, were: March, April, May, June, Quintilis, Sextilis, September, October, November, and December. The years for many centuries thereafter were counted from 753 and were designated A.U.C., in the year of the founding of the City. Two months, January and February, were added later and were eventually placed at the beginning, so that the number months have ever since then appeared in the calendar out of their proper order.

In its 12-month form the Roman calendar was of the lunisolar type. The day began at midnight instead of at sunset as with most early people. An occasional extra month was added to keep the calendar in step with the seasons. The calendar was managed so unwisely, however, that it fell into confusion; its dates drifted back into different seasons from the ones they were supposed to represent.

When Julius Caesar became the ruler of Rome, he was disturbed by the bad condition of the calendar and took steps to correct it. He particularly wished to discard the lunisolar form with its troublesome extra months. Caesar was impressed with the simplicity of the solar calendar the Egyptians were using, and he knew of their discovery that the length of the tropical year is very nearly $365\frac{1}{4}$ days. He accordingly formulated his reform with the advice of the astronomer Sosigenes of Alexandria. In preparation for the new calendar the "year of confusion," 46 B.C., was made 445 days long in order to correct the accumulated error of the old one. The date of the vernal equinox was thereby brought to March 25. The Julian calendar began on January 1, 45 B.C.

4·16. The Julian Calendar was of the solar type, and so neglected the moon's phases. Its chief feature was the adoption of $365\frac{1}{4}$ days as the average length of the calendar year. This was accomplished conveniently by the plan of leap years. Three common years of 365 days are followed by a fourth year containing 366 days; this *leap year* in our era has a number evenly divisible by 4.

In lengthening the calendar year from the 355 days of the old lunisolar plan to the common year of 365 days, Caesar distributed the additional 10 days among the months. With further changes made in the reign of Augustus, the months assumed their present lengths. After Caesar's death in 44 B.C., the month Quintilis was renamed July in honor of the founder of the new calendar. The month Sextilis was later renamed August in honor of Augustus.

Because its average year of 365^d 6^h was 11^m 14^s longer than the tropical year, the Julian calendar fell behind with respect to the seasons about 3 days in 400 years. When the council of churchmen convened at Nicaea in A.D. 325, the vernal equinox had fallen back to about March 21. It was at that convention that previous confusion about the date of Easter was ended.

4·17. Easter was originally celebrated by some early churches on whatever day the Passover began, and by others on the Sunday included in the Passover week. The Council of Nicaea decided in favor of the Sunday observance and left it to the church at Alexandria to formulate the rule, which is as follows.

Easter is the first Sunday after the 14th day of the moon (nearly the full moon) which occurs on or immediately after March 21. Thus if the 14th day of the moon occurs on Sunday, Easter is observed one week later. Unlike Christmas, Easter is a movable feast because it depends on the moon's phases; its date can range from March 22 to April 25.

DATES OF EASTER SUNDAY

1961, Apr. 2	. 1966, Apr. 10	1971, Apr. 11
1962, Apr. 22	1967, Mar. 26	1972, Apr. 2
1963, Apr. 14	1968, Apr. 14	1973, Apr. 22
1964, Mar. 29	1969, Apr. 6	1974, Apr. 14
1965, Apr. 18	1970, Mar. 29	1975, Mar. 30

4·18. The Gregorian Calendar. As the date of the vernal equinox fell back in the calendar, March 21 and Easter which is reckoned from it came later and later in the season. Toward the end of the 16th century the equinox had retreated to March 11. Another reform of the calendar was proposed by Pope Gregory XIII.

Two rather obvious corrections were made in the Gregorian reform. First, ten days were suppressed from the calendar of that year; the day following October 4, 1582, became October 15 for those who wished to adopt the new plan. The date of the vernal equinox was restored in this way to March 21. The second correction made the average length of the calendar year more nearly equal to the tropical year, so that the calendar would not again get so quickly out of step with the seasons. Evidently the thing to do was to omit the 3 days in 400 years by which the Julian calendar year was too long. This was done conveniently by making common years of the century years having numbers not evenly divisible by 400. Thus the years 1700, 1800, and 1900 became common years of 365 days instead of leap years of 366 days, whereas the year 2000 remained a leap year as in the former calendar. The average year of the new calendar is still too long by 26 seconds, which is hardly enough to be troublesome for a long time to come.

The Gregorian calendar was gradually adopted, until it is now in use, at least for civil purposes, in practically all nations. England and its colonies including America made the change in 1752. By that time there were 11 days to be suppressed; for that century year was a leap year in the old calendar and a common year in the new one. September 2, 1752, was followed by September 14. The countries of eastern Europe were the latest to make the change, when the difference had become 13 days.

4·19. Suggested Calendar Reform. Irregularities in our present calendar are frequently cited as reason for reforming it. The calendar year is not evenly divisible into quarters; the months range in length from 28 to 31 days, and their beginnings and endings occur on all days of the week; the weeks are split between months. Some people say that the irregularities should be corrected. Others are not sure that the improvement would be great enough to offset the confusion in our records that the change might bring.

Recent proposals for calendar reform are based on the period of 364 days, a number evenly divisible by 4, 7, and also 13. An extra day is added each year in such a way as not to disturb the sequence of weekdays, and another is added every 4 years in the same manner, except in the century years not evenly divisible by 400. Two proposed calendars are the 13-month perpetual calendar and the 12-month perpetual calendar known as the world calendar.

The first plan divides the year into 13 months of 28 days each. In this plan a calendar for one month would serve for every other month forever if it is remembered when to add the two stabilizing days. This proposal met with approval for a time, but lost favor because it seemed too drastic a change from the present calendar.

The second plan divides the 364-day period into 12 months. The four equal quarters of the year remain the same forever. Each quarter begins on Sunday and ends on Saturday. Its first month has 31 days, and its second and third months have 30 days each. One stabilizing day is added each year at the end of the fourth quarter; it is called Year-End Day, December Y, and is an extra Saturday. The second extra day is added every fourth year, with the usual exceptions, at the end of the second quarter; it is called Leap-Year Day, June L, and is also an extra Saturday. This plan is a more moderate change from the present calendar; it was disapproved, however, by the United Nations in 1956.

<h3 style="text-align:center">QUESTIONS ON CHAPTER 4</h3>

1. If the star Arcturus were selected as the time reckoner of the clock in the sky, what would be the definitions of noon, day, and time of day? Why would this plan be inconvenient for ordinary purposes?

2. If a certain star rises tonight at 10 o'clock by your watch, at what time will it rise tomorrow night? a month from now?

3. Give two reasons why apparent solar days are longest near the beginning of winter.

4. What is the advantage of predicting the time of a future celestial event in ephemeris time rather than universal time?

5. At noon, universal time, what are the corresponding standard times at New York, Chicago, and San Francisco?

6. State the difference between the time divisions employed on land and at sea, and the reason for the difference.

7. At 2:00 A.M., universal time May 10, the local mean solar time at a certain place is 9:40 P.M., May 9. Explain that the longitude of the place is 65° W.

8. At 11:55 P.M. on Tuesday, an airplane flying west over the ocean is about to cross the 180° meridian. State the time and date for the plane 10 minutes later.

9. Name the terms that are defined as follows.

(a) Hour angle of the vernal equinox.
(b) Hour angle of the mean sun plus 12 hours.
(c) Time by the sundial.
(d) Standard time near the meridian 90° west of Greenwich.

10. Distinguish between the lunar, lunisolar, and solar calendars.

11. State the two chief changes made in our calendar in the Gregorian reform, and the reasons for the changes.

12. Give some reasons for a proposed reform of our present calendar and a possible argument against a reform.

<h3 style="text-align:center">REFERENCES</h3>

The American Ephemeris and Nautical Almanac. Published yearly. Superintendent of Documents, U.S. Government Printing Office, Washington 25, D. C.

Shaw, R. William, and Samuel L. Boothroyd, *Manual of Astronomy.* A guide to observation and laboratory interpretation in elementary astronomy. Third edition. F. S. Crofts and Co., New York, 1947.

5

TELESCOPES AND THEIR USES

REFRACTING TELESCOPES — REFLECTING TELESCOPES
— THE SPECTROSCOPE — RADIO TELESCOPES

The chief optical feature of the telescope is its *objective,* which receives the light of a celestial object and focuses the light to form an image of the object. The image may be formed either by refraction of the light by a lens or by reflection from a curved mirror. Optical telescopes are accordingly of two general types: *refracting telescopes* and *reflecting telescopes.* Schmidt telescopes are modifications of the reflecting type. In the *radio telescopes* the radio radiations from a celestial source are received by an antenna which concentrates them on receiving and recording apparatus.

REFRACTING TELESCOPES

5·1. Light Comes to Us in Waves which spread from a source, such as the sun, in something like the way that ripples spread over the surface of a pond when a stone is dropped into the water. *Light* may be defined as the sensation that is produced when waves of appropriate lengths enter the eye, or more generally in terms of the wave motion itself.

The *wavelength* is the distance from crest to crest of successive waves. In the limited range which causes the sensation of light, the wavelengths vary from 1/70,000 inch for violet light to nearly twice that length for the reddest light we can see. The total *radiation* from a source has a far greater range of wavelength than the eye can detect, from gamma rays of the order of a billion waves to the inch to radio waves which may be many miles long. The *frequency* of the radiation is the number of waves emitted by the source in a second; it equals the velocity of light divided by the wavelength.

The *velocity of light* is about 186,300 miles a second; it is the speed of all the radiation in a vacuum. The speed is reduced in a medium, such as air or glass, depending on the density of the medium and the wavelength. This is the reason for the refraction of light.

5·2. Refraction of Light is the change in the direction of a ray of light when it passes obliquely from one medium into another of different density, as from air into glass. A "ray" of light denotes the direction in which a narrow section of the wave system is moving.

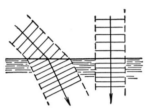

When a ray of light obliquely enters a denser medium, where its speed is reduced (Fig. 5·2), one side is retarded before the other. The wave front is accordingly swung around, and the ray becomes more nearly perpendicular to the boundary between the two media. When the oblique ray enters a rarer medium instead, it is refracted away from the perpendicular. Evidently the direction of the ray is not altered if it is originally perpendicular to the boundary.

FIG. 5·2. Refraction of Light. A ray of light passing obliquely from one medium into another is changed in direction.

Fig. 5·2A shows how a double convex lens forms by refraction a real inverted image of an object that is farther from the lens than is the focal point, F, the point where rays parallel to the axis of the lens are focused. Rays which pass through the center of the lens are unchanged in direction. When the image formed by this lens is brought within the focal distance of a similar lens, the sec-

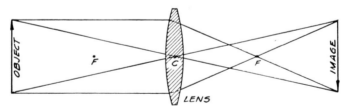

FIG. 5·2A. A Simple Convex Lens Forms an Inverted Real Image of a Celestial Object.

ond lens serves as an eyepiece with which to view and magnify the image, leaving it inverted. A single lens, however, does not give a sharp image, mainly because it refracts shorter waves more than longer ones, violet light more than red, so that it does not bring them together at the same focus. This confusion of colors is partly corrected by the use of a compound lens.

5·3. The Refracting Telescope. The objective of a refracting telescope is generally a combination of two lenses. Its *aperture,* or clear diameter, is given in denoting the size of the telescope. The *focal length,* or distance from the objective to its focus, is often about 15 times the aperture. Thus a 12-inch telescope has an aperture of 12 inches and may be about 15 feet long. For visual use the inverted image formed by the objective is viewed with an *eyepiece,* a magnifier of small lenses set in a sliding tube. The objective of a visual refractor focuses together the yellow and adjacent colors of the spectrum, to which the eye is especially sensitive, but not the blue and violet light which most affects the ordinary photographic plate. Without a correcting device it does not serve well for photography.

Where a telescope intended for visual purposes is used as a camera, a plate holder replaces the eyepiece. A yellow filter and a yellow-sensitive plate may be combined to utilize the light that is sharply focused, or a correcting lens may be introduced for a particular kind of plate. Refracting telescopes intended only for photography often have more than two lenses in the objective; they generally have shorter focal lengths and give clear pictures of greater areas of the sky.

5·4. The 40-inch Telescope of Yerkes Observatory at Williams Bay, Wisconsin, is the largest refracting telescope; its focal length is 63 feet. It has about the greatest permissible aperture for an instrument of this kind, where the objective can be supported only at the edge. A larger lens might sag seriously under its own weight.

The *equatorial mounting* of the 40-inch telescope (Fig. 5·4) is an example of the type generally used for the larger refracting telescopes. The *polar axis* is parallel to the earth's axis; around it the telescope is turned parallel to the celestial equator. The *declination axis* is supported by the polar axis; around it the telescope is turned along an hour circle, from one declination to another.

The polar axis carries a graduated circle showing the hour angle of the star toward which the telescope is pointing. There is also a dial on the pier, which indicates the star's right ascension. A circle on the declination axis shows the declination of the star. By the use of these circles the telescopes can be pointed toward a celestial object of known right ascension and declination; it is then

FIG. 5·4. The 40-inch Telescope, Yerkes Observatory. This is an equatorial telescope; it can be moved parallel and perpendicular to the celestial equator.

kept pointing at the object by mechanism in the pier. The dome is turned by motor, so that the telescope may look out in any direction through the opened slit.

The 36-inch telescope of Lick Observatory on Mount Hamilton in California is second in size among refracting telescopes. About 40 refracting telescopes have apertures of 20 inches or more.

REFLECTING TELESCOPES

5·5. Reflection from a Concave Mirror.   The concave spherical mirror represented in Fig. 5·5 has its center of curvature at *C* and its focal point at *F*, to which rays parallel to the axis of the mirror are reflected. Rays passing through the center strike the mirror normally and return without change in direction. The mirror forms an inverted real image of a distant object.

All mirrors are achromatic, because reflection does not disperse the light according to wavelength, as does refraction. The spherical mirror, however, does not form a clear image; its focal points are not the same for its inner and outer parts. A remedy is to

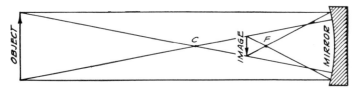

FIG. 5·5. A Concave Mirror Forms an Inverted Real Image of a Celestial Object.

make the mirror paraboloidal instead of spherical. A good image is then formed, which may be viewed with an eyepiece or photographed. Thus a concave mirror can serve as the objective of a telescope.

5·6. The Reflecting Telescope has as its objective a concave mirror at the lower end of the tube; this is a circular disk of glass having its upper surface ground to suitable curvature and coated with a film of metal, such as aluminum. The glass serves only to give the desired form to the metal surface, and it need not have the high optical quality required for a lens. The entire back of the disk may be supported. The focal length of the mirror is often about 5 times its aperture; sometimes it is less. Because the reflecting telescope is shorter than the ordinary refractor of the same diameter, it is less costly to construct and to house. These are reasons why very large telescopes are of the reflecting type.

The large mirror reflects the light of the celestial object to the *prime focus* in the middle of the tube near the upper end, where the image is accessible to the observer only in the very largest telescopes. In the *Newtonian form* a small plane mirror at an angle of 45° near the top of the tube reflects the converging beam from the large mirror to focus at the side of the tube. In the *Cassegrainian form* a small convex mirror replaces the plane mirror; it reflects the beam back through an opening in the large mirror to focus below it. Where the large mirror has no opening, which

is the case with the 100-inch Mount Wilson telescope, the return-
ing beam is reflected to focus at the side by a plane mirror in
front of the large one. This and some other large telescopes pro-

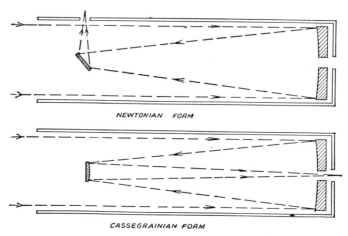

NEWTONIAN FORM

CASSEGRAINIAN FORM

Fig. 5·6. The Reflecting Telescope in Two Forms. In the Newtonian
form the converging beam from the large mirror is diverted to the side by
a small diagonal plane mirror. In the Cassegrainian form the beam is
reflected back to focus behind the large mirror.

vide another place of observation, the *coudé focus*, by reflection of
the beam through the polar axis to a laboratory below.

5·7. The 200-inch Hale Telescope on Palomar Mountain in southern California, completed in 1948, is the largest optical telescope.
Its large mirror is a disk of pyrex glass nearly 17 feet in diameter
and 27 inches thick, having its upper, concave surface coated with
aluminum. At the prime focus 55 feet above the mirror the observer is carried in a cage 5 feet in diameter, which obstructs less
than 10 per cent of the incoming light. Here a 5 × 7 inch photographic plate records an area of the sky 26′ × 36½′, or about the
apparent area of the full moon. Stars of the 19th magnitude
can be detected with an eyepiece, and stars as faint as the 24th
magnitude can be photographed or measured photoelectrically.

When the 41-inch convex mirror is set in the converging beam,
it reflects the light through the 40-inch opening in the large mirror
to focus below it. The effective focal length is 267 feet at the Cassegrainian focus and 510 feet at the coudé focus in the laboratory.
The telescope tube of skeleton construction moves in declination

F$_{IG}$. 5·7. The 200-inch Hale Telescope, Palomar Observatory. View from
the east.

within the yoke which forms the polar axis. The tube, together
with the mirror and observer's cage, weighs 140 tons. The dome is
137 feet in diameter.

5·8. Other Large Reflecting Telescopes. The 120-inch telescope
of the Lick Observatory on Mount Hamilton, California, is the
second largest reflector; its mirror has a focal length of 50 feet.
This telescope also has an observer's cage at the prime focus.
Next in order are the 102-inch telescope of the Crimean Astrophysical Observatory, the 100-inch telescope of the Mount Wilson Observatory in California, the 82-inch telescope of the McDonald Observatory on Mount Locke, Texas, and the 80-inch telescope of the
Kitt Peak National Observatory near Tucson, Arizona. Four others
complete for the moment the list of optical telescopes 6 feet or more
in diameter.

These telescopes are often employed as cameras; the photographic plate replaces the eyepiece at the focus. The photographs
provide permanent records of the heavens, which can be studied
deliberately. By cumulative effect of the light with prolonged

exposure they show features invisible to the eye at the same telescope. The telescopes are also employed to concentrate the light of
celestial objects on auxiliary apparatus, such as the spectroscope and
photoelectric photometer.

FIG. 5·8. Dome of the 120-inch Telescope, Lick Observatory.

The type of reflecting telescope thus far described is admirable
for photographing limited areas of the heavens. Another type is
more effective for recording larger areas distinctly.

5·9. The Schmidt Telescope is named after its designer, Bernhard
Schmidt, an optical worker at the Hamburg Observatory in Germany. Its objective is a spherical mirror, which is easy to make
but is not by itself suitable for a telescope. Parallel rays reflected
by the central part of such a mirror are focused farther away from
it than are those reflected from its outer zones. The appropriate
correction is effected by a special type of thin lens, the correcting
plate, at the center of curvature of the mirror. The lens slightly
diverges the outer parts of the entering beam with respect to the
middle, so that the entire beam is focused on a slightly curved surface. The photographic plate, suitably curved by springs in the
plate holder, faces the mirror between it and the correcting plate.

The size of this type of telescope is denoted by the diameter of the correcting plate. The Schmidt telescope can photograph rapidly and clearly a considerable area of the heavens, for example, a large part of the Milky Way.

The largest telescope of this kind is the 48-inch Schmidt telescope of the Palomar Observatory. Its 72-inch mirror has a radius

FIG. 5·9. The 48-inch Schmidt Telescope, Palomar Observatory.

of curvature of 20 feet, which is about the length of the tube. The focal length is 10 feet. An important achievement of this telescope is the National Geographic Society—Palomar Observatory Sky Survey, a photographic atlas of the heavens north of declination 27° S. The atlas consists of 879 pairs of negative prints from blue- and red-sensitive plates, each print 14 inches square and covering an area 7° on a side. The survey reaches stars of the 20th magnitude and exterior galaxies of the 19.5 magnitude.

Other examples of this newer type are the 24-inch Schmidt telescope at the Nassau Astronomical Station of the Case Institute of Technology, the similar telescope of the University of Michigan Observatory, and the 31½-inch Schmidt telescope of the Hamburg Observatory, dedicated in 1955. The 33-inch Baker-Schmidt telescope of the Boyden Station near Bloemfontein, South Africa, is a modified type.

5·10. Advantages of a Large Telescope. (1) A larger telescope has greater light-gathering power, which increases the depth of space to be explored. (2) It is likely to permit greater magnifying power. (3) It has greater resolving power, so that it reveals finer detail than can be observed with a smaller telescope.

The *light-gathering power* of a telescope increases in direct proportion to the area of the objective, or the square of its diameter. A particular star is accordingly 400 times as bright with the 200-inch telescope as with a 10-inch telescope. Thus stars can be observed with the former that are too faint to be detected with the latter.

The *magnifying power* of a telescope used as a camera increases with the length of the telescope. The diameter of a celestial object in the photograph equals the focal length of the telescope times the angular diameter of the object in degrees divided by 57°.3. Thus the moon, having an angular diameter of about ½°, appears 5¾ inches in diameter in a photograph at the prime focus of the 200-inch telescope, and about 1¼ inches with a 10-inch refracting telescope of the usual type. In either case, the size can, of course, be increased by enlargement of the photograph.

The *resolving power* of a telescope is the angular distance between two stars that can be just separated with the telescope in the best conditions. This least distance, d in seconds of arc, is related to the wavelength, λ, and the aperture, a, in the same units by the formula: $d'' = 1.03 \times 206{,}265'' \times \lambda/a$. For visual telescopes the formula becomes: $d'' = 4''.56/a$, where the aperture is expressed in inches; the value is $0''.023$ for the 200-inch telescope, and $0''.46$ for a 10-inch telescope. We notice presently how the much greater wavelengths employed in radio telescopes make them less effective in separating fine detail.

THE SPECTROSCOPE

5·11. Dispersion of Light. When a beam of light passes obliquely from one medium to another, as from air into glass, its direction is altered (5·2). Because the amount of the change in direction increases progressively with decrease in wavelength of the light, from red to violet, the beam is *dispersed* by refraction into a *spectrum*. Thus the rainbow is produced when sunlight is dispersed by raindrops. The spectrum is often obtained by passing the light through a glass prism (Fig. 5·11). It goes on beyond the visible

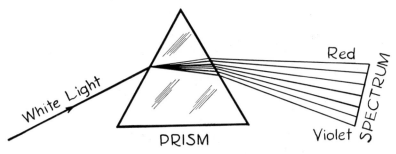

FIG. 5·11. Formation of a Spectrum by a Prism.

range into the ultraviolet in one direction and the infrared in the other, where it may be recorded by photography and other means.

5·12. The Spectroscope. A familiar type of spectroscope consists of a glass prism, toward which a collimator and view telescope are directed. The light enters the tube of the collimator through a narrow slit between the sharpened edges of two metal plates. The slit is at the focal point of the collimator lens. After passing

FIG. 5·12. The Spectroscope. (*Courtesy of Adam Hilger, Ltd.*)

through the lens, the rays are accordingly parallel as they enter the prism. The light is refracted by the prism and dispersed into a spectrum, which is brought to focus by the objective of the view telescope and magnified by its eyepiece. For purposes of astronomy the spectroscope is attached to the telescope, which serves to concentrate the light of the celestial body and to focus it on the slit.

Here, and in the laboratory as well, the eyepiece is generally replaced by a plate holder.

5·13. Emission and Absorption Spectra. The *bright-line spectrum,* or *emission-line spectrum,* is an array of bright lines. The source of the light is a glowing gas that radiates in a limited number of wavelengths. Each gaseous chemical element emits its characteristic selection of wavelengths and can, therefore, be identified by the

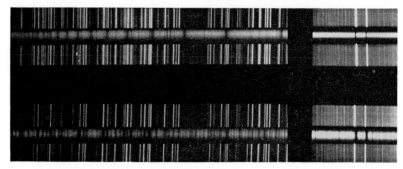

FIG. 5·13. Dark-Line and Bright-Line Spectra. At the left are the dark-line spectra of Alpha Cygni (above) and Betelgeuse (below). They are photographed between bright lines of the iron spectrum. At the right the dark D lines of sodium in the yellow region of the stars' spectra appear between bright comparison lines of sodium. Here the Doppler displacements of the dark lines are clearly shown. (*Mount Wilson Observatory photographs*)

pattern of lines of its spectrum. The glowing gas of a neon tube, for example, produces a bright-line spectrum.

The *continuous spectrum* is a continuous emission in all wavelengths. The source of the light is a luminous solid or liquid, or it may be a gas in conditions such that it does not emit selectively. The glowing filament of a lamp and the sun's surface produce continuous spectra. There may also be emission and absorption continuums of limited extent in the spectra of certain gases.

The *dark-line spectrum,* or *absorption-line spectrum,* is an array of dark lines on a bright background. Gas intervenes between the observer and the source of light, which by itself may produce a continuous spectrum. The gas abstracts from the light the pattern of wavelengths it emits in the same conditions, and thus reveals its own chemical composition. The spectrum of the sun is essentially a dark-line spectrum, because the sunlight has filtered through the atmospheres of the sun and earth before reaching us.

Where the gas consists of molecules, such as carbon dioxide or methane, the spectrum shows *bands* of bright or dark lines characistic of these molecules.

5·14. The Doppler Effect. When a source of sound waves, such as the whistle of a locomotive, is relatively approaching the observer, the waves come to him crowded together, so that the pitch of the sound is raised. When the source is receding, the pitch is lowered. The Austrian physicist C. J. Doppler pointed out, in 1842, that a similar effect is required by the wave theory of light; thus a star should appear bluer when it is approaching and redder when it is receding from us. The French physicist H. Fizeau explained in 1848 that the perceptible effect would be a displacement of the lines in the star's spectrum. The *Doppler effect* in the spectrum is as follows.

When a source of light is relatively approaching or receding from the observer, the lines in its spectrum are displaced respectively to shorter or longer wavelengths by an amount that is directly proportional to the speed of approach or recession.

The displacement of the spectrum lines to the violet or red from their normal positions is often our only means of observing the motion of a celestial body relative to the earth. Applications of this useful effect are noted in later chapters.

RADIO TELESCOPES

5·15. Radio Astronomy is the study of the heavens by reception of cosmic radiations at radio wavelengths. The radiations that can come through to the ground range in wavelength from less than 1 cm to about 30 meters. Waves much shorter than 1 cm are absorbed by molecules of our atmosphere, and those longer than 30 meters cannot ordinarily penetrate the electrified ionosphere. Selected parts of this continuous radio "window" are employed for various astronomical purposes, and the only known emission line at wavelength 21 cm, discovered in 1951, is useful where the velocity of the source in the line of sight is also required.

Cosmic radiation at radio wavelengths arises from two different causes. The first type, *thermal radiation,* is what would be expected only from the temperature of the source as ordinarily defined; it may come, for example, from an emission nebula, where the gas has been highly heated and ionized by a blue star in the vicinity. This kind of radiation is strongest in the centimeter lengths. The second type is *nonthermal radiation,* an excess over the first, which may be the sort of radiation emitted by fast-moving particles re-

FIG. 5·15. The 50-foot Radio Telescope at the Naval Research Laboratory, Washington.

volving in the synchrotron of the radiation laboratory; it is much stronger in the meter wavelengths than in the shorter ones.

Although radio reception from the heavens was achieved as early as 1931, extensive activity in radio telescope building and operation did not begin until 1946, after the end of World War II. Progress since then has been rapid in this new field in which physicists and radio engineers as well as astronomers are engaged. A list of radio astronomical observatories, compiled by J. L. Pawsey in 1957, includes 50 such observatories in 20 different countries.

5·16. The Radio Telescope is analogous to the optical telescope. Its antenna, like the optical objective, collects and focuses the radio beam from the celestial source toward which it is directed. Instead

FIG. 5·16.   The 96-Helix Radio Telescope of the Radio Observatory, Ohio State University.

of forming an image of the source, the antenna concentrates the beam on one or more small dipoles, whence the energy is conveyed to a sensitive receiver. The strength of the signal at a chosen wavelength is then recorded by a registering meter. The antennas are essentially of two kinds:

The *paraboloidal type* of radio antenna is a "dish" of sheet metal or wire mesh, resembling the large mirror of the optical reflecting telescope. The instrument in this form is generally steerable. Like many optical telescopes, it can be directed usually toward a selected point in the heavens and can follow that point in the daily westward movement.

The *flat-type antenna* is an array of collectors, which may be extended far enough to provide the desired resolving power. This

type of antenna has a variety of forms. As an example, J. D. Kraus
and associates at Ohio State University have employed the telescope
with which the radio map of the sky (Fig. 17·11) was made. The
antenna, which operates in the meridian (Fig. 5·16), consists of 96
helices mounted on a steel frame 160 feet long. The frame is
pivoted on a horizontal east-west axis so that it may face any part
of the meridian from the south horizon of Columbus to the north
celestial pole.

The Mills Cross, designed by B. Y. Mills at Sydney, Australia, is
a crossed array of dipoles, each arm 1500 feet long. It has the resolving power of a paraboloid of that diameter, but a smaller gather-
ing power. A similar crossed array having arms 2047 feet in length
is operated by the Carnegie Institution in Washington.

The radio telescope is as effective by day as by night. The long-
wave radiations it records are not obstructed by the clouds of our
atmosphere or by the interstellar dust clouds that conceal much of
the universe from the optical view. This type of telescope can locate in space the otherwise invisible clouds of neutral hydrogen,
which serve well as indicators of the spiral arms of our galaxy, and
it may be capable of recording strong radio sources at distances beyond the reach of optical telescopes.

5·17. The Resolving Power of a radio telescope is a measure of the
fineness of detail it can record. Calculated by the same formula
(5·10) as for the optical telescope, the resolving power is the least
angular distance between two radio point sources at which they can
be separated with a particular telescope. The value of this critical
angle is proportional directly to the wavelength of the radiation and
inversely to the diameter of the antenna. Because it operates with
the longer wavelengths, a radio telescope is less effective in separating
fine detail than is an optical telescope of the same aperture. Thus
the critical separation for a 50-foot radio dish at the wavelength of
21 cm is 47′ as compared with a least separation of only 0″.023 at
visual wavelengths with the 200-inch Hale telescope.

A partial remedy for the deficiency in resolving power of radio
telescopes is to employ larger antennae or interference methods, or
both.

5·18. Very Large Paraboloidal-Type Radio Telescopes. The 250-
foot paraboloid completed in 1957 at the Jodrell Bank Experimental Station of the University of Manchester is the largest steerable

radio telescope in operation. Its range of wavelength is from 10 cm to about 20 meters, so that it can record the 21-cm radiation of neutral hydrogen. The mounting is of the altazimuth type. Second in size is the 210-foot paraboloid of the Radiophysics Laboratory at Sydney, Australia. This telescope, situated about 200 miles west of

FIG. 5·18. The 250-foot Radio Telescope at the Jodrell Bank Experimental Station, University of Manchester.

Sydney, is designed to operate mainly in the range from 10 to 50 cm. It has an altazimuth mounting, but is also employed effectively in the equatorial system. Next is the 140-foot paraboloid of the National Radio Astronomy Observatory at Greenbank, West Virginia.

A steerable 600-foot paraboloid is under construction at the Naval Radio Research Station at Sugar Grove, West Virginia; it is designed primarily for military communications research, but will also be used for certain astronomical purposes.

The number of paraboloids having diameters less than 100 feet is increasing rapidly. Among these are the twin 90-foot paraboloids at

California Institute of Technology's radio observatory in the Owens Valley about 250 miles north of Pasadena. The two telescopes operate at wavelengths from 5 cm to 1 meter. They are equatorially mounted on flatcars that move on north-south and east-west tracks 1600 feet long, where they may be used either separately or together as an interferometer giving high resolution.

QUESTIONS ON CHAPTER 5

1. Distinguish between the refracting and the reflecting telescope. State the aperture and location of the largest telescope of each kind.

2. Give reasons why very large optical telescopes are all reflecting telescopes.

3. Mention some advantages of the equatorial mounting for a telescope as compared with an altazimuth mounting.

4. Distinguish between the Newtonian and Cassegrainian forms of the reflecting telescope.

5. Describe the Schmidt telescope. What are some of its advantages over the type of telescope considered in Question 4?

6. Give reasons why a telescope of larger aperture is superior to one of smaller aperture.

7. Explain how a spectrum is produced when a beam of light is passed through a glass prism. What is the purpose of the slit before the prism?

8. Describe the appearance of: (a) the bright-line spectrum; (b) the continuous spectrum; (c) the dark-line spectrum.

9. What is the physical nature of the source producing each kind of spectrum? What can be learned about the chemical composition of the source in each case?

10. State and explain the effect in the spectrum when the source is approaching or receding from the observer.

11. Explain that a radio telescope is less effective in separating fine detail than an optical telescope of the same aperture.

12. State an advantage and a disadvantage of a radio telescope as compared with an optical telescope.

REFERENCES

Brown, R. Hanbury, and A. C. B. Lovell, *The Exploration of Space by Radio.* John Wiley and Sons, New York, 1958.

Dimitroff, George Z., and James G. Baker, *Telescopes and Accessories.* Harvard University Press, Cambridge, 1945.

Fassaro, James S., *Photographic Giants of Palomar.* Drawings by R. W. Porter. Westernlore Press, Los Angeles, 1952.

Ingalls, Albert G., editor, *Amateur Telescope Making, Book 1; Amateur Telescope Making, Advanced; Amateur Telescope Making, Book 3.* Scientific American, New York.

King, Henry C., *The History of the Telescope*. Sky Publishing Corporation, Harvard Observatory, Cambridge, 1955.

Mount Wilson and Palomar Observatories, *Frontiers in Space*. The Bookstore, California Institute of Technology, Pasadena.

Wright, Helen, *Palomar*. The Macmillan Company, New York, 1952.

The 60-foot Radio Telescope at the Agassiz Station, Harvard Observatory.
(Photograph by Robert E. Cox)

6

THE MOON IN ITS PHASES

MOTIONS OF THE MOON – THE MOON'S SURFACE
FEATURES – ECLIPSES OF THE MOON

The moon is the earth's *satellite,* or attendant. Next to the sun, it is the most conspicuous in our skies, because it is the nearest celestial body to the earth. The moon and the earth revolve together around the sun, and mutually revolve meanwhile around a point between their centers. Some satellites of other planets are larger than the moon, but none of these reflects as much sunlight to its planet as does the moon to the earth. In this chapter we consider the moon's motion relative to the sun and to the earth, its surface features which are in marked contrast with those of the earth, and its eclipses when it enters the earth's shadow.

MOTIONS OF THE MOON

6·1. The Earth and Moon Are Like a Double Planet. Although the moon is not the largest of the satellites, it has the distinction of being the one most nearly comparable with its primary in size and

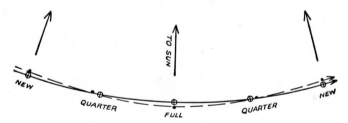

Fig. 6·1. Orbits of the Earth and Moon Around the Sun.

mass. The moon's diameter of 2160 miles is more than a quarter of the earth's diameter, and its mass is $\frac{1}{82}$ as much as the earth's mass.

Imagine the centers of the earth and moon joined by a stout rod. The point of support at which the two bodies would balance is the *center of mass* of the earth-moon system. It is this point around which the earth and the moon mutually revolve monthly; and it is the elliptical path of this point around the sun that we have hitherto called the "earth's orbit." The center of mass of the earth-moon system is only 2900 miles from the earth's center and is therefore within the earth. Thus the moon revolves around the earth, although not around its center. In the descriptions that follow it is convenient to consider the moon's revolution relative to the earth's center.

6·2. The Moon's Distance from the Earth. A frequent way of measuring the distance of a celestial body is by observing its parallax. *Parallax* is the difference between the directions of an

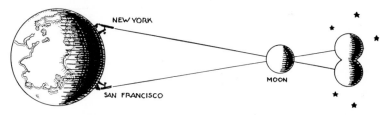

FIG. 6·2. The Moon's Directions Differ by Nearly Its Breadth as Viewed from New York and San Francisco.

object when it is viewed from two different places. Notice how a near-by object seems to jump back and forth against a distant background when it is viewed alternately with the two eyes. The nearer the object, the greater is its change in direction; and the amount of the parallax would be greater, of course, if our eyes were farther apart. Where the parallax has been measured and the distance between the two points of observation is known, the distance of the object is readily calculated.

The difference in the moon's directions from two widely separated places on the earth is so great that the parallax can be accurately measured. Observed at the same instant from New York and San Francisco, the moon's positions among the stars differ by nearly the full breadth of the moon, or nearly half a degree. When we speak of the moon's parallax ordinarily, it is as though one observer were at the center oi the earth and the other at the equator with the moon on his horizon. It is this equatorial horizontal parallax that is given for the sake of uniformity.

The moon's parallax at its average distance from the earth is nearly 1°. The average distance of the moon from the center of the earth is 238,857 miles, which is only about 60 times the radius of the earth, or less than 10 times its circumference. Close agreement with this value has been obtained by measuring the two-way travel times of many radio pulses reflected from the moon.

The distances which separate the celestial bodies are so great in comparison with the sizes of the bodies that it is often impractical to represent the two on the same scale in the diagrams. In Fig. 6·2, for example, the moon should be placed 2½ feet from the 1-inch earth.

6·3. The Moon's Orbit Relative to the Earth is an ellipse of small eccentricity, having the earth at one focus. At _perigee,_ where the moon is nearest us, the distance between the centers of the moon and earth may be as small as 221,463 miles. At _apogee,_ where the

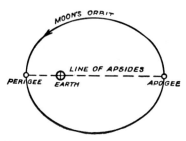

moon is farthest from us, the distance may be as great as 252,710 miles. The resulting variation of more than 10 per cent in the moon's apparent diameter is still not enough to be conspicuous to the unaided eye.

The moon's orbit around us is changing continually, mainly because of unequal effects of the sun's attraction for the moon and earth. For example, the major axis of the orbit rotates eastward in a period of about 9 years. This

FIG. 6·3. The Moon's Orbit Relative to the Earth. The orbit is an ellipse of small eccentricity (much exaggerated in the diagram) with the earth at one focus.

is one of the many variations which make the determination of the moon's motion an intricate problem, but a problem now being so well solved that the moon's course in the heavens is soon likely to be predictable with high accuracy.

6·4. The Moon's Phases are the different shapes it shows. The moon is a dark globe like the earth; one half is in the sunlight, while the other half turned away from the sun is in the darkness of night. The phases are the varying amounts of the moon's sunlit hemisphere that are turned toward us successively in the course of the month.

It is the _new moon_ that passes the sun; the dark hemisphere is toward us. The moon is invisible at this phase unless it happens to pass directly across the sun's disk, causing an eclipse of the sun. On the second evening after the new phase the thin _crescent_ moon is likely to be seen in the west after sundown. The crescent grows

thicker night after night, until the sunrise line runs straight across
the disk at the *first quarter*. Then comes the *gibbous* phase as the
bulging sunrise line gives the moon a lopsided appearance. Finally,
a round *full moon* is seen rising at about nightfall. The phases
are repeated thereafter in reverse order as the sunset line advances
over the disk; they are gibbous, *last quarter*, crescent, and new again.

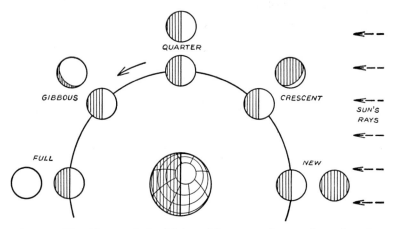

F IG. 6·4. The Phases of the Moon. The outer figures show the phases
as seen from the earth.

The horns, or *cusps*, of the crescent moon point away from the
sun's place, and nearly in the direction of the moon's path among
the stars. They are more nearly vertical in the evenings of spring,
and more nearly horizontal in the autumn. Their direction in
the sky follows the changing direction of the ecliptic with respect
to the horizon during the year.

6·5. Earthlight on the Moon. Often when the moon is in the
crescent phase we see the rest of the moon dimly illuminated.
This appearance has been called "the old moon in the new moon's
arms," for the bright crescent seems to be wrapped around the
faintly lighted part (Fig. 6·5).

The thin crescent is in the sunlight. The rest of the moon's disk
is made visible by sunlight reflected from the earth. Just as the
moon tempers the darkness of night for us, so the earth shines on
the moon. If anyone lived on the earthward side of the moon, he
would see the earth up among the stars in his sky (Fig. 1·3A) going
through all the phases that the moon shows to us. They are, of

FIG. 6·5. Earthlight on the Moon at the Crescent Phase in the Morning Sky. The planet Saturn had emerged from behind the moon half an hour before. (*Yerkes Observatory photograph*)

course, supplementary; full earth occurs at new moon. The full earth would look 4 times as great in diameter as the full moon appears to us, and something like 60 times as bright; for the earth is not only a larger mirror to reflect the sunshine but, owing to the atmosphere, it is a better reflector as well; it returns a third of the light it receives from the sun.

Earthlight is plainest when the moon is a thin crescent, for the earth is then near its full in the lunar sky. It is a bluer light than that of the sunlit moon, because a considerable part of it is sunlight reflected by our atmosphere. The air around us scatters the shorter wavelengths more effectively, as the blue sky shows.

6·6. The Month of the Phases, from new moon to new again, averages slightly more than 29½ days, and varies in length more than half a day. It is the *synodic month,* and the lunar month of the calendars. Because it is shorter than our calendar months, with a single exception, the dates of the different phases are generally earlier in successive months.

The length of the *sidereal month* averages 27⅓ days. It is the true period of the moon's revolution around the earth. At the end of this interval the moon has returned to nearly the same place among the stars. In the meantime the sun has been moving eastward as well, so that more than two days elapse after the end

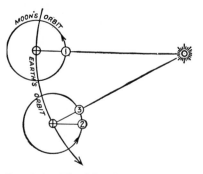

FIG. 6·6. The Month of the Phases Is Longer than the Sidereal Month. Between positions 1 and 2 the moon has made one revolution, completing the sidereal month. The synodic month does not end until the moon has reached the position 3.

of the sidereal month (Fig. 6·6) before the synodic month is completed.

6·7. The Moon's Path Among the Stars. Two apparent motions of the moon are observed by everyone. First, the moon rises and sets daily; it circles westward around us along with the rest of the celestial scenery, because the earth is rotating from west to east. Second, the moon moves eastward against the turning background of the stars, because it is revolving in this direction around the earth. In the course of a day the moon revolves 360°/27.3, or about 13°, moving slightly more than its own diameter in an hour.

The moon's apparent path among the stars is nearly a great circle of the celestial sphere, which is inclined about 5° to the ecliptic. It therefore crosses the ecliptic at two opposite *nodes*. The *ascending node* is the point where the moon's center crosses the ecliptic going north; the *descending node* is where it crosses going south. The nodes *regress*, or slide westward along the ecliptic. Regression of the nodes goes on at a much faster rate than does precession of the equinoxes (3·11). In only 18.6 years the nodes shift completely around the ecliptic. The moon's path through the constellations of the zodiac is considerably different from month to month.

6·8. Ephemeris Time by the Moon. The moon's revolution around the earth provides an important means of timekeeping that is independent of the earth's variable rotation. The practical problem is to be able to observe precisely the universal time when the center of the moon's large disk arrives at a particular place among the stars. The corresponding uniform ephemeris time (4·7) when the moon has this position can be determined by the theory of the moon's motion. Frequent comparisons of this kind permit accurate corrections from the predicted ephemeris times of celestial events to the universal times for ordinary use.

Occasions when the moon passes over, or *occults,* a star have been employed for a similar purpose. The star disappears almost instantly at the moon's eastern edge and reappears as abruptly at the western edge. Predictions of occultations for stations in the United States and Canada are published in *Sky and Telescope*. Approximate times of occultations of some planets and bright stars are listed in the *American Ephemeris and Nautical Almanac*. Occultations are also interesting to watch with the telescope or with the unaided eye when the objects are bright enough. The photograph of Jupiter and its satellites emerging from behind the moon (Fig. 6·8) illustrates a spectacular example.

A photographic device, known as the dual-rate moon position camera, is employed at the U.S. Naval Observatory and elsewhere for more convenient reading of the moon-clock. Attached to a telescope of moderate size, it holds the moon fixed relative to the stars during the exposure. In the photographs the positions of 30

FIG. 6·8. Jupiter and Its Satellites Emerging from Behind the Moon. (*Photographed by Paul E. Roques, Griffith Observatory*)

or 40 points on the bright edge of the moon are measured in relation to about 10 neighboring stars. This method not only gives a better control of our timekeeping but is also improving our knowledge of the moon's motions and its variations.

6·9. The Moon Rises Later from Day to Day. We have seen that the solar day is about 4 minutes longer than the sidereal day because the sun moves eastward relative to the stars. Due to the fact that the moon moves eastward still faster than the sun, the "lunar day" is longer than the solar day. The interval from upper transit of the moon to its next upper transit averages $24^h 50^m$ of solar time, varying as much as 15 minutes either way; it is of special importance to those who live beside the ocean, for it is twice the interval between high tides.

Not only its crossing of the meridian but also the rising and setting of the moon are delayed an average of 50 minutes from day to day. The variation from regularity in the moonrise is even more marked, and we notice it particularly in the rising of the moon near its full phase.

The *harvest moon* is the full moon that occurs nearest the time of the autumnal equinox. Then the moon near its full rises from night to night with the least delay as observed in our northern latitudes. In the latitude of New York the least delay is shorter by an hour than the greatest delay. Thus the harvest moon lingers longer in our early evening skies than does the nearly full moon of other seasons, giving more light after sundown for harvesting. It can be shown that the least delay in the moonrise on successive nights occurs when the moon's path among the stars is least inclined to the east horizon, as it is at sunset at the time of the autumnal equinox.

6·10. The Moon Moves North and South during the month, just as the sun does during the year and for the same reason. The moon's path among the stars is nearly the same as the ecliptic and is, therefore, similarly inclined to the celestial equator.

Consider the full moon. Opposite the sun at this phase, the full moon is farthest north when the sun is farthest south of the equator. The full moon near the time of the winter solstice rises in the northeast, climbs high in the sky, and sets in the northwest, as observed in middle northern latitudes; it is above the horizon for a longer time than are the full moons of other seasons. In summer it is the other way around. The full moon of June rises in the southeast, transits low in the south, and soon sets in the southwest, like the winter sun.

In some years the moon ranges farther north and south than in other years. The greatest range in its movement in declination occurs at intervals of 18.6 years. This was the case in 1950, when the moon was going fully 5° farther than the sun both north and south from the celestial equator, and many people remarked on it at the time. This variation in the range of the moon's north and south motion is a consequence of the regression of the nodes of its path (6·7).

6·11. The Moon's Rotation; Its Librations. As often as it is revealed in the changing phases, the face of the "man in the moon" is always toward us. This means that the moon rotates on its axis once in a sidereal month, while it is revolving once around the earth. Although the statement is true in the long run, anyone who

FIG. 6·12. The Moon at First Quarter. The moon is inverted and reversed, as it appears ordinarily through the telescope. The mountains are clearest near the sunrise line, at the right, where the shadows are longest.
(*Yerkes Observatory photograph*)

watches the moon carefully during the month can see that the same hemisphere is not turned precisely toward us at all times. Spots near the moon's edge are sometimes in view and at other times turned out of sight, as Figs. 6·12 and 6·12A clearly show. The moon seems to rock as it goes around us. These apparent oscillations, or *librations*, arise chiefly from two causes.

1. The moon's equator is inclined about 6½° to the plane of its

orbit. Thus its north pole is brought toward us at one time and its south pole is toward us two weeks later, just as the earth's poles are presented alternately to the sun during the year.

FIG. 6·12A. The Gibbous Moon About Two Days After First Quarter. The group of seas which form the "girl reading" is nearer the moon's western edge than in Fig. 6·12. The crater Copernicus is a little more than halfway down the bulging sunrise line. (*Yerkes Observatory photograph*)

2. The moon's revolution is not uniform. In its elliptical orbit around us, the law of equal areas (4·5) applies; the nearer the moon to the earth, the faster is its revolution. Meanwhile the rotation of the moon is practically uniform. Thus the two motions do not keep perfectly in step, although they come out together at the end of the month. The moon rocks in the east and west direction, allow-

ing us to see farther around it in longitude at each edge than we could otherwise.

Fully 59 per cent of the moon's surface has faced the earth when the month is completed. The remaining 41 per cent is never seen from the earth; and if anyone lived in that region of the moon, he could never see the earth. Three fourths of the hitherto unknown side of the moon was revealed for the first time in photographs from the space probe Lunik III on October 7, 1959. The only dark blotch that was then added was the Sea of Dreams, as it was named by Soviet scientists.

THE MOON'S SURFACE FEATURES

6·12. The Lunar Seas. Two features of the moon are plainly visible to the unaided eye. First, the changing phases are among the most conspicuous sights in the heavens and were the first to be correctly explained. Second, the large dark areas we see on the disk of the moon were as well known in early times, although they were not as well interpreted, as they are today.

The dark areas form the eyes, nose, and mouth of the familiar "man in the moon" and the profile of the "girl in the moon," which is easily seen when Fig. 6·12A is turned around to represent the view of the moon without the telescope. The "girl reading," the "hare," and the "frog" are all formed by the same group of seas in the telescopic aspect of the moon

Formerly supposed to be water areas, the lunar seas were given fanciful watery Latin names that have now survived their original meanings. One is Mare Serenitatis (Sea of Serenity); others are Mare Imbrium (Sea of Storms) and Sinus Iridum (Bay of Rainbows). The seas cover half the moon's visible surface and are especially prominent in its northern hemisphere. Roughly circular, they are mostly connected, with the conspicuous exception of Mare Crisium (Fig. 6·14). Although we still call them "seas," the dark spots are relatively smooth plains which are not all at the same level. A frequent explanation is that they are hardened pools of lava, resembling the great basaltic plateaus of the earth.

6·13. The Moon Through the Telescope. There is still another feature of the moon's surface to be detected occasionally with the naked eye; the sunrise and sunset lines are not perfectly smooth. Bright projections into the dark hemisphere show where the sunlight illuminates lofty peaks before the sun has risen or after it has set on the plains around them. The moon is mountainous, a feature that was verified as soon as the telescope came into use.

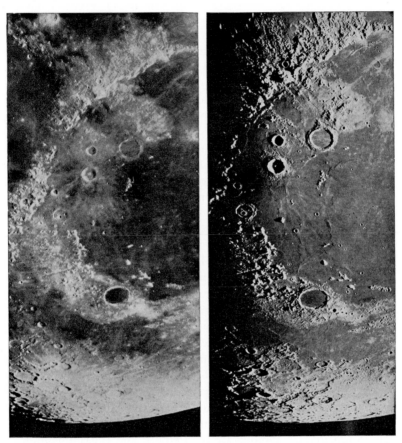

Fig. 6·13. Region of Mare Imbrium Under Different Illuminations. The lunar Apennines appear at the top, the Alps and the crater Plato below the center. (*Mount Wilson Observatory photographs*)

It was in 1609 that the Italian scientist Galileo heard of the discovery by a Dutch spectacle maker that two lenses held at suitable distances before the eye gave a clearer view of the landscape. Galileo fitted two small lenses into a tube and went out to view the heavens; he directed this telescope toward the moon first of all. Galileo observed the lunar mountains and estimated that they are comparable in height with terrestrial mountains. This he could do by noticing how far from the sunrise line into the darkness the peaks first catch the rays of the sun. Like little stars they appear at first, growing larger until they join the sunlit hemisphere. The heights of the lunar mountains may also be calculated from the lengths of their shadows and the altitude of the sun in their sky at that time.

The mountains on the moon are most distinct when they are near the sunrise or the sunset line. There the shadows are long, as they are with us in the early morning or late afternoon, so that the sunlit peaks stand out in bold relief among the shadows. The view of the mountains is especially good within about two days of the quarter phases.

Compare the two photographs (Fig. 6·13) of the same region at different phases of the moon. In the view at the left the sun is shining more directly on the region; the shadows are shorter, and the surface seems rather flat. In the photograph at the right the region is near the sunset line; the shadows are longer, and the mountains are more conspicuous.

6·14. The Lunar Mountains. There are only a few irregularities of the moon's surface that remind us at all of our own mountain ranges. Best known of these are the three ridges which form the curving western border of Mare Imbrium, the right eye of the "man in the moon" as we view the moon without the telescope, and which separate it from Mare Serenitatis. These are the Apennines, Caucasus, and Alps; their names are among the few that have survived from Hevelius' map of the moon of 1647, in which the lunar formations have the names of terrestrial ones. With a few exceptions the prominent mountains on the moon bear the names of scholars of former times, according to the system introduced by Riccioli in 1651. Examples are the Leibnitz and Doerfel mountains near the moon's south pole; some of their peaks rise as much as 26,000 feet above the plains.

The mountains around Mare Imbrium slope abruptly toward it and more gradually outward. It is as though they were all that remain of a nearly circular rampart 700 miles across which surrounded the great sea.

6·15. The Lunar Craters have nearly circular walls, steep and often shelving on the inside and sloping more gradually to the plain out-

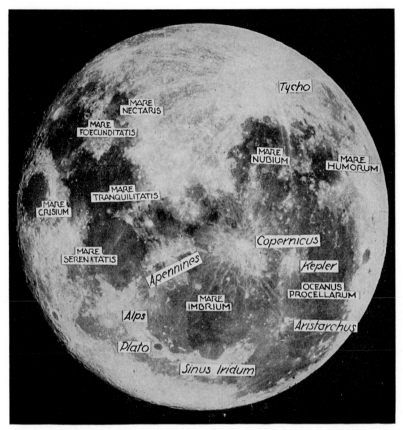

FIG. 6·14. The Moon Shortly After the Full Phase. The sunset line is appearing at the left. The longest ray system radiates from the crater Tycho near the moon's south pole. Shorter ray systems surround Copernicus and some other craters. (*Yerkes Observatory photograph*)

side. Lofty peaks surmount some of the walls, and peaks also appear near the centers of many craters. Some craters have floors depressed several thousand feet below the plain. In others the floors are elevated; the inside of the crater Wargentin is nearly as high as the top of the wall itself. Some craters have rough, bright floors; Aristarchus is the brightest of these. Others, such as Plato in the lunar Alpine region, are as dark inside as the seas.

More than 30,000 craters are recognized. They range in size from pits a few hundred feet across, which can be seen only with

Fig. 6·15. Lunar Landscape at Last Quarter. The crater Tycho is at the right of the center. The walled plain Clavius is near the top. (*Lick Observatory photograph*)

large telescopes, to "walled plains," such as Clavius (Fig. 6·15), about 150 miles in diameter, near the moon's south pole.

Two versions of the origins of the lunar craters and the other formations have long received attention, but without a firm decision as yet between them. One opinion is that the moon's surface features are mainly of igneous origin, having been formed during the cooling of the moon. The earliest and largest of the mountain rings provided the basins of the later lunar seas. As the moon's crust thickened, conditions became favorable for the forming of the smaller rings of the craters.

The second opinion is that the irregularities of the moon's surface were caused mainly by the fall of meteoritic masses. These blasted out the basins of the seas, scattering debris over the moonscape and perhaps producing great lava pools as well by the heat of their impacts.

6·16. Lunar Rays and Rills. The lunar *rays* are bright streaks often as wide as 5 or 10 miles and up to 1500 miles long, which radiate from points near a few of the craters and pass over mountain and plain alike without much regard for the topography. The longest and most conspicuous ray system radiates from the crater Tycho near the moon's south pole; it is a prominent feature of the full moon as viewed with any telescope. A system of shorter and more crooked rays is centered near the crater Copernicus.

The lunar *rills* are clefts as wide as half a mile and of unknown depth. Some are irregular, whereas others run nearly straight for many miles. They are generally not conspicuous through small telescopes. The rills might seem to have been caused by the parting of the crust as it cooled.

6·17. The Absence of Atmosphere. We can readily see that the moon has no perceptible amount of atmosphere around it. There is no twilight on the moon; the sunrise and sunset lines form a perfectly sharp division between day and night. The moon's disk is undimmed near the edge, where a greater thickness of atmosphere would intervene. When the moon occults a star, there is no dimming or reddening of the star before its abrupt disappearance behind the moon.

Two neighboring worlds share the sunshine together. One, the earth, has air around it and is the abode of life and activity. The other, the moon, is airless and therefore lifeless, a dead world where practically nothing happens. Why does the earth have an abundance of air, while the moon has none to speak of? The answer is found in the feebler surface gravity of the moon. The moon's attraction for objects near its surface is only one sixth the corresponding attraction of the earth; it is not effective enough to hold an atmosphere around the moon.

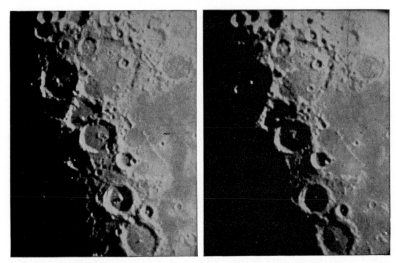

Fig. 6·17. Sunset on the Moon. The sunset line is moving toward the right. No twilight intervenes between day and night, as it does on the earth. (*McMath-Hulbert Observatory photographs*)

6·18. The Escape of Atmospheres. The molecules of a gas dart about incessantly. Their speeds increase as the temperature is raised, and at the same temperature are greater for lighter gases than for heavier ones. The molecules of hydrogen, the lightest gas, are moving as fast as a mile a second at the freezing temperature of water. The molecules of our air at ordinary room temperatures have speeds somewhat greater than half a mile a second.

These are averages. At the same temperature and for a particular kind of gas the speeds vary. Collisions between the molecules bring some of them momentarily almost to rest and propel others much faster than the average. Whether the molecules at their highest speeds can fly away into space depends on the strength of the restraining pull of gravity.

The *velocity of escape* is the speed that a molecule or anything else must attain to escape from a specified body. If a ball is thrown upward, it is soon brought down by the earth's attraction. Given a greater initial speed, the ball goes higher and returns to the ground after a longer time. With what speed must a ball be started so that it will never return? This critical speed is the velocity of escape. Its value at the earth's surface is nearly 7 miles a second, without allowance for air resistance. The molecules in our air do not ordinarily have speeds as great as this; hence, the earth has retained its atmosphere, except some of the very lightest gases. The velocity of escape at the moon's surface, however, is only $1\frac{1}{2}$ miles a second. An atmosphere could not remain there for a long time.

6·19. An Expedition to the Moon is considered by some people a possibility before the end of the century. Preliminary steps have been the launching of artificial earth-satellites (1·4), one of which

Fig. 6·19. The Lunar Apennines. (*Lick Observatory photograph*)

crash-landed on the moon, the placing of other unmanned vehicles in orbits around the sun, and experiments to determine what might be the reactions of human beings to space travel. The next step might be to assemble a space station in revolution around the earth, from which an expedition could take off for the moon.

Conditions the voyagers would find on the moon are quite well known to us. Some of them would differ drastically enough from conditions at home to threaten the survival of the party. The glaring sunlight during the long day on the moon heats its surface to the ordinary boiling point of water, and includes deadly ultraviolet rays. The temperature at nightfall drops abruptly, and at midnight is 500° F lower than at noon. The absence of air and water of course presents a difficult problem. The bare, lifeless landscape is not inviting. The moon is a perfect and dangerous desert.

ECLIPSES OF THE MOON

6·20. The Earth's Shadow. Like any other opaque object in the sunshine, the earth casts a shadow in the direction away from the sun. The *umbra* of the shadow is the part from which the sun-

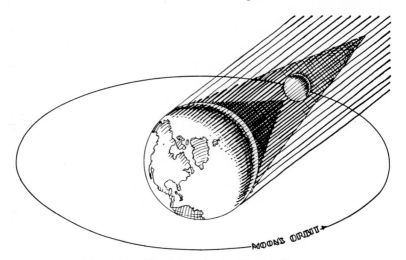

FIG. 6·20. The Moon in the Earth's Shadow.

light would be completely excluded if some light were not scattered into it by the earth's atmosphere. The umbra is a long, thin cone reaching an average of 859,000 miles into space before it tapers to a point. This darker part of the shadow is often meant when we speak of the *shadow.* It is surrounded by the *penumbra,* from which the direct sunlight is only partly excluded.

Suppose that a large screen is held at right angles to the direction of the shadow, and that it is moved out into space in that direction.

The umbra of the earth's shadow would fall on this screen as a dark circle growing smaller with increasing distance of the screen, until at the moon's distance the diameter of the shadow would be 5700 miles, or nearly 3 times the moon's diameter of 2160 miles.

Because the earth's shadow points away from the sun, it sweeps eastward around the ecliptic once in a year as the earth revolves. At intervals of a synodic month, the faster-moving moon overtakes the shadow and sometimes passes through it.

6·21. The Moon in the Earth's Shadow. *Umbral eclipses* occur when the moon passes through the umbra of the earth's shadow. The longest eclipses, when the moon goes centrally through the

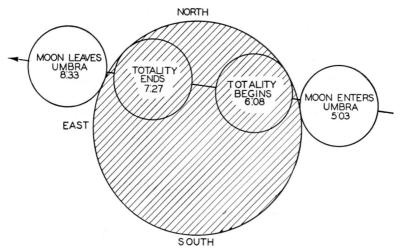

FIG. 6·21. Path of the Moon Through the Umbra of the Earth's Shadow During the Eclipse of the Moon, November 18, 1956. Universal times are given.

shadow, last about 3^h 40^m; this duration is counted from the first contact with the umbra until the moon leaves the umbra completely. Total eclipse can last as long as 1^h 40^m, preceded and followed by partial phases, each of about an hour's duration. Usually the eclipse is not central (Fig. 6·21), so that its duration is shorter. Often the moon passes so far from the center of the shadow that it is never completely immersed in the umbra, and the eclipse is partial throughout.

Penumbral eclipses occur when the moon passes through the penumbra of the earth's shadow without entering the umbra. The
weakened light of the part of the moon that is in the penumbra is
visible to the eye when the least distance of the edge of the moon
from the umbra does not exceed one third of the moon's diameter;
it is detected in the photograph (Fig. 6·21A) when the least distance

FIG. 6·21A. The Moon in the Penumbra of the Earth's Shadow, March
23, 1951. The weakening of the light of the northern (lower) part of the
moon was not visible to the eye. (*Photographed by Paul E. Roques,
Griffith Observatory*)

does not exceed two thirds of the moon's diameter and by photometric means when the distance is still greater.

A lunar eclipse is visible wherever the moon is above the horizon
during its occurrence, that is, over more than half the earth, count-
ing the region that is rotated into view of the moon while the eclipse
is going on. The ephemeris times of the circumstances of all umbral
eclipses and of penumbral eclipses when they occur are published in
advance in the *American Ephemeris*.

Ten umbral lunar eclipses are scheduled in the interval from
1961 to 1968 inclusive as visible, at least in part, in a considerable
area of the United States and Canada. Eight of these are total.

UMBRAL LUNAR ECLIPSES VISIBLE IN THE UNITED STATES AND CANADA

| Middle of Eclipse | | Duration of | |
Date	Universal Time	Umbral Phase	Totality
1961, Mar. 2	13 32	3 4	....
1961, Aug. 26	3 8	3 18	0 14
1963, Dec. 30	11 7	3 34	1 24
1964, June 25	1 7	3 40	1 38
1964, Dec. 19	2 35	3 28	1 4
1965, June 14	1 51	1 40	....
1967, Apr. 24	12 7	3 34	1 22
1967, Oct. 18	10 16	3 26	0 56
1968, Apr. 13	4 49	3 26	0 56
1968, Oct. 6	11 41	3 28	1 2

6·22. The Moon Is Visible in Total Eclipse. The first conspicuous effect of the lunar eclipse is seen soon after the moon enters the umbra. A dark notch appears at the eastern edge of the moon and

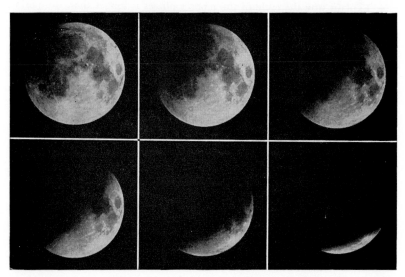

FIG. 6·22. Partial Eclipse of the Moon. Progress of the umbral eclipse until it became nearly total. (*Photographed by Albert W. Recht, Chamberlin Observatory*)

slowly overspreads the disk. The shadow is so dark in comparison with the unshaded part (Fig. 6·22) that the moon might be expected to disappear in total eclipse. As totality comes on, however, the moon usually becomes plainly visible.

The moon in total eclipse is still illuminated by sunlight which filters through the earth's atmosphere around the base of the shadow. The light is diffused by the air into the shadow and onto the moon. It is redder than ordinary sunlight for the same reason that the sunset is red, so that the totally eclipsed moon has an unfamiliar hue. The brightness of the moon then depends on the transparency of the atmosphere around the base of the shadow. Enough light usually sifts through to show the surface features clearly. On rare occasions the moon becomes very dim.

QUESTIONS ON CHAPTER 6

1. How would the moon's parallax compare with its present value (a) if the moon's distance were twice as great? (b) if the earth's radius were twice as great?

2. Describe the moon's orbit relative to the sun; relative to the earth.

3. Where is the moon in the sky at sunset when its phase is new? first quarter? full?

4. Explain why the cycle of the moon's phases is longer than the period of the moon's revolution around the earth.

5. Show that the interval between upper transits of the moon is about 50 minutes longer than the solar day.

6. At what time of year does the full moon pass nearest the zenith in middle northern latitudes? State its least possible distance from your zenith.

7. Explain the causes of two librations of the moon.

8. Name the terms which are defined as follows:

(a) The moon's phase between first quarter and full.
(b) The point of the moon's orbit which is nearest the earth.
(c) The true period of the moon's revolution around the earth.
(d) The interval between successive new moons.
(e) The moon near its full which rises with the least delay on successive nights.

9. Describe each of the following features of the lunar surface and state your idea of the origin of each: (a) the seas; (b) mountains; (c) craters; (d) rays.

10. If a manned rocket succeeds in reaching the moon, what conditions will the crew find there different from those at home?

11. Why does the moon remain visible in total eclipse?

12. When will the next umbral eclipse of the moon be visible in the United States and Canada? At what time will the middle of the eclipse occur where you are?

REFERENCES

Baldwin, Ralph B., *The Face of the Moon*.   University of Chicago Press, 1949.

Kuiper, Gerard P., editor, *Photographic Lunar Atlas*.   University of Chicago Press, 1960.

Moore, Patrick, *A Guide to the Moon*.   W. W. Norton and Company, New York, 1954.

Ryan, Cornelius, editor, *Conquest of the Moon*.   The Viking Press, New York, 1953.

The 16-inch Coronagraph Dome, Sacramento Peak Observatory, New Mexico.

7

THE PATHS OF THE PLANETS

MOTIONS OF THE PLANETS — THE LAW OF GRAVITATION — THE PLANETARY SYSTEM

Seven bright celestial bodies move about among the "fixed stars" that form the constellations. They are the sun, the moon, and the five planets—Mercury, Venus, Mars, Jupiter, and Saturn, which have the appearance of stars to the unaided eye. These were the *planeta,* or "wanderers," of the ancients. These 7 bodies are among our nearest neighbors in space. In the foreground of the starry scene they are conspicuous in our skies. Their brightness and their complex movements against the background of the stars have made them objects of special interest through the ages.

MOTIONS OF THE PLANETS

7·1. The Planets Move in Loops. Anyone who has viewed the spectacle of the heavens that is displayed in one of the larger planetariums knows how the planets swing back and forth in their courses among the stars. Celestial movements of a year can be represented in a short time in the sky of the planetarium. The looped paths of the planets are shown very clearly there.

For the most part, the planets move eastward through the constellations. This is their *direct* motion; for it is in this direction that they revolve around the sun. At intervals, which are not the same for the different planets, they turn and move backward, toward the west; they *retrograde* for a while before resuming the eastward motion. They are said to be *stationary* at the turns. Thus the planets seem to march and countermarch among the stars, progressing toward the east around the heavens in series of loops.

These apparent movements of the planets are readily observed in the sky itself. Watch the red planet Mars from week to week, for example, beginning as soon as it rises at a convenient hour of the evening. Notice the planet's position among the stars on each occasion, and mark the place and date on a star map. The line of dots will show presently, as it does in Fig. 7·1, that Mars steers a devious course.

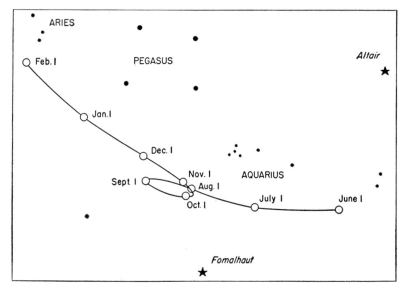

Fig. 7·1. Path of Mars Near the Favorable Opposition of 1956.

7·2. The Problem of the Planetary Motions. Just how do the planets move around the earth so as to proceed in loops among the constellations? By what combinations of uniform circular motions centered in the earth can their observed movements be represented? This was the problem the early scholars wished to solve. Intuitively they agreed that celestial motions ought to be uniform and in circles; then, too, the circle is an easy figure for calculations.

The globe of the earth was stationary at the center of their universe. The sphere of the stars turned daily around it. Within that sphere the 7 wanderers shared its daily turning, and also moved eastward around the earth at various distances from it.

7·3. The Geocentric System. The most enduring early plan for solving the problem of the planetary motions was developed by Ptolemy at Alexandria in the 2nd century and is, accordingly, known as the *Ptolemaic system.* It was a plan of epicycles. In the simplest form of the system (Fig. 7·3) each planet was supposed to move on the circumference of a circle, the *epicycle,* while the center of that circle revolved around the earth on a second circle, the *deferent.* By such combinations the attempt was made to represent the observed movements of the planets. The Ptolemaic plan became more complex as time went on. During many centuries that intervened between the decline of Greek culture and the revival of learning in Europe, Arabian astronomers undertook to improve the system so that it would more nearly represent the planetary movements. They tried to get a better fit by adding more epicycles and by other devices. Each planet was eventually provided with

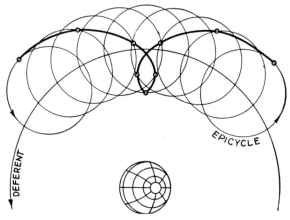

Fig. 7·3. The Motion of a Planet in the Ptolemaic System.

from 40 to 60 epicycles turning one upon another. It was then that King Alphonso of Castile remarked that had he been present at the Creation he might have given excellent advice. The theory of the central earth had begun to seem unreasonable.

7·4. The Earth in Motion. From the times of the early Greek scholars there was an undercurrent of opinion that the earth is not stationary. The followers of Pythagoras, who taught that the earth is a globe, supposed that it is moving. Aristarchus of Samos, in the 3rd century B.C., is said to have been convinced that the earth rotates daily on its axis and revolves yearly around the sun. There were others who caught glimpses of the truth. Such ideas, however, then seemed unbelievable to almost everyone and received little attention.

By the time that Columbus sailed west on his famous voyage, there was growing dissatisfaction with the theory of the central, stationary earth. Before the companions of Magellan had returned from the first trip around the world, a European scholar had reached the conclusion anew that the earth is in motion. His name, as we say it, was Nicholas Copernicus. His theory of the moving earth was published in 1543.

The *Copernican system* set the sun in the center instead of the earth which now took its rightful place as one of the planets revolving around the sun. It retained the original idea that the planets moved uniformly in circles, and accordingly remained a system of epicycles. Copernicus could offer no convincing proof of either the earth's revolution or daily rotation which he also advocated.

7·5. Tycho's Observations.   Tycho Brahe greatly improved the instruments and methods of observing the positions of the celestial bodies. He saw clearly that an improvement in the theory of the motions of the planets required more reliable data on their apparent movements among the stars. Born in 1546, the most fruitful years of his life were spent in his observatory on the formerly Danish island of Hven, 20 miles northeast of Copenhagen. He died in Prague in 1601.

It was before the invention of the telescope. Tycho's chief instruments were large quadrants and sextants having plain sights. With these, he and his assistants observed the planets night after night and determined their right ascensions and declinations with a degree of accuracy never before attained. He gave special attention to the planet Mars, a fortunate choice because its orbit is not as nearly circular as are the orbits of some of the other bright planets.

7·6. The Planets Move in Ellipses Around the Sun.   John Kepler was Tycho's assistant in his last years in Prague. He inherited the records of the positions of the planets, which his master had kept for many years. Kepler studied the records patiently in the hope of determining the actual motions of the planets. In 1609 he announced two important conclusions, and in 1618 he discovered the third. They are known to us as *Kepler's laws:*

1. *The planets move around the sun in ellipses having the sun at one of the foci.* Thus the planets do not go around the earth, and their orbits are not circles.

2. *Each planet revolves in such a way that the line joining it to*

the sun sweeps over equal areas in equal intervals of time. The nearer the planet comes to the sun, the faster it moves, as we have already noticed (4·5) in the case of the earth.

3. *The squares of the periods of revolution of any two planets are in the same ratio as the cubes of their mean distances from the sun.* This useful relation is called the *harmonic law.*

Here ended the attempts to represent the movements of the planets by uniform circular motions centered in the earth. There was still no evidence, however, that the earth itself revolves around the sun.

THE LAW OF GRAVITATION

While Kepler was deriving his laws which describe how the planets go around the sun, his contemporary, Galileo Galilei in Italy, was laying the foundations of mechanics. He questioned the traditional ideas about the motions of things and set out to determine for himself how they really move. It remained for Isaac Newton in England to formulate clearly the new laws of motion and to show that they apply not merely to objects immediately around us but to the celestial bodies as well. The principal feature of the new mechanics was the concept of an attractive force which operates under the same rules everywhere in the universe.

7·7. Force Equals Mass Times Acceleration. Before the time of Galileo, an undisturbed body was supposed to remain at rest. Hence, it seemed appropriate that the earth should be stationary. Anyone who asserted that the earth is moving might well be asked to explain by what process it is kept in motion.

Galileo's experiments led him to the new idea that uniform motion in a straight line is the natural state. An object will go on forever in the same direction with the same speed unless it is disturbed. Rest is the special case where the initial speed happens to be zero. Uniform motion in a straight line, therefore, demands no explanation. It is only when the motion is changing either in direction or in speed that an accounting is required. We say then that a force is acting on the body, and inquire where the force originates.

The strength of the *force* is measured by its effect on the body on which it acts; it equals the mass of the body multiplied by its *acceleration,* or the rate of change of its velocity (directed speed). The acceleration may appear as increasing or diminishing speed, or changing direction, or both. A stone falling vertically faster and faster is accelerated. An object moving in a circle with constant speed is accelerated. In both cases a force is acting.

7·8. The Laws of Motion were formulated by Newton in his *Principia* (1687) substantially as follows:

1. *Every body persists in its state of rest or of uniform motion in a straight line unless it is compelled to change that state by a force impressed upon it.* Where a force is applied:

2. *The acceleration is directly proportional to the force and inversely to the mass of the body, and it takes place in the direction of the straight line in which the force acts.*

3. *To every action there is always an equal and contrary reaction.*

The second law defines force in the usual way. The first law states that there is no acceleration where no force is acting; the motion of the body remains unchanged. The third law asserts that the force between two bodies is the same in the two directions. A bat exerts no greater force on the ball than the ball exerts on the bat; but the lighter ball experiences a greater acceleration than the heavier bat and batter combined.

Armed with these laws of motion, Newton succeeded in reducing Kepler's three laws of the planetary movements to a single universal law. It is said that the fall of an apple one day as Newton sat in his garden started the great mathematician to thinking of this problem. Does the attractive force that brings down the apple also control the moon's revolution around the earth? Does a similar force directed toward the sun cause the planets to revolve around it?

7·9. The Law of Gravitation. A force is continuously acting on the planets, because their courses around the sun are always curving. It is an attractive force directed toward the sun; this fact can be deduced from Kepler's law of equal areas, although we shall not stop to do so. From further studies of Kepler's laws, Newton discovered the law of the sun's attraction. He found that the force between the sun and a planet is proportional directly to the product of their masses, and inversely as the square of the distance between their centers.

Newton next calculated the law of the earth's attraction. An apple falls 16 feet in the first second. The moon, averaging 60 times as far from the earth's center, is drawn in from a straight-line course $\frac{1}{20}$ inch in a second, which is about 16 feet divided by the square of 60. Using more exact values than these, he showed that the force of the earth's attraction for objects around it is inversely proportional to the squares of their distances from its center. Although his studies could not extend beyond the planetary system, Newton concluded that he had discovered a universal law and so announced it in his *law of gravitation:*

Every particle of matter in the universe attracts every other particle with a force that varies directly as the product of their masses and inversely as the square of the distance between them.

7·10. How the Planets Revolve. Consider the earth as an example. By Newton's law there is an attractive force between the earth and the sun, which is the same in the two directions. Started from rest they would eventually come together. The earth is moving, however, nearly at right angles to the sun's direction at the rate of $18\frac{1}{2}$ miles a second, and in one second it is attracted less than an eighth of an inch toward the sun. It is this deviation from a straight line course second after second through the year that causes the earth to revolve around the sun.

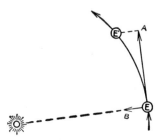

Properly speaking, the earth and sun mutually revolve around a point between their centers. The ancient problem of whether the sun or the earth revolves was not well stated. Both revolve. If the earth and sun were equally massive, the point around which they wheel yearly would be halfway between their centers. Because the sun is a third of a million times as massive as the earth, this center of mass is only 280 miles from the sun's center; and it is not far from the center for all the other planets.

Fig. 7·10. Earth's Revolution Explained by the Laws of Motion. At the position E the earth, if undisturbed, would continue on to A, by the first law of motion. It arrives at E' instead, having been attracted in the meantime toward the sun the distance EB.

Thus the planets revolve around the sun, although not precisely around its center. The first law of motion explains their continued progress, and the force of gravitation causes them to revolve around the sun instead of going away into space.

7·11. The Orbits of the Planets relative to the sun are ellipses having the sun's center at one of the foci. These *relative orbits* are the ones we employ for the planets generally, and similarly for the satellites revolving around their planets. They are the same in form as the actual orbits and differ from them only slightly in size.

Newton showed from his law of gravitation that the orbits of revolving bodies in general may be any one of the three *conics*. These are the ellipse, parabola, and hyperbola. The ellipse includes the circle, where the eccentricity is zero. The parabola, eccentricity 1, is open at one end, and the hyperbola is wider open. Evidently the permanent members of the sun's family have closed, elliptical orbits.

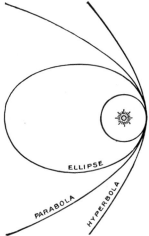

If the earth, now revolving in nearly a circle at the rate of 18½ miles a second, could be speeded up, its orbit would become larger and more eccentric. At the speed of 26 miles a second the orbit would become a parabola,

Fig. 7·11.   Different Shapes of Orbits.

and the earth would depart from the sun. This is the velocity of escape from the sun at the earth's distance.

7·12. The Masses of the Planets. The law of gravitation views the physical universe as a scheme of masses and distances. It is, therefore, of considerable interest to inquire how the masses are measured. The *masses* of some planets, that is, the quantities of material they contain, can be found by Kepler's harmonic law (7·6) as Newton restated it more precisely:

The squares of the periods of *any two pairs* of mutually revolving celestial bodies, *each multiplied by the combined mass of the pair,* are in the same proportion as the cubes of the mean distances that separate the pairs.

Suppose that we wish to find the mass of the planet Saturn. We write this proportion, taking Saturn and one of its satellites as one pair and the earth and sun as the second pair. Let the unit of mass be the combined mass of the earth and sun, the unit of distance the mean distance between the earth and sun, and the unit of time the period of the earth's revolution around the sun. The relation becomes simply: The mass of Saturn and its satellite, which may be neglected, equals the cube of the mean distance of the satellite from Saturn divided by the square of its period of revolution around Saturn.

The masses of planets having satellites have been found in this way. It is more difficult to weigh planets, such as Mercury, Venus, and Pluto, which have no satellites; their masses are determined by their disturbing effects on the motions of neighboring bodies.

7·13. Courses and Forces. Early astronomers tried to represent the planetary movements by combinations of circular motions centered in the earth. Copernicus set the sun in the center instead of the earth. Kepler discovered that the planets revolve around the sun in ellipses instead of circles and epicycles. So far the interest was confined to the courses themselves.

Newton's law of gravitation directed the attention to mighty forces controlling the courses of the planets. This law has made possible the present accurate predictions of the planetary movements. It has promoted the discoveries of celestial bodies hitherto unknown, from their effects on the motions of known bodies. It applies equally well to mutually revolving stars.

For most purposes astronomers make their calculations on the basis of the law of gravitation. It is only rarely that the newer theory of relativity predicts celestial events with appreciably greater accuracy. The advance of Mercury's perihelion around the sun at a faster rate than is predicted by the law of gravitation is a well-known example. The apparent displacements of stars away from the sun's place in the sky at total eclipses of the sun is another example of the occasionally greater merit of relativity in representing what goes on.

THE PLANETARY SYSTEM

The meaning of the word *planet* as a body revolving around the sun began with the acceptance of the Copernican system which added the earth to the list of planets, subtracted the sun from the original list, and reduced the moon to its proper place as a satellite of the earth.

The known membership of the planetary system has increased greatly since Copernicus' time. Knowledge of satellites attending other planets began with Galileo's discovery, in 1610, of the four bright satellites of Jupiter. The planet Uranus, barely visible to the naked eye, was discovered in 1781. Neptune, which is always too faint to be seen without the telescope, was found in 1846. The discovery of the still fainter and more remote Pluto in 1930 completed the list of the 9 known *principal planets.* Ceres, the largest of the *asteroids,* or *minor planets,* was the first of these to be discovered, in 1801.

The earth is one of the principal planets. The moon is one of 31 satellites which accompany 6 of these planets. Thousands of asteroids and great numbers of comets and meteor swarms are also members of this large family which, including the sun itself, is known as the *solar system.*

7·14. The Planets Named and Classified. The names of the planets in order of mean distance from the sun are:

$$
\text{Inferior planets} \begin{cases} \text{Mercury} \\ \text{Venus} \\ \text{Earth} \\ \text{Mars} \end{cases} \Bigg\} \text{Inner planets}
$$

$$
\text{Superior planets} \begin{cases} \text{The Asteroids or Minor planets} \\ \text{Jupiter} \\ \text{Saturn} \\ \text{Uranus} \\ \text{Neptune} \\ \text{Pluto} \end{cases} \Bigg\} \text{Outer planets}
$$

They are classified as inferior and superior planets, and also as inner and outer planets. The *inferior planets* are nearer the sun than the earth's distance, and the *superior planets* revolve outside the earth's orbit. The *inner planets* revolve inside the main zone of the asteroids, whereas the outer planets have their orbits outside this zone. The 4 inner planets and Pluto as well are sometimes known as the *terrestrial planets,* because they are small as compared with the *giant planets:* Jupiter, Saturn, Uranus, and Neptune.

Not all the asteroids are confined to the main zone; some of them invade the regions of the principal planets. A part of the orbit of Pluto (Fig. 7·21) is nearer the sun than is Neptune's orbit.

7·15. Aspects and Phases of Inferior Planets. The *elongation* of a planet at a particular time is its angular distance from the sun.

Certain positions of the planet relative to the sun's place in the sky have distinctive names and are known as the *aspects* of the planet. The planet is in *conjunction* with the sun when the two bodies have the same celestial longitude, so that the planet's elongation is not far from 0°. It is in *quadrature* when the elongation is

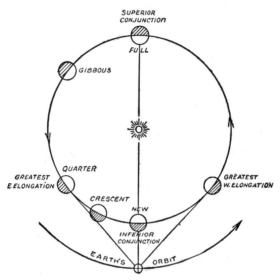

FIG. 7·15. Aspects and Phases of an Inferior Planet. The elongations are limited; the phases are like those of the moon.

90°, and is in *opposition* when its celestial longitude differs by 180° from the sun's, so that its elongation is near 180°.

The times of the aspects of the principal planets are predicted in *The American Ephemeris and Nautical Almanac.* For the conjunctions of the planets with one another and with the moon, the times predicted there are approximately when the two bodies have the same right ascension.

The inferior planets, Mercury and Venus, have limited elongations; they appear to us to oscillate to the east and west of the sun's place. From superior conjunction, beyond the sun, they move out to *greatest eastern elongation,* which does not exceed 28° from the sun for Mercury and 48° for Venus. Here they turn westward relative to the sun, pass between the sun and the earth at *inferior conjunction,* then move out to *greatest western elongation,* and finally return toward the east behind the sun. As Fig. 7·15 shows, the inferior planets go through the complete cycle of phases, just as the moon does. Their phases are nearly full at superior conjunction, quarter in the average at the greatest elongations, and nearly new at inferior conjunction.

7·16. Aspects and Phases of Superior Planets. The superior planets, such as Mars and Jupiter, revolve around the sun in periods longer than a year. They accordingly move eastward through the constellations more slowly than the sun appears to do. With respect to the sun's place in the sky, they seem to move westward (clockwise in Fig. 7·16), and attain all values of elongation in that direction from 0° to 180°. At *conjunction* they pass behind the sun to subsequently appear in the east before sunrise. At *western quadrature* they are near the celestial meridian at sunrise. At *opposition* they rise around the time of sunset, and at *eastern quadrature* they are near the meridian at sunset.

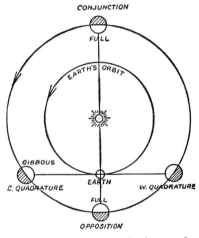

FIG. 7·16. Aspects and Phases of a Superior Planet. The aspects are similar to those of the moon. The only phases are full and gibbous.

From Fig. 7·16 we also see that the superior planets show the full or nearly full phase at all times to the earth. Mars near its quadrature appears conspicuously gibbous, because it is the nearest of these planets to the earth, so that its hemispheres turned toward the sun and earth are considerably different.

7·17. The Places of the Planets among the stars do not appear in the star maps, of course, because they are continually changing. Their right ascensions and declinations for a particular date can be found in an almanac and can then be marked in the maps. The positions of Jupiter and Saturn when they are opposite the sun's place are given in Table 7·I. The dates of oppositions of Mars and of its nearest approaches to the earth, from the latest to the next

TABLE 7·I   OPPOSITIONS OF JUPITER AND SATURN

Year	Jupiter			Saturn		
	UT	R.A.	Decl.	UT	R.A.	Decl.
1960	June 20^d 2^h	17^h 55^m	$-23°.7$	July 7^d 6^h	19^h 05^m	$-22°.2$
1961	July 25 10	20 18	-20 .1	July 19 11	19 54	-21 .0
1962	Aug. 31 15	22 39	$-$ 9 .7	July 31 19	20 43	-18 .9
1963	Oct. 8 11	0 55	$+$ 4 .5	Aug. 13 5	21 30	-16 .0
1964	Nov. 13 9	3 16	$+17$ .0	Aug. 24 20	22 17	-12 .3
1965	Dec. 18 9	5 43	$+23$ .1	Sept. 6 15	23 03	$-$ 8 .1

favorable opposition, are in Table 8·II. The dates of conjunctions and greatest elongations of Venus are in Table 8·I.

7·18. Retrograde Motions of the Planets. Consider again the loops in the planets' movements among the stars, which mystified the early astronomers and promoted the complex machinery of the Ptolemaic system. At intervals the planets interrupt their motions toward the east, and retrograde, or move back toward the west, for a while. The retrograde motions occur because we are observing from a planet that is revolving at a different rate from the others.

A superior planet, such as Mars, retrogrades near the time of its opposition; for the faster-moving earth then overtakes it and leaves it behind. On the other hand, Mars has its fastest direct motion near its conjunction with the sun, where its own motion and its displacement by ours are in the same direction. The inferior planets retrograde near inferior conjunction. In general, a planet retrogrades when it is nearest the earth.

7·19. The Distances of the Planets from the sun are given in Table 7·II, where other information about the planets and their orbits appears as well. These are mean distances; the distances vary because the orbits are ellipses with the sun at one focus. To find the greatest amount that a planet's distance departs from the mean, multiply the mean distance by the fraction representing the eccentricity of the planet's orbit. Thus the mean distance of

Mercury from the sun is 36 million miles, and the eccentricity of its orbit is 0.206; the greatest variation from the mean is therefore $7\frac{1}{2}$ million miles. Mercury is $28\frac{1}{2}$ million miles from the sun at perihelion and $43\frac{1}{2}$ million miles at aphelion.

A relation known as *Bode's law* is an easy way to remember the relative distances from the sun of all except the most remote planets. Write in a line the numbers: 0, 3, 6, 12, and so on, doubling the number each time to obtain the next one. Add 4 to each number, and divide the sums by 10. The resulting series of numbers: 0.4, 0.7, 1.0, 1.6, 2.8 . . . represents the mean distances of the planets expressed in astronomical units. The *astronomical unit* is the earth's mean distance from the sun.

Compare the distances found by this rule with the actual mean distances in astronomical units given in Table 7·II. The agreement is quite close except for Neptune and Pluto, although it would be less impressive for Mercury if the rule of doubling the number had been followed from the start.

7·20. The Scale of the Solar System. When the distance of one planet from the sun is given, the distances of the others can be calculated from their periods of revolution by Kepler's harmonic law (7·6). The earth's mean distance from the sun is taken as the yardstick which sets the scale for the distances of planets from the sun, of satellites from their planets (Table 7·III), and of the stars as well. This is the reason for calling it the astronomical unit and for wishing to determine its value as accurately as possible.

We have seen (6·2) that the moon's distance is found by observing its parallax from two stations on the earth. The distance of the sun is measured less reliably in this way, because its parallax is much smaller, and also because the stars are less available as reference points in the daytime. More dependable values of the astronomical unit have been derived by observing the larger parallaxes of the nearer planets, particularly of the asteroid Eros at its closest approaches to the earth.

The value of the solar parallax adopted in the astronomical almanacs by international agreement is 8″.80; this is the difference in the direction of the sun's center as it would be viewed from the center and equator of the earth, when the sun is on the horizon and at its average distance from us. The corresponding mean distance of the earth from the sun is 92,900,000 miles.

THE PATHS OF THE PLANETS

TABLE 7·II   THE PLANETS

Name		Symbol	Mean Distance from Sun		Period of Revolution		Eccentricity of Orbit	Inclination to Ecliptic
			Astron. Units	Million Miles	Sidereal	Synodic		
Inner	Mercury	☿	0.3871	35.96	days 87.969	days 115.88	0.206	7° 0'
	Venus	♀	0.7233	67.20	224.701	583.92	0.007	3 24
	Earth	⊕	1.0000	92.90	365.256	......	0.017	0 0
	Mars	♂	1.5237	141.6	686.980	779.94	0.093	1 51
	Ceres	①	2.7673	257.1	years 4.604	466.60	0.077	10 37
Outer	Jupiter	♃	5.2028	483.3	11.862	398.88	0.048	1 18
	Saturn	♄	9.5388	886.2	29.458	378.09	0.056	2 29
	Uranus	♅	19.1820	1783	84.013	369.66	0.047	0 46
	Neptune	♆	30.0577	2794	164.794	367.49	0.009	1 46
	Pluto	♇	39.5177	3670	248.430	366.74	0.249	17 9

Name	Mean Diameter in Miles	Mass ⊕ = 1	Density Water = 1	Period of Rotation	Inclination of Equator to Orbit	Oblateness	Stellar Magnitude at Greatest Brilliancy
Sun ☉	864,000	331,950	1.41	$24^d.65$	7° 10'	0	−26.8
Moon ☾	2,160	0.012	3.33	27 .32	6 41	0	−12.6
Mercury	2,900	0.05	6.1	88	7?	0	−1.9
Venus	7,600	0.81	5.06	30?	23?	0	−4.4
Earth	7,913	1.00	5.52	$23^h 56^m$	23 27	1/296	......
Mars	4,200	0.11	4.12	24 37	24	1/192	−2.8
Jupiter	86,800	318.4	1.35	9 50	3 7	1/15	−2.5
Saturn	71,500	95.3	0.71	10 02	26 45	1/9.5	−0.4
Uranus	29,400	14.5	1.56	10 45	98	1/14	+5.7
Neptune	28,000	17.2	2.29	15 48?	29	1/40	+7.6

TABLE 7·III   THE SATELLITES

Name	Discovery	Mean Distance in Miles	Period of Revolution			Diameter in Miles	Stellar Magnitude at Mean Opposition
Moon		238,857	27^d	7^h 43^m		2160	−12
SATELLITES OF MARS							
Phobos	Hall, 1877	5,800	0	7	39	10?	+12
Deimos	Hall, 1877	14,600	1	6	18	5?	13
SATELLITES OF JUPITER							
Fifth	Barnard, 1892	113,000	0	11	53	150?	13
I Io	Galileo, 1610	262,000	1	18	28	2000	5
II Europa	Galileo, 1610	417,000	3	13	14	1800	6
III Ganymede	Galileo, 1610	666,000	7	3	43	3100	5
IV Callisto	Galileo, 1610	1,170,000	16	16	32	2800	6
Sixth	Perrine, 1904	7,120,000	250	14		100?	14
Seventh	Perrine, 1905	7,290,000	259	14		35?	17
Tenth	Nicholson, 1938	7,300,000	260	12		15?	19
Twelfth	Nicholson, 1951	13,000,000	625			14?	19
Eleventh	Nicholson, 1938	14,000,000	700			19?	18
Eighth	Melotte, 1908	14,600,000	739			35?	17
Ninth	Nicholson, 1914	14,700,000	758			17?	19
SATELLITES OF SATURN							
Mimas	Herschel, 1789	115,000	0	22	37	300?	12
Enceladus	Herschel, 1789	148,000	1	8	53	350	12
Tethys	Cassini, 1684	183,000	1	21	18	500	11
Dione	Cassini, 1684	234,000	2	17	41	500	11
Rhea	Cassini, 1672	327,000	4	12	25	1000	10
Titan	Huygens, 1655	759,000	15	22	41	2850	8
Hyperion	Bond, 1848	920,000	21	6	38	300?	13
Iapetus	Cassini, 1671	2,210,000	79	7	56	800	11
Phoebe	Pickering, 1898	8,034,000	550			200?	14
SATELLITES OF URANUS							
Miranda	Kuiper, 1948	81,000	1	9	56	.....	17
Ariel	Lassell, 1851	119,000	2	12	29	600?	15
Umbriel	Lassell, 1851	166,000	4	3	28	400?	15
Titania	Herschel, 1787	272,000	8	16	56	1000?	14
Oberon	Herschel, 1787	364,000	13	11	7	900?	14
SATELLITES OF NEPTUNE							
Triton	Lassell, 1846	220,000	5	21	3	2350	13
Nereid	Kuiper, 1949	3,440,000	359	10		200?	19

7·21. The Revolutions of the Planets around the sun and of the satellites around their planets exhibit some striking regularities, which apply more generally to the larger ones. These and the

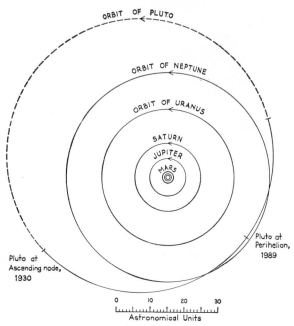

FIG. 7·21. Approximate Orbits of the Principal Planets. They are in general nearly circles around the sun, and are nearly in the same plane. The part of Pluto's orbit south of the ecliptic is indicated by the broken line.

exceptions in the cases of the less massive members provide important clues concerning the origin of the solar system.

1. *All the planets revolve from west to east.* This includes all the asteroids. Most satellites have direct revolutions, and this is also the favored direction of all rotations in the system.

2. *The orbits of the planets and satellites are nearly circles,* as a general thing. The orbits of the smallest principal planets, Mercury and Pluto, are considerably eccentric. Among the still smaller asteroids some orbits are even more eccentric.

3. *The orbits of most planets and satellites lie nearly in the same plane.* With the exception of Pluto's orbit, the orbits of the principal planets are inclined less than 8° to the ecliptic plane, so that these planets are observed always near the ecliptic, and mostly

within the boundaries of the zodiac. These three regularities do not apply to many comets and meteor swarms, especially to those having the longer periods of revolution.

The true periods of revolution of the planets, or their *sidereal periods,* increase with distance from the sun in accordance with Kepler's harmonic law, from 88 days for Mercury to nearly 250 years for Pluto. The *synodic periods* are also given in Table 7·II. They are the intervals between two successive conjunctions of the planet with the sun, as seen from the earth; for the inferior planets the conjunctions must both be either inferior or superior. In other words, the synodic period is the interval in which the faster-moving inferior planet gains a lap on the earth, or in which the earth gains a lap on the slower superior planet. Mars and Venus have the longest synodic periods because they are nearest the earth and run it the closest race around the sun.

QUESTIONS ON CHAPTER 7

1. In what respects did the Copernican system of the planetary motions differ from the Ptolemaic system? from the present view?

2. Suppose that a planet revolves around the sun in the period of 8 years. Show by Kepler's third law that its distance from the sun is 4 times the earth's distance.

3. Explain that an object moving in a circle with constant speed is continuously accelerated.

4. State the law of gravitation. How is the force between two bodies affected: (a) if the original distance between them is doubled? (b) if the distance is unaltered but the mass of one body is doubled?

5. Explain the revolution of a planet around the sun, employing the first law of motion and the law of gravitation.

6. Show that the mass of a planet is readily determined if the planet has a satellite.

7. Name: (a) an inferior planet; (b) a superior planet; (c) an inner planet; (d) an outer planet; (e) a minor planet.

8. State the earth's average distance from the sun. Why is it called the astronomical unit?

9. Why cannot the sun's distance from us be dependably measured by observing its parallax from two stations on the earth, as the moon's distance is determined?

10. Associate the appropriate term with each of the following definitions:

(a) The angular distance of a planet from the sun.
(b) The aspect of an inferior planet when it is between the sun and the earth.

(c) The aspect of a superior planet when it is opposite the sun's place in the sky.

(d) The motion of a planet from east to west among the stars.

(e) The interval of time between two successive conjunctions of a planet with a star as seen from the sun.

11. Why does Mars near its quadrature show the gibbous phase more noticeably than do the other superior planets?

12. Venus and Mars have the longest synodic periods (Table 7·II) of the principal planets. Explain.

REFERENCES

De Vaucouleurs, Gerard, *Discovery of the Universe*. An outline of the history of astronomy from the origins to 1956. The Macmillan Company, New York, 1957.

Dreyer, J. L. E., *History of the Planetary Systems from Thales to Kepler*. Photo-offset edition with title: *A History of Astronomy from Thales to Kepler*. Dover Publications, New York, 1953.

Smart, W. M., *Celestial Mechanics*. Longmans, Green and Co., New York, 1953.

Yerkes Observatory, Williams Bay, Wisconsin.

8

PLANETS AND THEIR SATELLITES

MERCURY AND VENUS – MARS, THE RED PLANET – THE
ASTEROIDS – JUPITER, THE GIANT PLANET – SATURN,
THE RINGED PLANET – URANUS AND NEPTUNE – PLUTO,
THE MOST REMOTE PLANET

MERCURY AND VENUS

These two planets revolve inside the earth's orbit, Mercury once
in 88 days, Venus in 225 days. They accordingly oscillate to the
east and west of the sun's place in the sky and are never very far
from it. At times they come out in the west at nightfall as evening
stars; at other times they rise before the sun as morning stars. Both
planets, as we view them with the telescope, show the whole cycle
of phases (7·15) just as the moon does. Neither planet has a
satellite.

Mercury is the nearest to the sun and the smallest of the principal
planets. Its diameter, 2900 miles, is less than half again as great
as the moon's diameter. Venus, the brightest planet, outshines
all the celestial bodies except the sun and moon. Its diameter,
7600 miles, is only slightly less than the earth's diameter. Our
nearest neighbor among the principal planets, it comes within an
average of 26 million miles of the earth.

8·1. Mercury as Evening and Morning Star. The terms "evening
star" and "morning star" are applied more often to the appearances
of the inferior planets in the west after sunset and in the east before
sunrise. They are employed for the superior planets as well, to
signify that they set soon after or rise not long before the sun.

Mercury is occasionally visible to the naked eye for a few days
near the times of its greatest elongations. It then appears in the
twilight near the horizon as a bright star, sometimes even a little
brighter than Sirius, and twinkling like a star because of its small
disk and low altitude. The elongations occur about 22 days before

and after inferior conjunction. Because the synodic period is only 116 days, several greatest elongations occur in the course of a year; they are, however, not equally favorable.

Mercury's altitude above the horizon at sunset and sunrise varies considerably on these occasions, in our latitudes. The altitude is greatest, and the planet is therefore most easily visible, when the ecliptic is most inclined to the horizon (3·7). On this account the most favorable times to see Mercury as evening star are at its greatest eastern elongations in the early spring, and as morning star at its greatest western elongations in the early autumn. Such occasions are especially favorable when the planet is then near its greatest distance from the sun. In its rather eccentric orbit Mercury's distance from the sun's place in the sky at its greatest elongations varies from 28° at its aphelion to as little as 18° at its perihelion.

8·2. Venus as Evening and Morning Star. Venus emerges slowly from superior conjunction, behind the sun, to appear as evening star, requiring 220 days to reach greatest eastern elongation. Then in only 72 days it moves back to inferior conjunction, this time between us and the sun, presently to become the morning star. In 72 days more it reaches greatest western elongation, where it turns again to begin the 220-day return to superior conjunction. Thus the entire synodic period is 584 days.

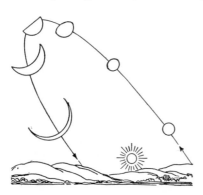

Fig. 8·2. Venus as Evening Star. Changing phase and apparent size of the planet as viewed with the telescope.

The greatest brilliancy of Venus as evening and morning star occurs about 36 days before and after inferior conjunction. On these occasions it appears 15 times as bright as Sirius, the brightest star, and 6 times as bright as the planet Jupiter. Then the planet appears through the telescope in the crescent phase, a crescent between 5 and 6 times as great from horn to horn as the apparent diameter of the fully lighted disk it shows over beyond the sun. Around the times of greatest brilliancy, Venus becomes visible in full daylight, like a star in the blue sky to the naked eye.

TABLE 8·I   DATES OF CONJUNCTIONS AND ELONGATIONS OF VENUS

Superior Conjunction	Greatest Elongation East (Evening Star)	Inferior Conjunction	Greatest Elongation West (Morning Star)
1960, June 22	1961, Jan. 29	1961, Apr. 10	1961, June 20
1962, Jan. 27	1962, Sept. 3	1962, Nov. 12	1963, Jan. 23
1963, Aug. 29	1964, Apr. 10	1964, June 19	1964, Aug. 29
1965, Apr. 12	1965, Nov. 15	1966, Jan. 26	1966, Apr. 6
1966, Nov. 9	1967, June 21	1967, Aug. 30	1967, Nov. 9

8·3. Mercury Resembles the Moon.   The best views of Mercury with the telescope are obtained in the daytime when the planet is well above the horizon.   In addition to the phases, some dark markings are glimpsed and are also recorded in photographs, which are remindful of the lunar seas.   The great increase in the planet's brightness from the quarter to the full phase, as the shadows become shorter, indicates that its surface is as mountainous as the surface of the moon.   Like the moon, too, Mercury has no atmosphere, and would not be expected to have any because of its small size and surface gravity.

Just as the moon rotates in the period of its revolution around us, so Mercury rotates once in 88 days while it is going once around the sun; the equality of the periods is verified by Dollfus in France, who finds that the equator is inclined about 7° to the ecliptic. Because of the considerable eccentricity of its orbit, the librations of Mercury leave only 30 per cent of the surface in permanent darkness. That part of the planet has a temperature not far above absolute zero, whereas the rocks on the sunward side are hot enough to melt lead; such extremes of temperature are unique in the planetary system.

8·4. Cloudy Atmosphere of Venus.   The surface of Venus is so concealed by the atmosphere around it that it has not been observed even in infrared photographs.   Photographs of the planet through violet filters reveal a variety of atmospheric markings which were studied by F. E. Ross as early as 1927.   The markings are ascribed to clouds of yellowish dust that is abundant there because of the lack of water. They frequently appear as alternate bright and dark bands which are presumably parallel to the equator. These bands inform us that the rotation period must be considerably less than the period of the planet's revolution around the sun. Yet the period cannot be as short as a day, because the spectrum lines are not noticeably slanting, as they are in the swiftly rotating

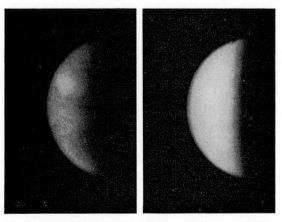

Fig. 8·4. Venus Near the Quarter Phase. In violet light (left) and red light (right). (*Photographed by Gerard P. Kuiper at McDonald Observatory*)

Saturn (Fig. 8·24). Ross estimated that the rotation period of Venus may be about 30 days.

More recently, Kuiper at McDonald Observatory and Richardson at Mount Wilson measured the directions of the cloud bands in their photographs of Venus. From the average of the two results, we conclude that the equator may be inclined to the ecliptic about as much as are the equators of the earth and Mars.

The spectrum of Venus also gives no evidence of water vapor or of free oxygen in its atmosphere. It reveals instead a surprising amount of carbon dioxide, many times as much in the available upper levels as in the entire atmosphere of the earth. Although Venus resembles the earth in size, mass, and distance from the sun, and has sometimes been called the "earth's twin sister," it seems unlikely that we would find this dust bowl of the planetary system a desirable place in which to live.

8·5. Transits of Mercury and Venus. The inferior planets occasionally *transit*, or cross directly in front of the sun at inferior conjunction. They then appear as dark dots against the sun's disk.

About 13 transits of Mercury occur in the course of a century; they are possible only within 3 days before or after May 8, and also within 5 days of November 10, when the sun passes the nodes of the planet's path. The latest one, on November 7, 1960, was visible in the United States and Canada. Transits are scheduled for the

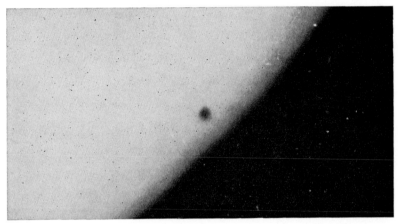

FIG. 8·5. Transit of Mercury, November 14, 1953. Photographed by J. L. Gossner at the Naval Observatory. (*U.S. Navy photograph*)

remainder of the century on May 9, 1970, November 10, 1973, November 13, 1986, November 6, 1993, and November 15, 1999, a grazing transit. Transits of Mercury are not visible without the telescope.

These transits, which can be timed rather accurately, have been useful for improving our knowledge of the planet's motions. A century ago, the French mathematician Leverrier discovered from records of many transits that the perihelion of Mercury's orbit is advancing faster than would be predicted by the law of gravitation. The major axis of the planet's orbit is turning eastward, mainly because of the attractions of other planets. The observed excess in its turning has now been explained by the theory of relativity.

Transits of Venus are less frequent; they are possible only when the planet arrives at inferior conjunction within about 2 days before or after June 7 or December 9, the dates when the sun passes the nodes of the planet's path. They are now coming in pairs having a separation of 8 years. The latest transits occurred in 1874 and 1882; the next ones are scheduled for June 8, 2004, and June 6, 2012. Transits of Venus are visible without a telescope.

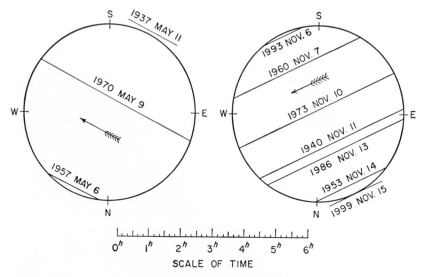

FIG. 8·5A.   Transits of Mercury, 1937–1999. (*Diagram by Fletcher G. Watson in* Sky and Telescope)

MARS, THE RED PLANET

Next in order beyond the earth, Mars revolves once in 687 days at the average distance of 142 million miles from the sun, and rotates on its axis once in $24^h 37^m$. Its diameter is 4200 miles, or slightly more than half the earth's diameter. Its atmosphere is not sufficiently extensive and clouded to hide its surface which exhibits a variety of markings. The persistent idea that Mars contains certain forms of life has made this planet an object of special interest, particularly at its closest approaches to the earth.

8·6. Oppositions of Mars with the sun recur at average intervals of 780 days, or about 50 days longer than 2 years. They accordingly come 50 days later in successive alternate years. Owing to the eccentricity of its orbit, Mars varies considerably in its distance from the earth at the different oppositions, from less than 35 million miles at perihelion to 63 million miles at aphelion.

TABLE 8·II OPPOSITIONS OF MARS

Date of Opposition	Nearest Earth	Distance in Million Miles	Magnitude
1956, Sept. 10	Sept. 7	35	−2.6
1958, Nov. 16	Nov. 8	45	−1.9
1960, Dec. 30	Dec. 25	56	−1.3
1963, Feb. 4	Feb. 3	62	−1.0
1965, Mar. 9	Mar. 12	62	−1.0
1967, Apr. 15	Apr. 21	56	−1.3
1969, May 31	June 9	45	−1.9
1971, Aug. 10	Aug. 12	35	−2.6

Favorable oppositions occur when the planet is also near its perihelion. At these unusually close approaches, which are always in the late summer, Mars becomes the most brilliant starlike object in the heavens with the single exception of Venus, and also attracts attention then because of its red color. With a telescope magnifying only 75 times, its disk appears as large as does the moon's disk to the unaided eye. The dates of oppositions of Mars from the latest to the next favorable opposition are given in Table 8·II.

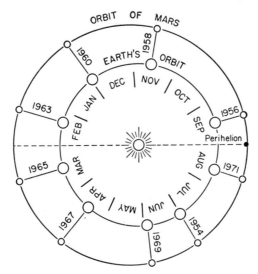

FIG. 8·6. Varying Distances of Mars at Oppositions from 1954 to 1971.

The oppositions of 1963 and 1965 will be equally unfavorable, although even then the planet will be superior in brightness to all the stars except Sirius. Following the favorable opposition of 1971, a pair about equally favorable will occur in 1986 and 1988.

8·7. The Seasons of Mars. Mars presents its poles alternately to the sun just as the earth does; its seasons resemble ours except that they are about twice as long. The winter solstice occurs near the time of perihelion, as in the case of the earth. Thus, as with us (3·16), the summer in the southern hemisphere begins when the planet is nearest the sun, and in the northern hemisphere when it is farthest from the sun. On the earth, as we have seen, the warmer summers and colder winters that might otherwise be expected in the southern hemisphere compared with the northern one are not appreciably so; the variation of our distance from the sun is relatively small, and our southern hemisphere has the more water to modify extreme temperatures.

The temperature difference is noticeable on Mars because of its more eccentric orbit, where the greatest distance from the sun exceeds the least by 20 per cent, or 26 million miles. The temperatures of the seasons are appreciably the more extreme in the Martian southern hemisphere. The snow cap around its south pole becomes larger in the winter season than does the north polar cap; and it completely disappears in the summer, which the other has not been observed to do. It is the south polar cap which is toward the earth at the favorable oppositions, and this is accordingly the one that more often appears in the photographs.

8·8. The Polar Caps; the Hazy Atmosphere. White caps, which appear alternately around the poles of Mars, are the most conspicuous features of the view with the telescope. Each snow cap expands rapidly as winter comes on in that hemisphere, and shrinks with the approach of summer. The southern cap has attained a diameter of 3700 miles, so that it then extended more than halfway from the pole to the equator. As the cap retreats toward the pole, the main body may leave behind for a time a small white spot, presumably on the summit or cooler slope of a hill.

The polar caps are more conspicuous in photographs in violet light, which reveal the areas of haze above them. The haze, as Kuiper has explained, may be caused by ice crystals similar to those in our cirrus clouds. Patches of haze also appear in the cooler air near the sunrise and sunset lines. Yellowish spots like clouds of dust are visible at times on various parts of the disk. Often the haze is widespread over the disk, making the view of the surface more difficult, and then it clears quite suddenly over large areas.

8·9. The Darker Markings appear through the telescope in a variety of shapes and sizes against the reddish background which imparts its color to the light of the planet. The reddish areas them-

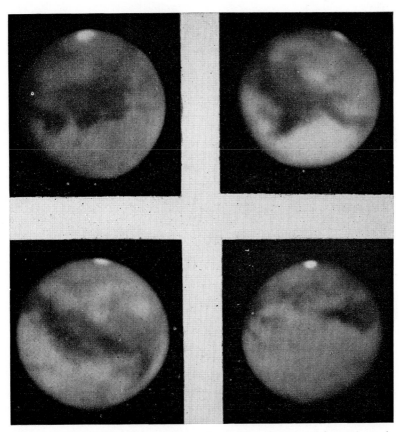

FIG. 8·9. Various Regions of Mars. South is at the top and east is at the right. In the *upper left* photograph, taken September 23, the dark central area is Mare Erythraeum. In the *lower left,* taken October 8, Mare Cimmerium is central, and in the *upper right,* taken 3½ hours later, Syrtis Major has come around to the center. The *lower right* photograph was taken October 19. Meanwhile, the south polar cap has shrunk considerably. (*Photographed in 1941 at Pic du Midi Observatory, France*)

selves are often called "deserts." Dollfus, observing at Pic du Midi in France, reports that their light resembles sunlight reflected from pulverized yellow oxide of iron.

The larger dark areas are known by watery names which have survived, like those of the lunar "seas," from the early maps. Prominent among them are the Syrtis Major (Great Bog) and Solis Lacus (Lake of the Sun). With the shrinking of each polar cap

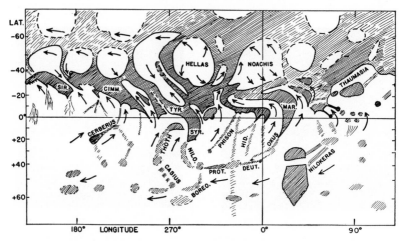

FIG. 8·9A. Sketch Map of Mars. It is based chiefly on a map by Antoniadi. Wind currents indicate the circulation during the Martian southern summer. (*Diagram by Dean B. McLaughlin*)

the dark markings of that hemisphere are more distinct; they become green during the Martian spring, and then fade and turn brown as winter approaches. Thus they might seem to behave as areas of vegetation would do.

An alternate explanation of the dark markings is offered by D. B. McLaughlin of the University of Michigan. He views them as frequently renewed areas of volcanic ash guided by prevailing winds into barlike and funnel-shaped forms which tend to terminate in triangular estuaries. The dark areas are more abundant in the southern hemisphere where the more extreme temperatures promote higher winds. The Margaritifer Sinus, abbreviated to Mar. in Fig. 8·9A, is illustrative. Notice how it changes direction after crossing the equator as though influenced by the Coriolis effect (2·1).

Changes in wind directions at certain seasons may bring in the red sands of the deserts to partly obliterate the darker markings. This interpretation would account for the variations in the forms and distinctness of the markings, and for the appearance of new ones, such as the new dark area "as large as Texas" reported by observers at the opposition of 1954.

The nomenclature of Mars was revised by the International Astronomical Union in 1958. The number of proper names for the large regions is reduced to 128, which are generally the same as before. Small details are designated only by their approximate Martian longitudes and latitudes. The official list of names and the maps for identifying the various features are shown in *Sky and Telescope* for November, 1958.

8·10. The Canals of Mars. A complex network of fine dark lines known as the *canals* of Mars was first reported by the Italian astronomer Schiaparelli, who observed it with a small telescope and

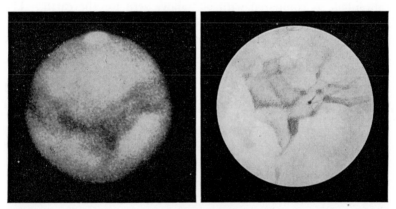

Fig. 8·10. Photograph and Drawing of Mars, Showing Some of the Larger Markings. The prominent marking below the center is Syrtis Major. (*Photograph by E. E. Barnard, Yerkes Observatory. Drawing by R. J. Trumpler, Lick Observatory*)

described the lines as like "the finest thread of spider's web drawn across the disk." This careful observer found the canals less difficult to see in the hemisphere where the snow cap was melting, and was tempted to suppose that vegetation bordering them might add to the width of the strips.

Many observers have viewed the network since then, often with telescopes of moderate size. The impression has been that it appears only during rare instants of exceptionally steady seeing.

Thus a continued succession of photographs with the very short exposures permitted by the largest telescopes might be expected to reveal the network eventually if it exists. Yet many other experienced observers have been unable to detect long narrow canals even visually, and have doubted their existence as such.

8·11. The Climate of Mars. The atmosphere of Mars is rarer than ours, and is deficient in certain ingredients necessary for animal life. Free oxygen is not detected in the spectrum analysis of sunlight reflected from the planet; it must be less than 1 per cent as abundant there as in the earth's atmosphere. The chief constitutent may be nitrogen, which is not revealed by this means. Water vapor is only a tenth of 1 per cent that of the earth, according to Kuiper, who has shown that carbon dioxide, however, is twice as abundant as in our atmosphere.

The average temperature of the surface of Mars is 40° below zero Fahrenheit as compared with 60° above zero for the earth. The climate of Mars seems to be too severe for the flourishing of even the hardiest known vegetation in such profusion as to color the dark areas.

8·12. Mars Has Two Satellites. Their names are Phobos and Deimos. Both are very small, probably not exceeding 10 miles

Fig. 8·12.   The Two Satellites of Mars.   (*Photographed by Gerard P. Kuiper, McDonald Observatory*)

in diameter, and are so near the bright planet as to be invisible except with large telescopes at favorable times.

Phobos has a direct revolution at the distance of only 3700 miles from the surface of Mars, once around in $7^h\ 39^m$, or less than one third the period of the planet's rotation in the same direction. Viewed from Mars, therefore, Phobos rises in the west and sets in the east. No other known satellite in the solar system revolves in a shorter interval of time than the rotation period of its primary.

Deimos, the outer satellite, revolves eastward around Mars once in $30^h\ 18^m$. It is smaller than Phobos and only a third as bright. This satellite rises in the east in the Martian sky, but drops behind the rotating planet so slowly that it goes through its whole cycle of phases for an observer there before it sets.

THE ASTEROIDS

The *asteroids,* or *minor planets,* revolve around the sun mainly between the orbits of Mars and Jupiter. Invisible to the naked eye, with the occasional exception of Vesta, they are "starlike" in the sense that few of them show disks even through large telescopes. The majority have periods of revolution between $3\frac{1}{2}$ and 6 years.

8·13. Discovery of Asteroids. Toward the close of the 18th century, the German astronomer Bode invited his colleagues to share in a search for a planet between the orbits of Mars and Jupiter. He explained that a series of numbers, which later came to be known as Bode's law (7·19), represented the relative distances of the known planets from the sun with a single exception. No planet had been found corresponding to the number 2.8.

While the search was being organized, the missing planet was discovered incidentally by Piazzi in Sicily on the 1st of January, 1801, because of its motion among the stars. The mean distance of the new planet, which Piazzi named Ceres, proved to be almost exactly 2.8 times the earth's distance from the sun. There was greater surprise when other minor planets were discovered later at about the same distance as Ceres.

Many thousand asteroids have been detected by the generally short trails they leave in the photographs by their motions against the background of the stars (Fig. 8·13) during the exposures. More than 1600 have had their orbits determined and have accordingly received permanent running numbers and names in the catalogs.

Many of even these, however, could readily become hopelessly lost because of considerable and rapid perturbations of their orbits by the attraction of Jupiter.   As an example of the concerted effort to prevent their being lost, F. K. Edmondson and associates at Indiana University have recovered a number of the fainter ones by moving the telescope to follow their expected motions during the exposures.   Thus the light of the asteroid is concentrated in a small image while the stars appear as trails.

Fig. 8·13.   Trails of Three Asteroids.   (*An early photograph by Max Wolf, Königstuhl-Heidelberg*)

The asteroids are small as compared with the principal planets. Ceres, the largest, is 480 miles in diameter.   Pallas, Juno, and Vesta are also among the larger asteroids.   The majority are less than 50 miles, and some are known to be scarcely a mile in diameter.

8·14. Orbits of Asteroids.   The motions of asteroids depart considerably from the regularities we have noted (7·21) in the movements of the larger planets.   Although they all have direct revolutions, some have orbits so much inclined to the ecliptic that they venture far outside the zodiac.   Some have rather highly eccentric orbits; one asteroid, Hidalgo, has its aphelion as far away as Saturn, and another, Icarus, comes at its perihelion nearer the sun than the orbit of Mercury.

The asteroids are not distributed at random through the zone they mainly frequent between the orbits of Mars and Jupiter. They avoid distances from the sun where the periods of revolution would be simple fractions, particularly one third, two fifths, and one half, of Jupiter's period. There they would be subject to frequent recurrences of the same types of disturbances by Jupiter. Where the periods are equal to Jupiter's, however, there are two regions in which asteroids congregate. The *Trojan asteroids* oscillate around two points near Jupiter's orbit, which are equidistant from that planet and the sun. They are named Achilles, Agamemnon, and so on after the Homeric heroes. More than a dozen are recognized.

8·15. Close Approaches of Asteroids. Several known asteroids come within the orbit of Mars and make closer approaches to the earth than do any of the principal planets. Among these is Eros that can come within 14 million miles, at which time this 15-mile object appears as bright as a star of the 7th magnitude. These favorable

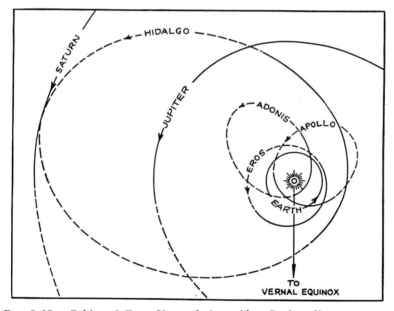

Fig. 8·15. Orbits of Four Unusual Asteroids. Broken lines represent parts of the orbits below the plane of the earth's orbit. (*Adapted from a diagram by Dirk Brouwer*)

oppositions, when Eros is also near perihelion, occur rather infrequently; the latest one was in 1931, and the next one is scheduled for 1975. The large parallax on such occasions permits accurate measurements of the distance, which have been valuable for verifying the scale of the solar system (7·20).

Examples of asteroids that come even nearer us are Apollo and Adonis (Fig. 8·15). The perihelion distance of Adonis is only slightly greater than Mercury's mean distance from the sun; this asteroid passes a little more than a million miles from the earth's orbit and about the same distance from the orbits of Venus and Mars. Another neighborly asteroid, Icarus, attracted Baade's attention in 1949 when it left a long trail on a photograph with the 48-inch Schmidt telescope. At perihelion its distance from the sun is less than 20 million miles.

Asteroids which have been observed within a few million miles of the earth are about a mile in diameter. At closest approach they appear as faint stars moving so swiftly across the heavens that they can easily be missed. Most of them have vanished before their orbits could be reliably determined.

8·16. Asteroids as Fragments. The erratic orbits of some asteroids suggest that these are fragments which have been propelled in various directions by the collisions of larger bodies. This theory may account not only for the smaller asteroids that pass near us but also for the meteorites which fall on the earth and are occasionally large enough to blast out meteorite craters.

Many asteroids fluctuate periodically in brightness, as would be expected of rotating fragments having irregular shapes. Eros is an example. In its rotation once in $5^h 16^m$, this asteroid shaped roughly like a brick presents its larger sides and smaller ends to us in turn. Thus it becomes brighter and fainter out there in the sunlight twice in each period. The light variation is greatest when the equator is presented edgewise to us, and it becomes less in other parts of the orbit when a polar region is turned more nearly in our direction.

An extensive photoelectric study of representative asteroids by G. P. Kuiper and associates has shown that over 90 per cent vary periodically in brightness, having two maxima and minima in each period of rotation. The periods range from $2^h 52^m$ to about 20 hours. The rotation axes have random orientations. In the case of the asteroid Eunomia the direction of rotation is definitely retrograde.

JUPITER, THE GIANT PLANET

Jupiter is the largest planet. Its equatorial diameter, 88,600 miles, is 11 times as great as the earth's diameter. Its mass exceeds the combined mass of all the other planets. With the exceptions of Venus and occasionally Mars, this planet is the brightest star-like object in our skies. Even a small telescope shows its 4 bright satellites and cloud belts clearly. Jupiter has 12 known satellites, the greatest number attending a planet.

At the distance of almost 500 million miles from the sun, Jupiter revolves around the sun once in nearly 12 years, so that it advances one sign of the zodiac from year to year. The period of its rotation, about $9^h 50^m$, is the shortest among the principal planets.

8·17. Jupiter's Cloudy Atmosphere. The markings on the disk of the giant planet, which run parallel to its equator, are features

FIG. 8·17. Jupiter, October 24, 1952, Showing the Great Red Spot. Photographed in blue light at the coudé focus of the Hale telescope. The 3rd satellite and its shadow appear near the top of the disk. (*Mount Wilson and Palomar Observatories photograph*)

of its atmosphere. Bright *zones* alternate with dark *belts*. The broad equatorial zone is bordered by the north and south tropical belts. Then come the north and south tropical zones, and beyond them a succession of dark and bright divisions extending to the polar regions. Bright and dark spots appear as well; they often change in form quite rapidly, as atmospheric markings might be expected to do. Yet some of them are of surprisingly long duration. The Great Red Spot (Fig. 8·17) is an extreme example; this oval spot 30,000 miles long, has been observed for at least a century; it behaves like a floating solid. The markings go around in the rotation at different rates, owing to the unequal horizontal movements of the clouds themselves.

The atmosphere consists mainly of hydrogen and helium. Its refraction effect on the light of a star was recently observed by W. A. Baum and A. D. Code as the planet began to occult the star, and was interpreted by them to mean that Jupiter's outer atmosphere has a molecular weight of about 3. Methane and ammonia contaminate the atmosphere, as is indicated by the presence of their bands in the spectrum. At the temperature of −200° F, methane is still gaseous, whereas ammonia is mainly frozen into crystals.

8·18. Structure of Jupiter. The bulging of Jupiter's equator, which is clearly shown in the figure, provides one clue to conditions in the interior. With its swift rotation the planet would be even more oblate if its mass were not highly concentrated toward its center. Other clues of what is hidden beneath the clouds are the low temperature and the low average density, about 1.3 times the density of water, of the whole planet, which requires very light material in the outer parts.

It is difficult to choose from among the different theoretical models that would justify the limited clues. As one extreme, Rupert Wildt of Yale University, about 20 years ago, designed a model in which the atmosphere is mainly of hydrogen and has a depth of 8000 miles. Beneath it there is a layer of ice 17,000 miles thick around a rocky core 38,000 miles in diameter; the core of the heavier elements is 6 times as dense as water, or somewhat more than the earth's average density. Hydrogen contributes 50 per cent of the mass of this model, an abundance now considered too low.

At the opposite extreme, Wildt, DeMarcus, and others have proposed a model of the planet consisting entirely of hydrogen. Anything resembling an atmosphere in this model is only a few miles thick. Solid hydrogen begins at a depth of 2000 miles. Metallic hydrogen extends from a depth of 8000 miles to the center; it becomes highly compressed under the very great pressure, which increases to 32 million atmospheres at the center. Intermediate models have been discussed by these and other investigators. Whatever the choice may be, we conclude that Jupiter has little resemblance to the earth.

8·19. Jupiter's Twelve Satellites. Next to the moon the 4 bright satellites of Jupiter are the most conspicuous in our skies. They could be glimpsed with the naked eye if they were farther removed

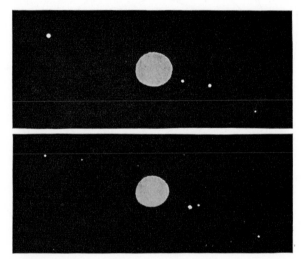

Fig. 8·19. Jupiter's Four Bright Satellites. The lower photograph was taken 3 hours later than the upper one. (*Yerkes Observatory photographs*)

from the glare of the planet. They were discovered by Galileo early in 1610.

The bright satellites are numbered in order of distance from the planet; they have personal names as well, although these are not so often used. The 1st and 2nd satellites are about the size of the moon. The 3rd and 4th satellites are half again as great; they are the largest of all satellites and surpass even the planet Mercury in diameter. Like the moon they have equal periods of rotation and revolution.

These satellites have direct revolutions in nearly circular orbits, which are nearly in the plane of the planet's equator and of its orbit around the sun. Because their paths are almost edgewise to the earth, the satellites seem to oscillate from one side of the planet to the other (Fig. 8·19). At times they disappear behind the planet's disk or into its shadow. At other times they pass in

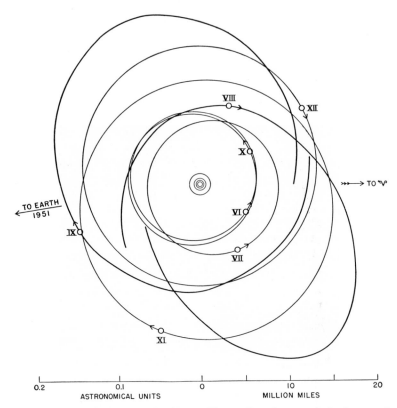

FIG. 8·19A. Orbits of Jupiter's Satellites. Showing marked changes in two orbits during a single revolution. (*Diagram by Seth B. Nicholson*)

front of the planet; their transits across its disk are visible with telescopes of moderate size, and the shadows they cast upon it are visible as well.

The other satellites of Jupiter are too small and faint to be easily seen through the telescope. They are designated by numbers from 5 to 12 in order of their discovery. The 5th satellite is the nearest of all to the planet; in the small eccentricity and inclination of its orbit and in its direct revolution it resembles the bright satellites. The 7 outer satellites have orbits of considerable eccentricity and inclination to the ecliptic. They fall into two groups. The 6th, 7th, and 10th satellites have direct revolutions at mean distances of a little more than 7 million miles from the planet. The 8th, 9th, 11th, and 12th satellites have retrograde revolutions at distances about twice as great.

The data on the outer satellites in Table 7·III are as given by Nicholson. The order of distance of the outermost four, as he points out, has little significance, because disturbances of their motions by the sun's attraction may change that order in a few years. The diameters of the faint satellites, which do not appear as disks with the largest telescopes, are estimated from their brightness.

SATURN, THE RINGED PLANET

Saturn is the most remote of the bright planets and is, therefore, the most leisurely in its movement among the constellations. It revolves once in 29½ years at the mean distance of 886 million miles from the sun. A bright yellow star in our skies, it ranges from equality with Altair to twice the brightness of Capella. This planet ranks second to Jupiter in size and mass; its equatorial diameter is 74,100 miles. It has the lowest average density, 0.7 times the density of water, and the most prominent bulge at the equator of any of the planets. Its unique system of rings makes it one of the most impressive celestial sights with the telescope.

8·20. The Planet Itself. Saturn resembles Jupiter except for its smaller size, mass, and density. The core is relatively smaller in the model that assigns it a rocky core. Methane bands are stronger

FIG. 8·20. Bright Spot on Saturn. (*Photographs with ultraviolet, violet, and yellow filters, August 7, 1933, by W. H. Wright, Lick Observatory*)

in its spectrum, and there is less evidence of ammonia, presumably because this ingredient is frozen out of its atmosphere at the lower temperature there of −240° F.

From its broad, yellow, equatorial zone to its bluish polar caps, the cloud markings of Saturn show less detail than do those of

Jupiter. A large bright spot which appeared in the equatorial zone in 1933 was exceptional; it was an oval spot 10,000 miles long at first, and quickly became longer. The rotation period derived from some spots in intermediate latitudes is around $10\frac{1}{2}$ hours, whereas the period from the Doppler effect in the spectrum at its equator is about half an hour less.

8·21. The Satellites of Saturn. Titan, the largest and brightest of Saturn's 9 known satellites, is considerably larger than the moon. It is the only satellite in the solar system known to have an atmosphere, although an atmosphere is now suspected in the case of Neptune's larger satellite. Titan's spectrum shows methane bands in Kuiper's photographs at McDonald Observatory. This satellite resembles Mars in its reddish color, probably because of similar action of the atmosphere on the surface rocks.

Four or five other satellites can be seen with telescopes of moderate size, appearing as faint stars in the vicinity of the ringed planet. All the satellites have direct revolutions around the planet with the exception of Phoebe, the most distant and the faintest one; Phoebe has retrograde revolution like Jupiter's outer group of satellites. Some of the satellites vary in brightness in the periods of their revolutions; they evidently rotate and revolve in the same periods, and are either irregular in form or have surfaces of uneven reflecting power. The very high reflection from the inner satellites suggests to Kuiper that they have icy surfaces, and their low densities may mean that they are composed mainly of ice.

8·22. Saturn's Rings are invisible to the naked eye and were, therefore, unknown until after the invention of the telescope. When Galileo began observing Saturn, in 1610, he glimpsed what seemed to be two smaller bodies in contact with the planet on opposite sides. The supposed appendages disappeared two years later and subsequently reappeared. This changing appearance of the planet remained a mystery until about half a century later, when the Dutch scientist Huygens, with a larger telescope, concluded that Saturn is encircled by a broad flat ring. In still later times it was found that there are 3 concentric rings instead of a single one.

The entire ring system is 171,000 miles across, but is scarcely more than 10 miles thick. The width of the *outer ring* is 10,000 miles. The middle or *bright ring* is 16,000 miles wide. It is separated from the outer ring by the 3000-mile *Cassini division,* named after its discoverer; this is the only real division in the rings. The inner or *crape ring,* which is continuous with the bright ring, is about 12,000 miles wide. Much fainter than the others and not

FIG. 8·22.   Saturn in 1939.   (*Photographed by Hamilton M. Jeffers, Lick Observatory*)

very clearly shown in the figures, the crape ring is nevertheless rather easily visible with telescopes of moderate size, although it was not discovered until 1850.

FIG. 8·22A.   Saturn in 1943.   (*Photographed by George H. Herbig, Lick Observatory*)

8·23. Different Aspects of the Rings.   Saturn's rings are inclined 27° to the plane of the planet's orbit, and they keep the same direction during its revolution. They accordingly present their northern and southern faces alternately to the sun, and also to the earth which is never more than 6° from the sun as viewed from Saturn. Twice during the sidereal period of 29½ years the plane of the rings passes through the sun's position (Fig. 8·23), requiring nearly a year each time to sweep across the earth's orbit. In that interval our own revolution brings the rings edgewise to us from 1 to 3 times, when they disappear through small telescopes and are only very narrow bright lines with larger ones.

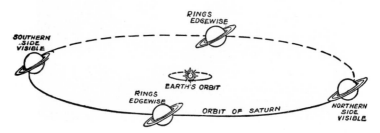

Fig. 8·23. Saturn's Rings at Different Angles. Twice in the course of Saturn's revolution its rings become edgewise to the sun. Each time the plane of the rings requires about a year to sweep across the earth's orbit.

The latest widest opening of the rings occurred in 1958, when Saturn with the northern face of the rings toward us was near the position of the winter solstice. When the rings are widest open, their apparent breadth is 45 per cent of their greatest diameter and one sixth greater than the planet's polar diameter. On these occasions Saturn appears brighter than usual, because the rings at this angle reflect 1.7 times as much sunlight as does the planet's disk. The next edgewise presentation will come in 1966.

8·24. Texture of the Rings. Saturn's rings consist of solid particles which revolve like satellites around the planet in nearly circular orbits in the plane of its equator and in the direction of its rotation. They are mainly icy particles, as Kuiper's study of the sunlight reflected from the rings suggests. The light from the separate pieces runs together at the great distance of Saturn to give the appearance of a continuous surface.

If the rings were really continuous, all parts would rotate in the same period, and the outside, having farther to go, would go around faster than the inside. The spectrum shows (Fig. 8·24), however, that the inside has the faster motion, as it should have in accordance with Kepler's harmonic law if the rings are composed of separate pieces.

The outer edge of the outer ring has the longest period of rotation, $14^h 27^m$. The inner edge of the bright ring rotates once in $7^h 46^m$, and the material of the crape ring must go around in still shorter time. Meanwhile the planet itself rotates in a period of about 10 hours. Thus the outer parts of the ring system move from

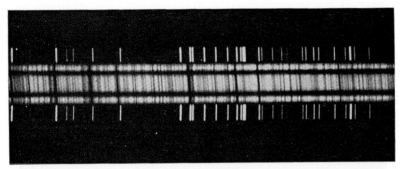

FIG. 8·24. Spectrum of Ball and Rings of Saturn. In the spectrum of the ball of the planet, in the middle, the lines slant because of the planet's rotation. In the spectrum of the rings, above and below, the lines have the opposite slant. This shows that the rings revolve more rapidly at their inner edges, proving their discrete nature. (*Lowell Observatory photograph*)

east to west across the sky of Saturn, whereas the inner parts seem to go around from west to east, like Phobos in the sky of Mars.

URANUS AND NEPTUNE

8·25. Discoveries of Uranus and Neptune. The discovery of Uranus, in 1781, was accidental and unexpected. William Herschel in England was examining a region in the constellation Gemini when he noticed a greenish object which seemed to him somewhat larger than a star. The object eventually proved to be a planet more remote than Saturn, and it received the name Uranus. Forty years later, when this planet had gone nearly halfway around the sun, its orbit was calculated from many observed positions, with allowance for the disturbing effects of other known planets. The new planet, however, did not follow thereafter precisely the course it was expected to pursue. Astronomers finally concluded that its motion in the heavens was being altered by the attraction of a planet still more remote and as yet unseen.

Neptune was discovered by Leverrier, in France, in 1846. By comparing observed positions of Uranus during the preceding quarter of a century with the predicted ones, he was able to calculate the place at that time of the unseen disturber in the sky. An astronomer at the Berlin Observatory, where an accurate star map was available, directed the telescope toward the specified region in the constellation Aquarius and soon found Neptune within a degree of the place assigned it by Leverrier. The discovery was acclaimed as a triumph for the law of gravitation, on which the calculation was based.

8·26. Uranus, the first planet to be discovered, is nearly 30,000 miles in diameter; it revolves once in 84 years at 19 times the earth's distance from the sun. It rotates once in less than half a

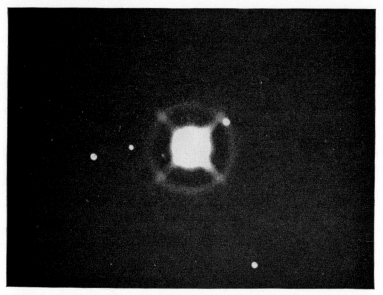

Fig. 8·26. The Five Satellites of Uranus. The recently discovered satellite appears inside the halation ring at the left of the planet. (*Photographed by Gerard P. Kuiper at McDonald Observatory*)

day, having its equator inclined nearly at right angles to the ecliptic. Barely visible to the unaided eye, Uranus shows a small greenish disk through the telescope, on which the markings are not clearly discernible. The spectrum includes a dark band in the infrared observed by Kuiper and identified by Herzberg with molecular hydrogen, the first direct evidence of the presence of this element in the atmospheres of the major planets. Bands of the contaminating methane appear in the spectra of both Uranus and Neptune.

Five satellites revolve around Uranus in nearly circular orbits in the plane of its equator and therefore inclined nearly at right angles to the ecliptic. The orbits were presented flatwise to the earth in 1945, and will appear edgewise to us in 1966. The 5th satellite, discovered by Kuiper at McDonald Observatory in 1948, is the faintest and nearest to the planet.

8·27. Neptune, about the same size as Uranus, revolves once in 165 years. It has a direct rotation once in 15.8 hours, according to earlier spectroscopic measures. Using other means, however,

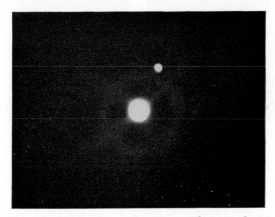

Fig. 8·27.   Neptune and Its Inner Satellite. *(Photographed by Gerard P. Kuiper at McDonald Observatory)*

O. Gruenther in Germany has recently reported a period of 12.7 hours. Always invisible to the naked eye, Neptune appears with the telescope as a star of the 8th magnitude, and shows a small greenish disk on which markings have not been seen. It seems to closely resemble Uranus.

Neptune has two known satellites. The first, Triton, is somewhat larger than the moon and is slightly nearer the planet than the moon's distance from the earth; it is nearly twice as massive as the moon and perhaps has an atmosphere. Triton has a retrograde revolution, contrary to the direction of the planet's rotation. The second satellite, discovered by Kuiper in 1949, is much the smaller and the more distant from the planet. It has a direct revolution in an orbit having an eccentricity of 0.76, the greatest for any known satellite.

PLUTO, THE MOST REMOTE PLANET

8·28. The Discovery of Pluto was announced by Lowell Observatory on March 13, 1930, as the successful result of a long-continued search at that observatory for a planet beyond Neptune. The

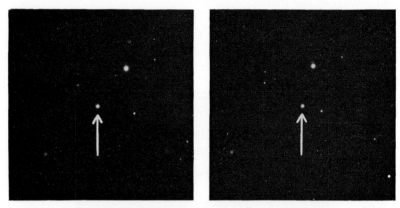

FIG. 8·28. Pluto. Showing its motion among the stars in one day. (*Mount Wilson and Palomar Observatories photograph*)

planet was discovered by Clyde Tombaugh in his photographs taken in January of that year. The search had been instituted by Percival Lowell, who had calculated the orbit of a transneptunian planet from slight discrepancies between the observed and predicted movements of Uranus, which seemed to remain after the discovery of Neptune.

Pluto is visible with the telescope as a star of the 15th visual magnitude. Its diameter is 3600 miles, as measured by Kuiper with a disk meter on the 200-inch telescope. Unless the density is greater than would be expected, its mass cannot exceed a tenth of the earth's mass. Pluto is thought to have a gritty snow-covered surface and perhaps an atmosphere that is considerably rarer than ours. Its period of rotation is 6.390 days, as determined by M. F. Walker and Robert Hardie from periodic fluctuations in its brightness.

8·29. The Orbit of Pluto. At its average distance the planet is $39\frac{1}{2}$ astronomical units, or 3670 million miles, from the sun. It revolves once in 250 years, which is half again as long as the period of Neptune's revolution. Its orbit is inclined 17° to the ecliptic, the highest inclination for any principal planet, so that Pluto ventures at times well beyond the borders of the zodiac.

The eccentricity, 0.25, of Pluto's orbit is the greatest for any principal planet. On this account and because of the great size of its orbit, its distance from the sun varies enormously. At aphelion it is 1800 million miles beyond Neptune's distance from the sun, whereas at perihelion it comes 35 million miles nearer the sun than the orbit of Neptune; yet in their present orbits the two planets cannot approach each other closer than 240 million miles. At the time of its discovery Pluto was near its ascending node (Fig. 7·21) and also near its mean distance from the sun. The distance will diminish until the planet reaches its perihelion in the year 1989. In the figure the part of the orbit south of the ecliptic is indicated by the broken line.

QUESTIONS ON CHAPTER 8

1. Name the principal planets in order of distance from the sun. State a unique feature of each.

2. Mention some points of resemblance between Mercury and the moon; Venus and the earth. What conditions on Venus seem to make that planet uninviting to life?

3. Why is Venus brightest at the crescent phase and not at the full phase, as in the case of the moon?

4. Mention some features of Mars which might suggest the presence of life, and some conditions which would seem discouraging to life.

5. Why is there some doubt as to the existence of a network of canals on Mars?

6. In what respects do some asteroids depart from the regularities (7·21) in the revolutions of the principal planets? Why might Pluto be considered not a principal planet?

7. The periodic fluctuations in the brightness of many asteroids inform us of their irregular shapes and possible origins. Explain.

8. Describe the telescopic view of Jupiter.

9. Jupiter's satellites are sharply divided into 3 groups. Explain.

10. Why are Saturn's rings presented to us at varying angles? Explain their edgewise presentation at intervals of 15 years.

11. What is the evidence that Saturn's rings have discrete constitution rather than continuous surfaces?

12. Describe the discoveries of Ceres, Uranus, Neptune, and Pluto.

REFERENCES

Kuiper, Gerard P., editor, *The Atmospheres of the Earth and Planets.* Revised edition. University of Chicago Press, 1951.

Richardson, Robert S., *Exploring Mars.* McGraw-Hill Book Company, New York, 1954.

Whipple, Fred L., *Earth, Moon and Planets.* Grosset and Dunlap, New York, 1958.

The 26-inch Refracting Telescope of the U.S. Naval Observatory.
(Photograph by Underwood and Underwood)

9

OTHER FEATURES OF
THE SOLAR SYSTEM

COMETS – METEORS AND METEOR STREAMS –
METEORITES AND METEORITE CRATERS

Comets and meteors revolve around the sun in orbits that are generally more eccentric than are those of the planets. Meteors are products of the disintegration of comets; meteor streams are associated with the orbits of comets. Meteorites, which are allied more closely with asteroids, come through to the ground, and very large ones produce meteorite craters.

COMETS

A conspicuous comet has a head and a tail. The head consists of a hazy, globular *coma,* sometimes having a brighter *nucleus* near its center. The luminous *tail* is directed away from the sun and occasionally extends a considerable distance across the heavens. Many comets, however, are never more than tailless telescopic objects. Spectacular comets, such as Halley's comet, are infrequent.

9·1. Halley's Comet is named in honor of Edmund Halley, contemporary of Isaac Newton, who predicted its return. Halley calculated as a parabola the orbit of a bright comet of 1682 and noted its resemblance to the orbits of comets of 1531 and 1607, which he had also determined from records of their observed places in the sky. Deciding that these three were appearances of the same comet, which must therefore be revolving in an ellipse, Halley predicted its return to the sun's vicinity "about the year 1758." The comet was sighted on Christmas night of that year and reached perihelion early in 1759. It came around to perihelion again in 1835 and in 1910, its latest appearance.

Twenty-eight returns of this comet are identified from the records as far back as 240 B.C. .It was Halley's comet that appeared in the

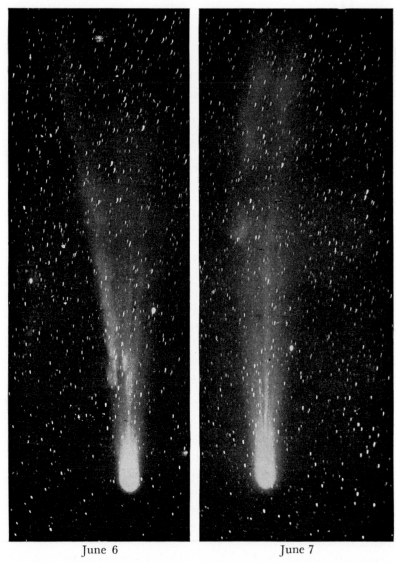

June 6   June 7

FIG. 9·1.   Halley's Comet at Its Latest Appearance in 1910.   (*Lick Observatory photographs*)

year 1066 at the time of the Norman conquest of England and is depicted on the Bayeux tapestry. The intervals between returns to perihelion have averaged 77 years, varying a few years because of disturbing effects of planets.

Halley's comet is not only the first periodic comet to be recognized, but it is also the only conspicuous one of the many periodic comets known today that return to perihelion oftener than once in a century. It has a retrograde revolution around the sun in an elongated orbit (Fig. 9·1A) at distances from the sun that range from

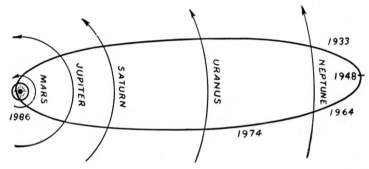

Fig. 9·1A. Orbit of Halley's Comet. The comet will return to perihelion in 1986.

one half to more than 35 times the earth's distance. Invisible at present near its aphelion, which is more remote than Neptune's distance, it will return to the sun's vicinity in 1986.

9·2. Discovery of Comets. Comets are likely to be discovered either in photographs of regions of the heavens often taken for other purposes or in visual searches with small telescopes. The western sky after nightfall or the eastern sky before dawn are most promising for the search. The comet generally appears as a small hazy spot, and its gradual movement among the stars shows presently that it is not a faint star cluster or nebula. Having found a comet, the observer would do well to report its position, direction of motion, and brightness to Harvard Observatory, which serves as a receiving and distributing station in this country for such astronomical news.

As soon as three positions of the comet (its right ascension and declination) have been observed at appropriate intervals, a preliminary orbit is calculated. Then it is usually possible to decide from the records whether the comet is a new one or the return of a comet already known.   A catalog of cometary orbits prepared by F. Baldet in 1952 includes 763 comets.   Five or six comets are picked up each year in the average, and two thirds of them have not been previously recorded.

The provisional designation of a comet is by the year of the discovery followed by a small letter in the order of which the discovery is announced; an example is Comet 1956 h.   The permanent designation is the year (not always the year of discovery) followed by a Roman numeral in order of perihelion passage during that year;

Fig. 9·2.   Motion of Mrkos' Comet (1955 e) in 22 Minutes.   (*Photographed by Richard Fink and William Konig, Milwaukee Astronomical Society*)

an example is Comet 1956 II.   Many comets are also known by the name of the discoverer, or discoverers, or of the astronomer whose investigations of the comet entitle him to the distinction; Halley's comet is an example.

9·3. The Orbits of Comets depart from the regularities we have noted (7·21) in the case of the principal planets.   These orbits are generally of high eccentricity and are often much inclined to the ecliptic.   With respect to their motions the comets are divided into two groups by a somewhat indefinite dividing line.

(1) Comets having *nearly parabolic orbits*.   In this more numerous group the orbits are so eccentric that they are not readily distinguished from parabolas in the small portions near the sun where the comets are visible.   The orbits extend far beyond the region of the planets, and the undetermined periods are all so long that only one appearance of each comet is likely to be found in the records.   In this sense the comets are "nonperiodic."   About half the revolutions are direct (west to east) and the other half are retrograde.

(2) Comets having *definitely elliptic orbits*. These "periodic comets" revolve in periods not exceeding a few hundred years. The orbits are allied more closely with the planetary orbits. Although most of them have high eccentricity, they are frequently more moderately inclined to the ecliptic, and the revolutions are mainly direct; the retrograde revolution of Halley's comet is one of the exceptions.

The Schwassmann-Wachmann comet (1925 II) is unusual in having a nearly circular orbit. It revolves around the sun once in about 16 years entirely between the orbits of Jupiter and Saturn, and remains visible at aphelion. This comet is also unusual in its occasional surprisingly great and rapid flare-ups; an increase of 100 times in brightness has occurred within less than a day. Oterma's comet is similar in having a nearly circular orbit, but it shows no unexplained variation in brightness. It revolves in a period of about 8 years entirely between the orbits of Mars and Jupiter.

The bright comets of 1668, 1843, 1880, 1882, and 1887, which passed very close to the sun, had orbits that were nearly the same in the sun's vicinity. Presumably they were fragments of a comet that was disrupted at a previous close approach. Indeed, the comet of 1882 was itself observed to break into four parts; these are expected to return as separate comets between the 25th and 28th centuries.

9·4. Jupiter's Family of Comets. Two dozen or more comets revolve around the sun in periods averaging 6 years, or half of Jupiter's period. Their aphelions and one node of each orbit are not far from Jupiter's orbit, so that these comets can come close to the planet itself. They constitute *Jupiter's family of comets*. Their direct revolutions and the low inclinations of their orbits to the ecliptic suggest that Jupiter has assembled the family by capture of comets passing by in originally larger orbits. At successive encounters the planet's attraction has progressively reduced the orbits to their present sizes. The membership is unstable; further approaches of these comets to the planet may occur in such ways as to remove some of them from the family. Three members of Jupiter's family have been especially noteworthy

Encke's comet, discovered in 1786, was the first member of Jupiter's family to be recognized, in 1819. Its period of revolution, 3.3 years, is the shortest for any known comet. Its aphelion is a whole astronomical unit inside Jupiter's orbit, having gradually drawn in by this amount. Since 1819, the comet has not been missed at a single return to perihelion. Like other members of the family, Encke's comet never becomes at best more than faintly visible to the unaided eye.

Biela's comet, having a period of 6½ years, came to an end in a spectacular way. At its return in 1846 it was divided into two

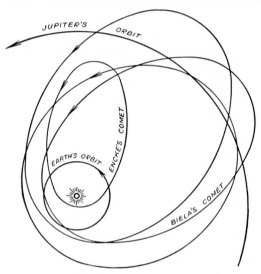

FIG. 9·4. Orbits of Four Comets of Jupiter's Family. Encke's comet has the smallest orbit of all comets.

separate comets traveling side by side, and at the next return the separation had increased to 1½ million miles. The comet was never seen again; but a stream of meteors in its orbit, the Andromedids or Bielids, gave fine showers when it encountered the earth in 1872 and 1885. The Giacobini-Zinner comet, having a similar period, is associated with a meteor stream that in 1933 and 1946 provided the most abundant showers of this century.

9·5. The Nature of a Comet. A comet's nucleus is a conglomerate of frozen material, mainly methane, ammonia, and water, having meteoric particles embedded in it. In this theory, proposed by F. L. Whipple in 1950, the nucleus of the average comet does not exceed a mile or two in diameter. It is known that the mass of a comet is too small to disturb appreciably the motions of planets and satellites at close approaches, whereas the comet's orbit may be greatly altered by the attractions of these bodies.

Some of the ices evaporate at each approach of the comet to the sun. The gases issue explosively into the coma, from which they are swept out through the tail by radiations from the sun and dis-

Fig. 9·5. Comet Arend-Roland (1956 h). The meteoric material fanning out below the comet's head is more clearly shown in the picture at the left. (*Photographs, April 27 and May 1, 1957, by Henry L. Giclas, Lowell Observatory*)

persed into space. These gases are transformed in the coma by action of sunlight mainly to carbon, methyne, hydroxyl, ammonia radicals, and cyanogen, as the spectra of the comets show, and are soon converted in the tail to more durable molecules such as carbon monoxide, carbon dioxide, and nitrogen. As the surface of the ices in the nucleus is made increasingly gritty by the meteoric particles that remain, the evaporation is retarded, so that the comet may return to the sun many times before its material is completely dissipated.

The meteoric particles originally embedded in the ices of the nucleus are released by the evaporation of the ices and are scattered along the comet's orbit as a meteor stream. The fanning out of this material behind Comet Arend-Roland (1956 h) is clearly shown in the photograph at the left in Fig. 9·5, taken on April 27, 1957, when the plane of the material was presented more nearly edgewise to us. The earth had passed through the plane of the comet's orbit on April 25.

The light of a comet that is more than 3 astronomical units from the sun is almost entirely reflected sunlight; the spectrum is then a faint replica of the solar spectrum. If the comet comes close enough to the sun to be spectacular, it glows mainly with luminescence stimulated by action of sunlight in the gases of the coma and tail, so that bright bands become prominent in the spectrum. Bright lines of sodium and some other metals may also appear in the spectrum of a comet that makes an unusually close approach to the sun.

METEORS AND METEOR STREAMS

The trails of "shooting stars" across the starlit sky inform us of the flights of meteors through the air. *Meteors* are stony and metallic objects revolving around the sun. Those that become visible to the unaided eye range generally from a millimeter in diameter to not larger than a golf ball. They can be seen separately only when they chance to plunge into our atmosphere, where they are heated intensely by impact with the air molecules. In the short intervals while they are being consumed they produce luminous *trails*. The brighter meteors sometimes leave *dust trains* that remain visible from a few seconds to generally not longer than half an hour, while they may become twisted by air currents.

9·6. The Influx of Meteors. The total number of meteor trails brighter than visual magnitude +5 over all the earth's surface is determined by G. S. Hawkins as 90 million in a 24-hour period. The meteors producing these trails add several tons a day to the earth's mass, and the great majority are *sporadic meteors,* not belonging to recognized meteor streams. The frequency of trails visible to a single observer is likely to increase somewhat during the night. In the morning we are on the forward side of the revolving earth, where we are more exposed to the incoming meteors, whereas in the evening we are in the rear and are more protected except from the meteors overtaking us.

The swiftness of the meteor flights in the air increases through the night. At our distance from the sun the speeds of meteors in their highly eccentric orbits approach the parabolic value of 26 miles a second (7·11). Their speeds relative to the revolving earth

Fig. 9·6. Trail of a Brilliant Meteor. The meteor was brighter than the planet Venus. The left end of the trail is a little way south of Capella. The middle of the trail is nearly halfway between Algol and the Pleiades, and the right end is between Triangulum and the triangle of Aries. The Hyades appear in the lower left corner. (*Harvard Observatory photograph*)

accordingly range from about 26 minus 18½ miles a second for meteors that overtake us to 26 plus 18½ miles a second for head-on collisions, with a little added because of the earth's attraction. The morning meteors are heated more intensely in their swifter flights, so that they are brighter than the evening meteors.

9·7. Determining the Orbits of Meteors. When the same meteor trail is observed from two stations several miles apart, it is possible to determine the distance of the meteor from the stations. From the observed angular speed and direction of the meteor's flight the linear velocity is then obtained, providing enough data for calculating the meteor's orbit around the sun. Earlier visual methods are replaced for this purpose by the more precise photographic and radar techniques.

The first effective photography of meteor trails from two stations, employing cameras provided with rotating shutters for interrupting the images of the trails at regular intervals to facilitate the timing, was initiated by F. L. Whipple and associates at Harvard Observ-

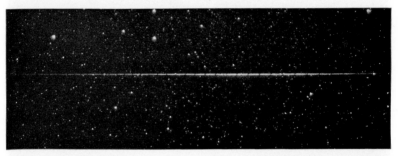

Fig. 9·7. Meteor Trail Interrupted at Intervals of a Twentieth of a Second. The meteor's flight was from left to right. The breaks in the trail are closer together at the left because the meteor was then farther away. (*Photograph from Harvard Observatory Meteor Program*)

atory in 1936. The later extension of this program with a pair of "super-Schmidt" cameras in New Mexico has produced double photographs of more than 6000 meteor trails and the calculation of many orbits of meteors. Another pair of these cameras is in operation by P. M. Millman and associates north of Edmonton, Canada. Meteor orbits so determined are ellipses resembling the orbits of comets. Thus the meteors were members of the solar system and did not come from outside the system.

The meteor's speed by itself is enough to determine the status of the meteor in this respect. If the speed on entering the atmosphere, with allowance for the motion and attraction of the earth, exceeds 26 miles a second, the meteor may have come from outside the solar system. If the speed is less than this critical value, the meteor is a member of the system. The speeds of more than 10,000 meteors down to the 8th visual magnitude were determined by D. W. R. McKinley at Ottawa from records of radio beams returned from the trails. In not a single case was the speed great enough to suggest certainly that the meteor came from outside the system.

9·8. Meteor Streams and Showers. A *meteor stream* consists of many meteors revolving around the sun in about the same orbit, at least when they are in the earth's vicinity. A *meteor shower* occurs where the orbit of the stream crosses the earth's orbit at either one or two points, and whenever part of the stream and the earth arrive together at an intersection. The shower occurs around the same date, either annually if the stream is far extended or at longer intervals for a short stream. Only rarely have the showers been spectacular enough to attract the attention of people who are not watching for them.

The trails of the meteors in a shower are directed away from a small area of the sky, the center of which is the *radiant* of the shower. Because the trails are nearly parallel, they spread out over the sky from the radiant (Fig. 9·8), just as the parallel

FIG. 9·8. The Radiant of a Meteor Shower.

rails of a track seem to diverge from a distant point. Showers of meteors and the streams that produce them are named from the positions of the radiants among the constellations at the heights of the displays. Examples are the Perseids and the Delta Aquarids. The place of the radiant is shifted during the progress of a shower as the earth changes the direction of its revolution.

9·9. Major Showers of Meteors. The more abundant meteor showers are listed in Table 9·I, which is taken principally from more extended data by F. L. Whipple and G. S. Hawkins in the *Handbuch der Physik*, Volume 52, 1959. The table gives in each case the date of maximum display, in universal time, the position of the radiant, so that it may be located in the star maps, and the name of the parent comet.

The Perseids provide in August the most familiar of the annual showers; the display from this wide stream extends through two

TABLE 9·I   METEOR SHOWERS AND ASSOCIATED COMETS

Shower	Maximum Display (UT Date)	Radiant at Max. (Equinox of 1950)		Associated Comet (and notes)
		R. A.	Decl.	
Quadrantids	Jan. 3	$15^h\ 20^m$	$+48°$	
Lyrids	Apr. 21	18 0	$+33$	1861 I
Eta Aquarids	May 4	22 24	0	Halley(?)
*Arietids	June 8	2 56	$+23$	(=Delta Aquarids)
*Zeta Perseids	June 9	4 8	$+23$	
*Beta Taurids	June 30	5 44	$+19$	Encke
Delta Aquarids	July 30	22 36	-11	(two streams)
Alpha Capricornids	Aug. 1	20 36	-10	1948 n
Perseids	Aug. 12	3 4	$+58$	1862 III
Draconids	Oct. 10	17 36	$+54$	Giacobini-Zinner
Orionids	Oct. 22	6 16	$+16$	Halley(?)
Taurids	Nov. 1	3 28	$+17$	Encke (two streams)
Andromedids	Nov. 14	1 28	$+27$	Biela
Leonids	Nov. 17	10 8	$+22$	Temple
Geminids	Dec. 14	7 32	$+32$	
Ursids (Ursa Minor)	Dec. 22	13 44	$+80$	Tuttle

* Shower in daytime

or three weeks and the trails are frequently rather bright. The showers of the Orionids and Geminids are also among the most faithful of the annual showers. The radiant given for the Delta Aquarids in late July is the mean of two radiants several degrees apart, and the same is true for the Taurids of November. Both streams make second crossings to produce the daytime showers of the Arietids and Beta Taurids, respectively.

The Leonids and Andromedids, which produced fine showers at intervals in the 19th century, have since given only sprinkles at the predicted times. Showers of Draconids in the evenings of October 9 in 1933 and 1946 were the most impressive of the present century, and an afternoon display on that date was recorded by radar at the Jodrell Bank Experimental Station in England, in 1952. Three previously unknown showers, listed in the table, were also recorded in the daytime at this station.

Fig. 9·9. Draconid Meteors During the Shower of October 9, 1946. The camera was stationary during the 12-minute exposure, while the stars were describing small arcs of their daily circles around the pole. The meteor trails are straight and diverge from the radiant in Draco. (*Photographed by Kenneth Spain, Vanderbilt University*)

9·10. The Zodiacal Light. The triangular glow of the *zodiacal light* can be seen extending up from the west horizon after nightfall in the spring and from the east horizon before dawn in the autumn in our northern latitudes. Broadest and brightest near the horizon it tapers upward, leaning toward the south. The glow is symmetrical with the ecliptic and is accordingly most conspicuous when the ecliptic is most nearly vertical.

Near the equator, where the ecliptic is always nearly perpendicular to the horizon, the zodiacal light can be observed all year around. Here it is said to have been seen as a faint, narrow band encircling the sky. The light is mainly sunlight scattered by meteoric dust, which forms a ring around the sun in the plane of the earth's orbit and is continually being replenished by disintegration of comets. Near the sun the light is identified by a replica of sunlight in the spectrum of the corona.

Opposite the sun's position the zodiacal glow brightens a little and widens into the *gegenschein,* or *counterglow,* which is faintly visible to the unaided eye in the best conditions as an oval spot 10°

AUTUMN   SPRING

FIG. 9·10. The Zodiacal Light in the Evening. It is most conspicuous in the evening in middle northern latitudes around the beginning of spring, because the ecliptic is then most nearly perpendicular to the horizon.

to 15° long. This spot is recorded effectively with the photoelectric cell and is shown clearly in photographs with very wide-angle cameras.

METEORITES AND METEORITE CRATERS

9·11. Stones from the Sky. Near noon one day in November, 1492, a number of stones came down in a field near Ensisheim, Alsace. The largest one, weighing 260 pounds, was placed in a church in that town; a smaller stone is exhibited in the Chicago Natural History Museum. This is the oldest observed fall of meteorites on record, of which samples are still preserved.

The idea that stones fall from the sky goes back to very early times. There were stones preserved in some of the ancient temples that were doubtless of celestial origin, and these "stones from heaven" were objects of veneration. In later times, however, all reports of stones falling from the sky came to be regarded with suspicion. The stones seemed to choose remote places where there

were no reliable observers. It may be, too, that the accounts of ter-
rified spectators of some of the falls were so exaggerated that no one
could believe them. Finally, in April, 1803, a shower of two or
three thousand stones fell at Laigle, France, and was reliably reported. Yet the news spread so slowly that when 300 pounds of
meteorites came down near Weston, Connecticut, in December,
1807, the first observed fall on record in the United States, many
people were reluctant to believe that it was true.

9·12. Falls of Meteorites. *Meteorites* are masses of stony or metallic
material, or both, which survive their flights through the air and
fall to the ground. They arrive either singly or in many pieces.
Several thousand individuals have come down in one fall, and in
such cases are likely to be distributed over an elliptical area having
its major axis several miles long in the direction of the flight. Although meteors are products of the disintegration of comets, many
meteorites are believed to be fragments of shattered asteroids (8·16).

Their speeds greatly reduced by air resistance, most meteorites
cool before they reach the ground. In their brief flights through the
air the heat has not gone far into their cold interiors, and the melted
material has been swept away in droplets from their surfaces. They
are usually cool enough to be handled comfortably when they are
picked up immediately after landing and they do not penetrate
far into the ground. Larger meteorites are less impeded by the
air; some very massive ones have struck at such high speeds that
they have blasted out large craters in the earth's surface (9·15).

9·13. The Meteorites Themselves are essentially of two kinds, the
stones (aerolites) and the irons (siderites). There are gradations
between them (siderolites) from stones containing flecks of nickel-
iron to sponges of metal with stony fillings. Inside their varnish-
like fusion crusts the *stony meteorites* are often grayish, having a
characteristic granular structure that serves to establish their celestial
origin. The rounded granules are crystalline, chiefly silicates similar
to those in our native igneous rocks. The largest known example,
weighing at least a ton, fell on February 18, 1948, in Furnas County,
Nebraska (Fig. 9·13).

Iron meteorites are silvery under their blackened exteriors. They
are composed mainly of alloys of iron and nickel, which are affected
by acid in various degrees. When they occur in crystal forms, a
characteristic pattern of intersecting bands parallel to the faces of

an octahedron may be etched with dilute nitric acid on a polished section.

Individuals from about 1600 falls have been recovered. They are generally named after the locality in which they were found; examples are the Canyon Diablo, Arizona, meteorites and the Willamette, Oregon, meteorite. Collections are exhibited in the

FIG. 9·13. The Furnas County, Nebraska, Meteorite. (*Official photograph of the Institute of Meteoritics, University of New Mexico*)

Chicago Natural History Museum, the American Museum of Natural History, New York City, and many other places.

Micrometeorites are so minute that they are not greatly altered when they enter the atmosphere. Their presence in interplanetary space is indicated by the scattered sunlight of the zodiacal light (9·10). Meteoritic dust is also produced by the larger meteoritic bodies themselves either when they are crumbled by collision or are partly melted to form droplets in the air.

9·14. The Large Iron Meteorites. About 35 individual meteorites weighing more than a ton are listed in F. C. Leonard's catalog. With the exceptions of the Furnas County stone, two stony irons, and a

FIG. 9·14. The Hoba Meteorite. (*Photograph by W. J. Luyten*)

FIG. 9·14A. The Ahnighito Meteorite. (*American Museum of Natural History, New York*)

2-ton iron individual from the 1947 Siberian fall, their falls were not observed. All the others are irons; the two largest are the Hoba meteorite and the Ahnighito meteorite.

The Hoba meteorite lies partly buried in the ground in the Grootfontein district, Southwest Africa. Its rectangular upper surface measures 9×10 feet and its greatest thickness exceeds 3 feet; its weight is unknown. The Ahnighito meteorite is the largest of three that the explorer R. E. Peary found near Cape York, Greenland, in 1894, and brought back to New York City. This meteorite measures about $11 \times 7 \times 6$ feet and weighs a little more than 34 tons (68,085 pounds); it is exhibited in the American Museum— Hayden Planetarium. The Willamette meteorite, also in the Hayden Planetarium, weighs 15 tons. The largest meteorite found in the United States, this conical mass of nickel-iron was discovered, in 1902, ten miles south of Portland, Oregon. It evidently kept the same orientation in its flight and was fashioned by the rush of hot air. Some meteorites turned over and over as they fell and were rounded in the air.

Three large iron meteorites, each weighing more than 10 tons, were found in Mexico. They are the Bacubirito (29 tons), the Chupaderos (21 tons, in two pieces that fit together), and the Morito (11 tons). The last two are exhibited in the School of Mines in Mexico City.

9·15. Two Siberian Falls of large meteorites in the present century have attracted attention. The first occurred on June 30, 1908, in a forested region of the Tunguska River in north central Siberia, devastating an area 20 or 30 miles in radius. The trees were felled without bark or branches and with their tops pointing away from the center of the area. Many craters were formed near the center, the largest one 150 feet in diameter. Although larger remnants of the Tunguska meteorite have not been recovered, soil samples from the region are found to contain microscopic chips and spherules of nickel-iron dust.

The second fall occurred on February 12, 1947, on the western spurs of the Sikhote-Alin mountain range near the Pacific coast in southeastern Siberia. The meteorite broke into many pieces before the fall and came down as an "iron rain" over a square mile. The fragments produced a field of smaller holes and larger craters, the largest one 90 feet in diameter. The field was strewn with an estimated 100 tons of meteoritic material.

9·16. The Barringer Meteorite Crater, near Canyon Diablo in northeastern Arizona, is a circular depression 4200 feet across and 570 feet deep. Its rim, which rises 130 feet above the surrounding plain, is composed of debris thrown out of the pit, from fine rock dust to blocks of limestone and sandstone weighing up to 7000 tons apiece.

Fig. 9·16.   Barringer Meteorite Crater, Arizona.   (*Photograph by John Farrell, Fort Worth, Texas*)

This crater is a scar left by the fall of a great meteorite probably not less than 50,000 years ago. The meteorite is estimated, at the minimum, to have had a diameter of 200 feet and a weight of a million tons. So massive that it was only slightly retarded by the air, it struck the earth a mighty blow. The intense heat of the collision partly fused the meteorite and the rocks in contact with it; the gases expanded explosively, scattering what was left of the meteorite over the surrounding country and blasting out the crater. Thirty tons of meteoritic iron have been picked up within a radius of 6 miles around the crater. The largest individual, weighing more than 1400 pounds, is exhibited in the museum on the north rim of the crater. Samplings indicate that the total amount of crushed meteoritic material around the crater is 12,000 tons.

Other craters and groups of craters in various parts of the world are recognized to be of meteoritic origin. The Wolf Creek crater in West Australia has a diameter of 2800 feet at the bottom and a depth of 160 feet. Among the very large circular depressions suspected of having meteoritic origin are the Ungava crater in northern Quebec, the Brent and Holleford craters in Ontario, and the Talemzane crater in southern Algeria.

QUESTIONS ON CHAPTER 9

1. Give two reasons why Halley's comet is noteworthy. Name three other comets and mention an interesting feature of each.

2. What is characteristic of the orbits of Jupiter's family of comets?

3. Describe and explain some changes in the appearance of comets as they approach the sun.

4. Account for the association of meteor streams and comets. State one such association.

5. Meteors are likely to be swifter and brighter in the morning than in the evening sky. Explain.

6. What is the evidence that most meteors are members of the solar system and have not come in from outside it?

7. Explain the radiant of a meteor shower. How are the separate showers named? Give an example.

8. Why is spring the most favorable season for viewing the zodiacal light in the evening in middle northern latitudes?

9. Distinguish between two kinds of meteorites. Name an example of a large meteorite of either kind and state where it may be seen.

10. Describe a large meteorite crater and state its location.

REFERENCES

Leonard, Frederick C., *A Classification Catalog of the Meteoritic Falls of the World.* University of California Press, 1956.

Lovell, A. C. B., *Meteor Astronomy.* Oxford University Press, New York, 1954.

Rush, J. H., *The Dawn of Life.* Hanover House, Garden City, N. Y., 1957.

Watson, Fletcher G., *Between the Planets.* Revised edition. Harvard University Press, Cambridge, 1956.

10

THE SUN WITH ITS SPOTS

THE PHOTOSPHERE; SUNSPOTS – THE SUN'S ATMOS-
PHERE – ECLIPSES OF THE SUN; THE CORONA

The sun is the only star near enough to us for its features to be examined in detail. Our account of the sun is accordingly associated both with the preceding descriptions of the solar system and with those of the stars in the following chapters.

10·1. Observing the Sun. The sun is too bright to be safely observed on a clear day without protection of the eye from its glare. Viewed through a dark glass it appears as a disk about as large as the full moon, and as a perfectly blank disk generally to the eye alone. With the telescope the disk is enlarged and its features are revealed. It would be unwise, of course, to look directly through the telescope at the sun without a device for diverting most of the light and heat which it concentrates at its focus. A convenient procedure is to let the telescope project the image on a smooth cardboard screen held back of the eyepiece. In this way many people can observe at the same time.

Photographic records of the sun's surface and its surroundings are obtained in a variety of ways. Fixed telescopes into which the sunlight is directed by coelostats have often been employed. These permit the use of long-focus objectives that form large images of the sun. Examples of such vertical telescopes are the 150-foot and the 60-foot towers of the Mount Wilson Observatory and the 70-foot and 50-foot towers of the McMath-Hulbert Observatory.

The solar telescope under construction at the Kitt Peak National Observatory has a sloping tube 500 feet long that is parallel to the earth's axis and three fifths below the ground. A heliostat, a rotating plane mirror 80 inches in diameter will reflect the sunlight down the tube to a 60-inch concave mirror near the bottom. This mirror, having a focal length of 300 feet, will form an image of the sun averaging 33½ inches in diameter in the observing room at the ground level.

Fig. 10·1. The McMath-Hulbert Observatory of the University of Michigan.

Photographs of the sun and its spectrum from high-altitude stations, balloons, and rockets are giving new information, and radio telescopes are providing data about the sun that are not available to optical instruments.

10·2. The Structure of the Sun. In the ordinary view the sun is a gaseous globe 864,000 miles in diameter, or 109 times the earth's diameter. The sun has therefore 1⅓ million times the volume of the earth; and since its mass is a third of a million times as great, it averages one fourth the earth's density, or 1.4 times the density of water. Its temperature increases from 10,000° F at its lowest visible level to many million degrees at the center.

The *photosphere,* the visible surface, is mottled with brighter granulations and faculae and is often marked with darker sunspots. The gases above the photosphere constitute the *sun's atmosphere.* The *chromosphere,* extending to the height of several thousand miles, is so named because of its color, which is imparted chiefly by the red glow of its hydrogen. It is normally the region where the spectacular solar flares are observed. The red *prominences* appear above the chromosphere, at times attaining heights of many hundred thousand miles. They are visible during total solar eclipses, and together with the inner corona are studied effectively with special devices at other times. The *corona,* the outermost solar envelope, appears as a filmy halo of intricate structure.

THE PHOTOSPHERE; SUNSPOTS

10·3. The Photosphere is as far into the sun as we can see. Here, where the pressure is only a hundredth of our air pressure at sea level, the gas becomes opaque. From this level the sunlight emerges, distributing energy equivalent to 5×10^{23} horsepower to light and heat the members of the planetary system. Each square yard contributes 70,000 horsepower. The sun has been pouring out energy at this great rate for at least a billion years, during all the geological ages, and is expected to continue to do so for several billion years in the future.

The temperature of the photosphere averages 5750° on the absolute centigrade scale, or less than 10,000° F. It is somewhat higher near the center of the disk, where we look in directly, and is reduced to 8000° F near the edge, where our slanting view is obstructed at higher and cooler levels. Thus the sunlight from the edge is less bright and redder than from the center of the disk.

Through the telescope the photosphere presents a mottled appearance. Bright *granules* a few hundred miles in diameter cover a considerable part of the surface; they are hotter spots in the seething furnace formed by gases coming from below. Each granule lasts only a few minutes before it cools to the temperature of its surroundings. Larger bright spots, the *faculae,* are often conspicuous

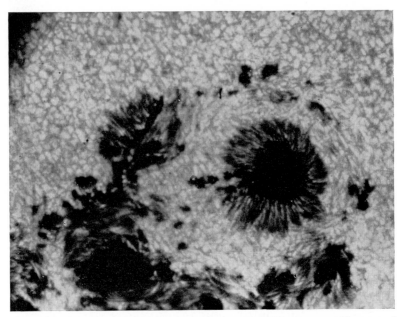

Fig. 10·3. The Sun Photographed August 17, 1957, from an Unmanned Balloon. Photograph from an altitude exceeding 80,000 feet with a special 12-inch Perkin-Elmer telescope in a project directed by Martin Schwarzschild, Princeton University. (*Courtesy of Perkin-Elmer Corporation*)

against the less luminous background near the edge of the disk. Dark spots on the sun have held the greater interest.

10·4. Sunspots in Groups. *Sunspots* appear dark in contrast with the brighter general surface of the sun. They range in size from specks scarcely distinguishable from the spaces between the bright granules to the great spots visible without the telescope. They usually consist of two distinct parts: the *umbra,* the inner, darker part which is often divided, and the lighter *penumbra* around it.

Sunspots occur in groups; where a single spot is seen, it is likely to be a survivor of a group. A normal group develops in about a week and then begins to decline. Two *principal spots* grow larger than the others which form mostly between them. The *preceding spot* in the direction of the sun's rotation frequently becomes the larger of the two. The *following spot* is the largest of the spots in the rear. It subdivides and vanishes along with the smaller spots, until only the preceding spot is left to shrink and disappear. There are exceptions to this pattern.

One of the largest groups ever recorded (Fig. 10·4) appeared early in 1946 and lasted more than 3 months, an exceptionally long duration. The group attained the length of 200,000 miles and the area

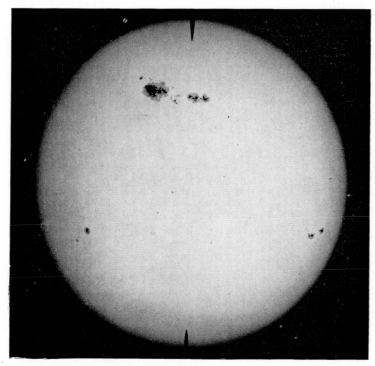

FIG. 10·4. The Sun, February 4, 1946. An exceptionally large group of sunspots appears above the center of the disk. (*Mount Wilson Observatory photograph*)

of 5700 million square miles. Its largest spot, in this case the following spot, measured 90,000 by 60,000 miles. A slightly larger group (Fig. 10·5) appeared in 1947.

10·5. The Sun's Rotation is shown by the gradual movement of sunspots across its disk. The spots come into view at the eastern edge, disappear two weeks later at the western edge if they last that long, and may reappear at the eastern edge after another two weeks. Because the sun's equator is inclined 7° to the plane of the earth's orbit, the paths of the spots across the disk are generally curved; the curve is greatest early in March, when the sun's south pole is toward us, and again early in September, when its north pole is toward us. The axis of the sun's rotation is directed toward a point in the heavens midway between Polaris and Vega.

Unlike the earth which rotates in the same period in all latitudes, the rotation period of the gaseous sun is longer as the distance from

Fig. 10·5. Sunspots Show the Sun's Rotation. The large group of 1947 lasted for more than 3 months. (*Mount Wilson and Palomar Observatories photographs*)

its equator is greater. Spots near the equator, which survive long enough, go completely around in 25 days, although they seem to us to require 4 weeks, because the earth has revolved partway around the sun in the meantime. At 35° from the equator, beyond which the sunspots are rarely seen, the true period is 27 days. In solar latitude 75° the Doppler effect in the spectra of the approaching and receding edges shows that the period has increased to 35 days.

10·6. The Sunspot Number Cycle. In some years the sun's disk is seldom free from spots, whereas in other years it may remain unspotted for several days in succession. Sunspot groups vary in number in a roughly periodic manner, a variation first announced in 1843 by Schwabe, an amateur astronomer in Germany. The intervals between the times of maximum spottedness have averaged 11.1 years, but for the past half-century have been more nearly 10 years. The numbers of groups at the different maxima are not the same. The rise to maximum is faster than the decline.

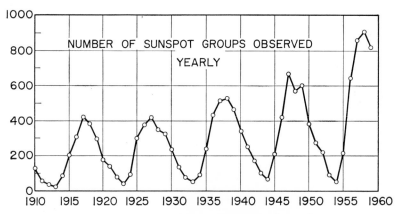

FIG. 10·6. The Sunspot Number Cycle. The point for each year represents the number of groups observed during the year. The curve shows the roughly periodic variation in the numbers. (*From data by Mount Wilson Observatory*)

The latest maximum, which occurred in 1958, was the highest on record in number of groups, but the groups and individual spots were generally smaller than at the maximum around 1948. The latest minimum occurred early in 1954, and the next minimum would be expected in 1964.

10·7. The Shifting Sunspot Zones. Sunspots are confined mainly between latitudes 5° and 30° north and south of the sun's equator; very few have as yet been reported beyond 45°. At any particular time they are likely to appear in two rather narrow zones equidistant from the equator. As spots vanish and others appear, the zones shift toward the equator in cycles that parallel the sunspot number cycles.

About a year before sunspot minimum, small spots break out in the higher latitudes. Thereafter, the two zones of spot activity draw in toward the equator, and when the next minimum is reached, a few surviving members of the fading cycle are seen around latitudes 5°. Meanwhile some spots of the new cycle have already become visible in the higher latitudes. Thus at the minimum of 1954 the Mount Wilson observers recorded 15 groups near the equator and 31 groups of the new cycle.

The cause of the one-way shifting of the spot zones, like the cause of the number cycle and indeed of the spots themselves, is not as yet known. Nor is it clearly understood why sunspots are magnetic, and why their magnetism reverses with the beginning of each new cycle.

10·8. Sunspots Are Magnetic. When the image of a sunspot is focused on the slit of a spectroscope, the dark lines of the solar spectrum appear split into two or more parts (Fig. 10·8). This

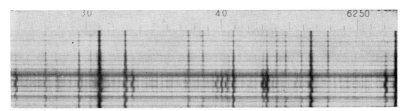

Fig. 10·8. Zeeman Effect in the Sunspot Spectrum. The slight splitting of the dark lines is emphasized by a device which alternately suppresses the violet and red components of the lines. Thus the lines have a zigzag appearance. (*Mount Wilson Observatory photograph*)

Zeeman effect, known by the name of the Dutch physicist who discovered it in the laboratory, in 1896, is the splitting of the spectrum lines where the source of the light is in the field of a strong magnet. The effect in the sunspot spectrum shows that the spot is magnetic and also reveals its *polarity*—whether the positive or negative pole of the magnet is toward us.

Most sunspot groups are *bipolar;* their two principal spots have opposite polarities which conform to the following rule: During a particular cycle the preceding spots in the sun's northern hemisphere have their positive poles toward us, and the following spots their negative poles. In the southern hemisphere the preceding spots present their negative magnetic poles, and the following spots their positive poles.

A remarkable feature of sunspot magnetism is the complete reversal of the pattern with the appearance of the groups of the next cycle (Fig. 10·8A). The preceding spots in the northern hemisphere now present their negative poles, and so on. First reported by Mount Wilson astronomers around the sunspot minimum of 1913, this reversal of polarities has been observed at each succeeding minimum.

The sun's magnetism is being studied by H. W. and H. D. Babcock by means of their effective scanning device, the *magnetometer*.

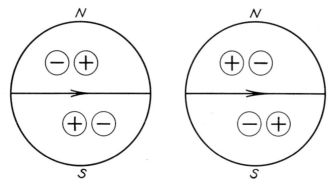

FIG. 10·8A. Reversal of Polarities of Sunspots with the Beginning of a New Cycle. The circles represent preceding and following spots of groups in the two hemispheres.

The general field, as they assume, has two components: (1) Polar fields of opposite polarity around the two poles; these reversed sign at the sunspot number maximum in 1958. (2) Ring-shaped fields parallel to the sun's equator have opposite field direction in the two hemispheres and migrate toward the equator in the sunspot cycle. They are replaced at sunspot minimum by new rings of opposite directions in the higher mid-latitudes. These fields are serving as a convenient basis for tentative magnetohydrodynamic interpretations of observed features at and above the solar surface.

THE SUN'S ATMOSPHERE

10·9. The Spectrum of Sunlight, as it is observed visually, is an array of colors from violet to red, which is interrupted by thousands of dark lines. The lines are not seen in the rainbow or in the spectrum formed by the prism alone. They require the selectivity given by the narrow slit before the prism and, accordingly, were not discovered

until the slit was used. The German optician Fraunhofer was the
first, in 1814, to see them clearly; he mapped several hundred dark

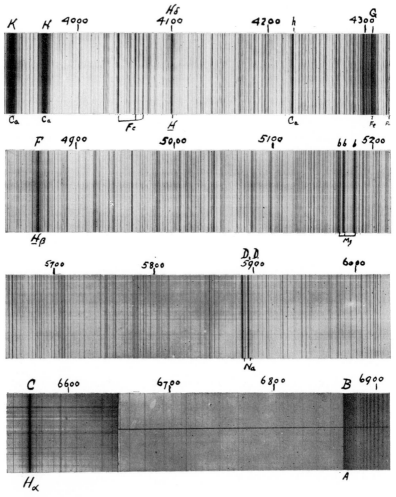

FIG. 10·9. Parts of the Visible Solar Spectrum. (*Photographed with the
13-foot spectrograph, Mount Wilson and Palomar Observatories*)

lines and labeled them with Roman letters beginning at the red end
of the spectrum. The lines are still known by the letters which he
assigned them.

The dark lines are images of the slit of the spectroscope at the
wavelengths that are darkened in the sunlight; these are abstracted

from the continuous light of the photosphere mainly by gases of the different chemical elements in the sun's atmosphere. The strongest solar lines are the Fraunhofer H and K of calcium near the violet end of the visible spectrum. There are also *telluric bands*—groups of lines abstracted from the sunlight by molecules of the earth's atmosphere. The B band formed by terrestrial oxygen molcules is prominent in Fig. 10·9. The separate lines of the solar spectrum itself are produced by atoms of the different elements in the sun's atmosphere, which cannot generally combine into molecules at that high temperature.

The wavelengths of the lines are expressed in *angstroms,* abbreviated A; one angstrom is 10^{-8} centimeter. The visible region of the solar spectrum is between 3900 and 7600 A. Some conspicuous lines and bands are the following:

Fraunhofer Letter	Wavelength	Identification
A	7594 A	oxygen (telluric)
B	6867	oxygen (telluric)
C	6563	hydrogen
D	5893	sodium (double)
E	5270	iron
F	4861	hydrogen
H	3968	calcium
K	3934	calcium

The ultraviolet region of the solar spectrum can be photographed ordinarily as far as 2900 A, beyond which it is hidden by absorption of ozone and other constituents of our atmosphere. Features of the extreme ultraviolet spectrum are being recorded from rockets above the absorbing levels. Shortward from 1700 A the separate dark lines become so crowded that they disappear. Only the bright lines of the chromosphere are then recorded, and by far the brightest of these is the alpha line of the Lyman series of hydrogen. The infrared region has been mapped by photography and other means as far as 200,000 A. Here the solar lines are frequently obscured by broad telluric bands.

10·10. Chemical Elements in the Sun. More than 60 chemical elements are recognized in the sun's atmosphere. They have been identified by comparing their laboratory spectra with the lines in the solar spectrum. Some unrecognized elements would not be expected to make much impression there, and some have not had

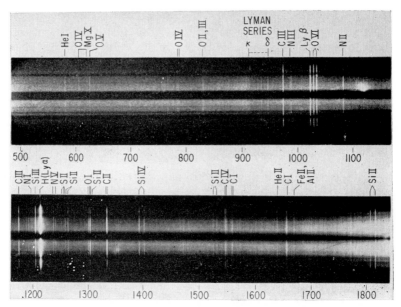

FIG. 10·9A. Ultraviolet Spectrum of the Sun. Photographed, March 3, 1959, from a Naval Research Laboratory Aerobee rocket. (*Official U.S. Navy photograph*)

their laboratory spectra determined well enough for dependable comparisons. Some inert gases and halogens have their strongest lines in the far ultraviolet. The conclusion is that practically all the chemical elements are present in the sun.

The hot gases of the sun are generally composed of dissociated atoms. The molecules of 18 compounds are recognized as well by their dark bands in the spectrum. Examples are titanium oxide and the hydrides of calcium and magnesium, which occur in the cooler areas of sunspots. Only a few hardy compounds hold together above the unspotted regions.

Hydrogen is the most abundant element in the sun's atmosphere, and helium is second. These two elements also predominate in the sun's interior, in the stars, and in the universe generally. Hydrogen contributes about 55 per cent of the mass of the cosmic material, helium 44 per cent, and the heavier elements the remainder. Exceptions to these proportions occur in the earth and other smaller bodies from which most of the lighter gases have escaped.

10·11. The Chromosphere appears as a red fringe around the dark disk of the moon when it completely conceals the photosphere at the time of total solar eclipse. On these occasions the bright-line spectrum of the chromosphere can be observed; it is also known as the *flash spectrum,* because it flashes into view in the spectroscope near the beginning of the total eclipse, replacing the dark lines of the ordinary solar spectrum. The red Fraunhofer C line gives its color to the chromosphere and the prominences above it.

As it is photographed with a slitless spectroscope near the beginning or end of total solar eclipse, the flash spectrum (Fig. 10·11) appears as a succession of images of the narrow crescent of the chromosphere left uncovered by the moon. The different lengths

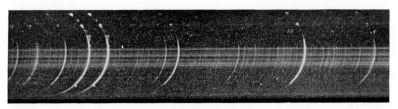

FIG. 10·11. The Spectrum of the Chromosphere. The pair of long crescents at the left are the H and K lines of calcium. Projections to the right of the crescents are prominences. Breaks in the crescents are caused by irregularities in the moon's surface. (*Mount Wilson Observatory photograph*)

of the crescents show that some of the chemical elements which produce them are effective to greater heights above the photosphere than are others. Hydrogen, calcium, and helium give the longest images.

The strong helium lines of the flash spectrum, by which this useful element was discovered in the sun before it was recognized on the earth, are almost entirely missing in the dark-line solar spectrum. Aside from this and some other explainable exceptions, the lines of the chromospheric and ordinary solar spectra are similar, illustrating the rule that a luminous gas emits the same pattern of wavelengths that it absorbs from light passing through it.

10·12. The Chromosphere Outside Eclipse. Much of our knowledge of the exterior features of the sun is being obtained with special apparatus when the sun is uneclipsed. Examples are the spectroheliograph and the coronagraph. The latter is effective at high altitudes where purer and thinner air produces less glare around the edge of the sun. Such instruments are in operation on the Pic du Midi in the French Pyrenees and at several other mountain observatories, including the high altitude stations at Climax, Colorado, and on Sacramento Peak in New Mexico.

The *spectroheliograph* is an attachment to the telescope employed to record the chromosphere over the whole disk of the sun. An adaptation of the spectroscope, it is a device for photographing the sun in the light of a single line of the spectrum, and therefore of the chemical element in the sun's atmosphere that produces the chosen line. We will understand that the "dark" lines are dark

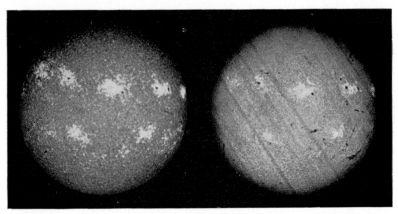

FIG. 10·12. The Sun in Calcium and Hydrogen Light. Spectroheliograms taken with the K line of calcium (left) and the red hydrogen line (right). (*Mount Wilson Observatory photographs*)

by contrast with the brighter background of the solar spectrum; they contain the weaker light of the chromosphere, which is recorded in the photograph, or *spectroheliogram*. The K line of calcium and the C line of hydrogen are the ones generally used for the purpose.

Photographs of the chromosphere (Fig. 10·12) show the bright *flocculi*. Where these are bunched around sunspot groups and other active centers, they are known as *plages*. Photographs beyond the edge of the sun show the chromosphere as a fairly uniform layer from which bright *spicules* keep emerging, forming a grass-like upper surface. Each spicule reaches a height of about 10″ above the edge and soon vanishes.

Monochromatic filters are also employed to transmit a very narrow range of wavelength of the sunlight. The polarizing monochromator is an example; the filter here may be a succession of quartz crystal and polaroid sheets. Such devices are effective in viewing the solar prominences outside eclipse.

10·13. The Solar Prominences appear flame-like beyond the chromosphere during total solar eclipse, their vivid red in striking contrast with the white glow of the corona. In the photographs in

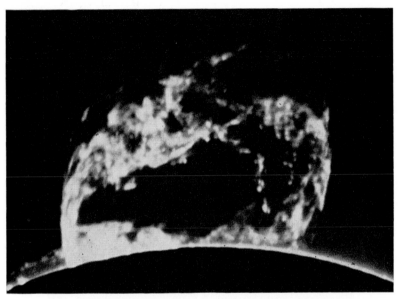

FIG. 10·13. Solar Prominence, June 28, 1945. (*Photographed by Walter Orr Roberts, High Altitude Observatory, Climax, Colorado*)

hydrogen light taken outside eclipse they often appear as long dark filaments against the brighter background of the chromosphere. Where they are carried beyond the disk by the sun's rotation, they appear bright against the sky. The prominences can be photographed in their hydrogen or calcium light, or can be viewed directly with the spectrohelioscope. Effective studies of their behavior have been made at the McMath-Hulbert Observatory and at high altitude stations in America and Europe in successions of photographs taken on motion picture film. The projections of the films give dramatic and very instructive portrayals of their activities.

Most prominences are of the *active* type; they originate high above the chromosphere and pour their streamers down into it. *Quiescent* prominences are the least active and have the longest

lives; their most common form is the "haystack." *Eruptive* prominences are among the rarer types. These rise from active material
above the chromosphere, attaining high speeds and great altitudes
before they vanish. A prominence of 1938 attained a speed of 450
miles a second. A prominence of June 4, 1946, rose to a distance
of more than a million miles above the sun's surface.

10·14. Solar Flares are remarkable outbursts generally in the
vicinities of large and active sunspot groups of irregular polarity.
Viewed with the spectrohelioscope or monochromatic filter they

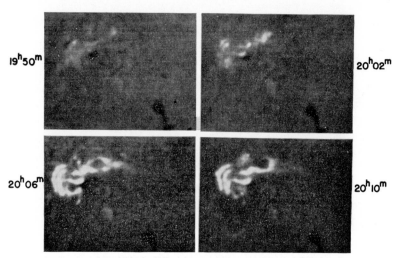

Fig. 10·14. A Solar Flare, May 10, 1949. A series of hydrogen spectroheliograms showing development of the flare. Universal times are given.
(Photographed by Helen W. Dodson, McMath-Hulbert Observatory)

appear as brilliant areas of the chromosphere. They vary from
smaller flares of a few minutes' duration to more intense and rarer
ones which require up to 15 minutes to attain their greatest brightness, and then disappear in an hour or more. They have been
attributed to masses of glowing gas brought up from below the
photosphere in the wakes of upheavals whch cause the bursts observed with radio telescopes.

These hot gases emerge explosively and rise to considerable
heights. The first report of their rapid ascent was given by Helen
Dodson at the McMath-Hulbert Observatory from her photographs
with a motion picture camera. The flare of May 8, 1951, at the
edge of the disk rose in the first minute of its life at the rate of 450

miles a second, comparable with the speeds of some eruptive prominences, and continued to the height of 30,000 miles.

10·15. The Radio Sun. The reception of noise from the sun was first detected, in 1942, by radar defense stations in Great Britain, where the source of the disturbance was traced to a large spot group near the central meridian of the sun. This accidental discovery provided a new means of studying the sun, which is being utilized with radio telescopes in various parts of the world. The radio emission is produced by the interactions of fast-moving electrified particles from below with the exterior gases; it is strongest at wavelengths of 1 to 10 meters, where it originates at different levels of the corona, and is weakest at centimeter ranges, from the lower chromosphere.

With the shorter wavelengths the Australian radio astronomers have devised apparatus for rapidly scanning the whole disk. They record bright spots which are generally associated with visible sunspot groups, but may last much longer than do the spots. From the *quiet sun,* in the years when sunspots are scarce, the radio emission has its least strength, which is fairly constant.

From the *active sun,* when sunspots are numerous, *bursts* of irregular and much greater strength are superposed. The explanations of how they occur and of their relation to the visible flares are still tentative. J. P. Wild in Australia suggests that the upheaval in the sun produces clouds of particles moving outward at a sixth the speed of light; when they reach the corona in seconds, they produce the radio *flashes* of a few seconds' duration. The following shock wave may carry great numbers of trapped particles into the corona at the rate of 1000 miles a second, where they cause a radio *outburst* lasting from 10 to 20 minutes.

10·16. Terrestrial Associations. The appearance of an intense solar flare is likely to be soon followed by a deterioration of our radio communications in the higher frequencies. Powerful ultraviolet radiations from the flare arrive with visible evidence of the flare itself, and the very swift particles which cause the radio flashes from the corona reach the earth less than an hour later. These disrupt ionized layers of the upper atmosphere, which normally keep reflecting our own radio beams back to the ground (1·14).

Less swift electrified particles from the upheaval in the sun arrive here about a day after the solar flare was observed, and after the particles have produced the outburst of radio emission in their passage through the corona. They then excite the gases of our upper atmosphere and set them glowing in an auroral display (1·19). The appearance of the aurora is generally accompanied by unusual gyrations of the magnetic compass, which inform us that a *geomagnetic storm* is in progress.

ECLIPSES OF THE SUN; THE CORONA

10·17. The Moon's Shadow on the Earth. An eclipse of the sun occurs when the moon passes directly between the sun and the earth, screening part or all of the sun's disk. The earth is then partly darkened by the moon's shadow.

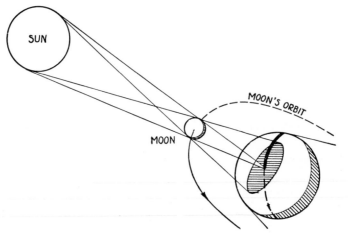

Fig. 10·17. Path of Total Solar Eclipse. The moon's shadow moves in an easterly direction over the earth's surface. The eclipse is total for an observer in the umbra, and is partial in the larger area of the penumbra.

The average length of the umbra of the moon's shadow is 232,000 miles, which is 3000 miles less than the average distance of the moon from the earth's surface. In the average the umbra does not reach the earth's surface; the fact that it often does reach is because of the eccentricity of the moon's orbit around the earth and of the earth's orbit around the sun. When the moon is nearest the earth and the earth is also farthest from the sun, the conical umbra of the moon's shadow falls on the earth 18,000 miles inside its apex.

10·18. Total and Annular Eclipses. A *total eclipse* of the sun occurs when the umbra of the moon's shadow extends to the earth's surface. The area encompassed by the umbra rarely exceeds 150 miles in diameter when the sun is overhead, and is generally smaller. The observer within the area sees the dark circle of the moon completely hiding the sun's disk.

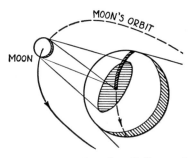

An *annular eclipse* occurs when the umbra is directed toward the earth but is too short to reach it. Within a small area of the earth's surface the moon is seen nearly centrally projected upon the disk of the sun, but the moon appears slightly the smaller of the two, so that a ring, or annulus, of the

Fig. 10·18.   Annular Eclipse of the Sun.   The umbra of the moon's shadow does not reach the earth's surface.

sun's disk remains uncovered.   Annular eclipses are 20 per cent more frequent than total eclipses.

Around the small area of the earth from which the eclipse appears total or annular is the larger area, some 2000 to 3000 miles in radius,

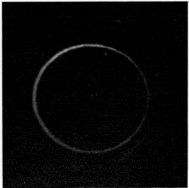

Fig. 10·18A.   Annular Solar Eclipse, September 1, 1951.   Immediately before (left) and after (right) the beginning of the annular phase.   The sun was near the horizon.   (*Photographs by Luc Secretan*)

which is covered by the penumbra of the shadow.   Here a *partial eclipse* is visible, and the fraction of the sun that is hidden decreases as the observer's distance from the center is greater.   Eclipses are entirely partial where the axis of the shadow is directed slightly to

one side of the earth. All total and annular eclipses are preceded
and followed by partial phases.

10·19. The Path of the Moon's Shadow. The revolution of the
moon causes its shadow to sweep eastward at the average rate of
2100 miles an hour. Because the earth is rotating toward the east

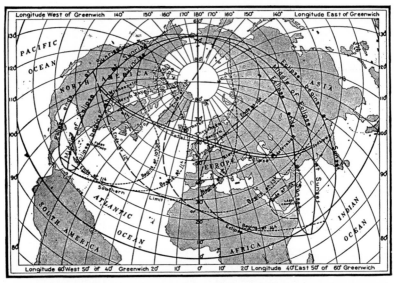

FIG. 10·19. Path of Total Solar Eclipse of June 30, 1954. The umbra of
the moon's shadow touched the earth in Nebraska and left it in northern
India. (*From the* American Ephemeris and Nautical Almanac)

at the rate of 1040 miles an hour at the equator, the speed of the
shadow over the surface is 1060 miles an hour at the equator when
the sun is overhead. The effective speed becomes greater with increasing distance from the equator, where the rotation is slower, and
may reach as much as 5000 miles an hour when the sun is near the
horizon.

Considering its high speed and small area, we see that the umbra
can darken any part of its path for only a short time. The greatest
possible duration of total solar eclipse at a particular place can
scarcely exceed 7½ minutes, and that of annular eclipse can be only
a little greater. The partial phase accompanying either type of
eclipse may have a duration of more than 4 hours from beginning
to end, but is usually much less.

The *path of total eclipse,* or of annular eclipse, is the narrow track of the darkest part of the shadow over the earth's surface, from the time it first touches the earth at sunrise until it departs at sunset. Meanwhile the penumbra moves over the larger surrounding region in which the eclipse is only partial. Occasionally the umbra is long enough to reach the earth at the middle of its path but at the beginning and end fails to extend to the surface. In this event the eclipse is total around the middle of the day and is otherwise annular.

10·20. Eclipse Seasons. In order to eclipse the sun, the moon must be almost directly between the sun and the earth. This condition is not fulfilled every time the moon arrives at its new phase, because

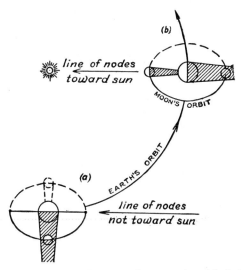

FIG. 10·20. Eclipse Seasons. Because the moon's orbit is inclined about 5° to the plane of the earth's orbit, eclipses can occur only at two opposite seasons, as at *b*, when the sun is near the line of nodes of the moon's path. At other times in the year, as at *a*, the moon does not pass between the earth and the sun or into the earth's shadow.

the moon's path around the heavens is inclined 5° to the ecliptic. Thus the new moon is more likely to pass north or south of the sun.

Eclipses occur during two *eclipse seasons* around the times when the sun is passing the two opposite nodes of the moon's path. Owing to the rapid westward shifting of the nodes along the ecliptic (6·7), these seasons come about half a month earlier in the calendar from year to year; in 1960 they were around March and September. The length of the *eclipse year* is 346.6 days, which is the interval between two successive returns of the sun to the same node. Thus if the first season is early in the year, another season around the same node may begin before the end of the year.

Each solar eclipse season lasts a little more than a month, or somewhat more than the month of the moon's phases. During each interval the moon becomes new at least once, and may do so twice. Two eclipses of the sun are accordingly inevitable each year, one near each node. Five may occur, two near each node and an additional eclipse if the sun comes around again to the first node before the year ends. Similarly, it can be shown that three umbral eclipses of the moon are possible in the course of the year, although a whole year may pass without a single one.

10·21. Predictions of Solar Eclipses. Accurate predictions of solar eclipses, of when they will occur and where they will be visible, are published in various astronomical almanacs a year or two in advance. Tracks of total solar eclipses for several years in advance are published in the U.S. Naval Observatory *Circulars.* The approximate times and places of eclipses from 1208 B.C. to A.D. 2163 can be found in Oppolzer's *Canon der Finsternisse,* which also contains maps showing the tracks of total and annular solar eclipses.

The predictions of eclipses are made possible by knowledge of the motions of the earth and moon. They are facilitated by a relation between the occurrences of eclipses which has been known from very early times. The *saros* is the interval of 18 years 11⅓ days (or a day less or more, depending on the number of leap years included) in which eclipses of the same series are repeated. It is equal to 223 synodic months which contain 6585.32 days, and is nearly the same as 19 eclipse years having 6585.78 days. After this interval the relative positions of the sun, moon, and node are nearly the same as before. The sun is about one diameter west of its former position relative to the node; the paths of the eclipses of a series are accordingly displaced progressively in latitude, being shifted gradually from pole to pole until the shadow fails to touch the earth and the particular series is completed.

The third of a day in the saros period causes the path of each eclipse to be displaced in longitude a third of the way around the earth with respect to its predecessor. After 3 intervals, about 54 years and a month, the path returns to about the same region as before.

Total Solar Eclipses

Date	Duration (minutes)	Region
1961, Feb. 15	3	Europe, Siberia
1962, Feb. 5	4	East Indies
1963, July 20	2	Alaska, Canada
1965, May 30	5	New Zealand, Peru
1966, Nov. 12	2	South America, South Africa
1970, Mar. 7	3	Mexico, Florida, Georgia, Carolinas
1972, July 10	3	NE Asia, Alaska, Canada
1973, June 30	7	South America, Africa

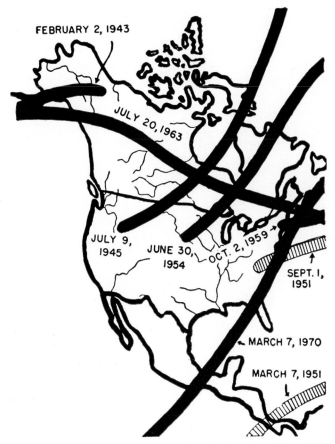

Fig. 10·21. Recent and Coming Total and Annular Solar Eclipses in North America. (*Diagram by Charles H. Smiley, Brown University*)

The dates, durations at noon, and land areas in which current total eclipses of the sun are visible are shown in the table; the paths of the eclipses that will be visible in North America until 1970 appear in Fig. 10·21. The path of the 1963 eclipse will pass near northern Maine, and that of the 1970 eclipse will follow along our Atlantic Coast.

10·22. The Sun in Total Eclipse is an impressive sight to be always remembered. The beginning of eclipse is manifested by the appearance of a dark notch at the sun's western edge. Gradually the sun's

FIG. 10·22. The Total Solar Eclipse of June 30, 1954. (*Photographed by John R. Winckler, University of Minnesota*)

disk is hidden by the moon. When only a thin crescent remains uncovered, the sky and landscape have assumed a pale and unfamiliar aspect, because the light from the sun's rim is redder than ordinary sunlight.

The light fades rapidly as total eclipse approaches. There is a chill in the air; birds seem bewildered; some flowers begin to close. As soon as the last sliver of the sun breaks into brilliant beads and disappears, the filmy corona bursts into view.   Red prominences are often seen close to the edge of the eclipsing moon; some planets and bright stars may appear.   Totality ends as abruptly as it began; the sunlight returns and the corona vanishes.

The scientific value of total solar eclipse is owing to the availability on these rare occasions of features which are revealed less

FIG. 10·23.   The Sun's Corona.   (*Photographed at the total eclipse of August 31, 1932, by Paul A. McNally, Georgetown University*)

clearly or not at all at other times.   Precise measurements of the positions of stars in the vicinity of the darkened sun have shown that they are apparently displaced slightly outward from the sun's edge, as they should be according to the theory of relativity.   Many features of the sun's corona, particularly the streamers of the outer corona, can be well observed only during total solar eclipse.

10·23. The Corona is the outer envelope of the sun and the chief contributor to the splendor of the total solar eclipse; its brightness is half that of the full moon.   The corona is characterized by delicate streamers which vary in the sunspot cycle.   Near sunspot maximum the form is roughly circular; petal-like streamers all around give the appearance which has been likened to that of a dahlia. Near sunspot minimum the corona is flattened in the polar regions (Fig. 10·23), where short, curved streamers are remindful of the lines of force around a bar magnet. Long streamers may reach out more than a million miles from the equatorial regions. The in-

Fig. 10·23A. An Artist's Conception of the Corona and Zodiacal Light Observed from Space. (*Drawing by Charles A. Federer, Sr., for* Sky and Telescope)

fluence of the corona is far more extended than the photographs show. While the sun was passing near the Crab nebula in Taurus, a source of radio emission, the occulting effect of the corona on radio reception from the nebula was detected to a distance of 18 solar radii from the sun's center.

The light of the corona is partly reflected sunlight, as the dark Fraunhofer lines in its spectrum show; it decreases slowly in intensity outward, and is ascribed mainly to the reflection by a portion of the dust ring that causes the zodiacal light (9·10). The rest of the light, which gives a bright-line spectrum, comes from the luminous gases of the corona itself, and is stronger near the sun's equator than at its poles. The bright lines in the spectrum of the corona were first identified, in 1941, by the Swedish physicist Edlén. They are emitted by shattered atoms of iron, nickel, calcium, and argon, which have been stripped of from 9 to 15 electrons. Such disruption of the atoms would occur at a temperature of 2 million degrees F, whereas a temperature of less than 6000° F would normally be expected for material at that distance from the sun's radiating surface.

Features of the inner corona around the uneclipsed sun were first photographed, in 1930, by the French astronomer B. Lyot with the coronagraph on the Pic du Midi. This type of telescope, having special precautions against bringing in direct sunlight to blot out the faint coronal light, is now in use at other high-altitude stations. With an appropriate filter both still and cine photographs of the corona are being made around the uneclipsed sun.

QUESTIONS ON CHAPTER 10

1. Suppose that the sun is represented by a ball 3¼ inches in diameter (about its diameter in Fig. 10·4). Show that the earth on this scale would be $\frac{1}{32}$ inch in diameter. Find a sunspot of this size in the photograph.

2. Explain the advantage of a long-focus telescope in photographing the sun.

3. Describe the growth and decline of a normal sunspot group.

4. Describe the sunspot number cycle and the shifting of the spot zones during the cycle.

5. Describe the magnetism of sunspot groups in the two hemispheres and its change from cycle to cycle.

6. Associate each of the following definitions with the feature of the sun to which it applies:

(a) The surface that is ordinarily visible.
(b) The two principal members of a sunspot group.
(c) The darkest part of a sunspot.
(d) The red layer surrounding the visible surface.
(e) The outermost envelope of the sun.

7. Name: (a) four chemical elements which produce strong dark lines in the solar spectrum; (b) a fifth element producing prominent bright lines in the spectrum of the chromosphere.

8. Why do the prominences appear dark against the sun's disk and bright when they project beyond its edge? Account for their red color.

9. What is a solar flare? Distinguish between bursts and outbursts recorded with radio telescopes.

10. Mention some terrestrial effects which are frequently associated with solar flares.

11. Distinguish between total and annular eclipse of the sun as to cause and appearance.

12. Describe the changes in the appearance of the corona during the sunspot cycle.

REFERENCES

Abetti, Giorgio, *The Sun*. Revised edition. The Macmillan Company, New York, 1957.

Dyson, Frank, and R. v. d. R. Woolley, *Eclipses of the Sun and Moon*. Oxford University Press, 1937.

Kuiper, Gerard P., editor, *The Sun*. University of Chicago Press, 1954.

Menzel, Donald H., *Our Sun*. Revised edition. Harvard University Press, Cambridge, 1959.

Mitchell, S. A., *Eclipses of the Sun*. Fifth edition. Columbia University Press, New York, 1951.

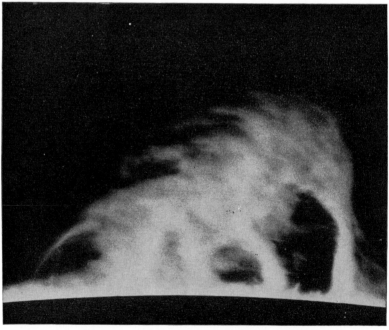

A Solar Prominence. *(Photographed by R. B. Dunn with the 15-inch Camera, Sacramento Peak Observatory)*

11

THE STARS IN THEIR SEASONS

THE CONSTELLATIONS — STARS OF SPRING — STARS OF
SUMMER — STARS OF AUTUMN — STARS OF WINTER —
THE SOUTHERN CONSTELLATIONS

THE CONSTELLATIONS

In the original sense the constellations are configurations of stars. The brighter stars form patterns of dippers, crosses, and the like. Some of the star-figures we recognize today were well known to the people of Mesopotamia 5000 years ago, who had named them after animals and representatives of occupations, such as the herdsman and the hunter. The plan was later adopted by the Greeks who renamed some of the characters after the animals and heroes of their mythology.

11·1. The Original Constellations. Forty-eight constellations were known to the early Greeks. Nearly all of these are described in the *Phenomena*, which the poet Aratus wrote, about 270 B.C., and which can be found in many libraries today. The popularity of Aratus' poem did much to perpetuate the imagined starry creatures which he vividly described.

Interest in the celestial menagerie was also promoted by the publication of Ptolemy's *Almagest*, about A.D. 150, where the places of the stars are designated by their positions in the mythological figures. Then, too, famous artists of later times vied with one another to produce the liveliest pictures of the imagined creatures.

These creatures do not appear on modern maps and globes of the heavens. They have nothing to do with the astronomy of today, except the connection with which they began; their names are still the names of constellations. Meanwhile, the constellations have increased in number and have taken on a new significance, although their oldest one as groups of stars survives as well.

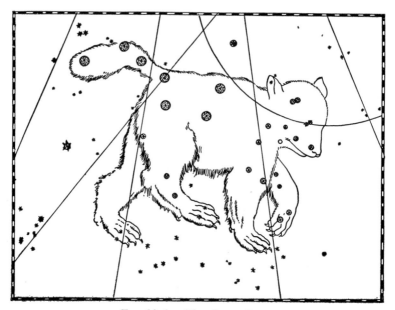

Fig. 11·1. The Great Bear.

11·2. Constellations as Divisions of the Sky. The original constellations did not cover the skies of the Greeks completely; they did not include the duller areas where there were no striking configurations of stars to claim attention. At that time, only those stars within the imagined creatures belonged to constellations. In addition, the part of the heavens around the south celestial pole that did not rise above the horizon of the Greeks remained uncharted.

Celestial map makers of later times filled the vacant spaces with new constellations which they named after scientific instruments, birds, and other things having no connection with the creatures of the legends. Not all of them survived. At present we recognize 88 constellations, which completely cover the sphere of the stars from pole to pole. Seventy of them are visible, either wholly or in part, from the latitude of New York.

For the purposes of astronomy, the constellations are now definite divisions of the heavens marked off by boundary lines, just as the states are bounded. The boundaries first appeared in the star maps at the beginning of the 19th century. They were frequently irregular, making detours to avoid cutting across outstretched arms and paws of the legendary creatures. These devious dividing lines were straightened for most of the southern constellations by the American astronomer Gould, in 1877, and finally for all the constellations by decision of the International Astronomical Union, in 1928. The boundaries now run only from east to west and from north to south, although they zigzag considerably so as not to

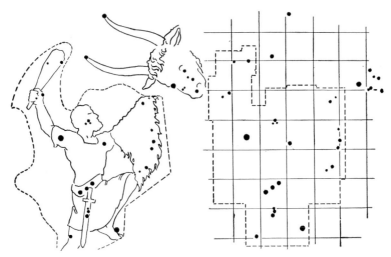

FIG. 11·2. Old and New Boundaries of Orion.

expatriate bright stars and variable stars from constellations with which they have long been associated.

11·3. Names of the Stars. The brightest stars and other especially famous ones are known to us by personal names which have been handed down through the ages. Some of these names are of Greek and Latin origin. Some are derived from the Arabic; names such as Algol, Altair (*al* is the Arabic definite article), and many others are survivals from earlier times when astronomy was a favorite study of the Mohammedan scholars. The stars were also named by shepherds, sailors, and nomads of the desert.

Procyon, meaning "before the dog," precedes the Great Dog Star in its rising. Aldebaran means "the follower"; it rises after the Pleiades. Antares is the "rival of Mars," owing to its red color. These are examples of how some of the stars were designated. Other star names have come to us in a different way.

In the earliest catalogs, such as Ptolemy's, the stars were distin-

TABLE 11·I NAMES OF THE CONSTELLATIONS

Latin Name	Possessive	English Equivalent	Map
*Androm'eda	Androm'edae	Andromeda	4, 5
Ant'lia	Ant'liae	Air Pump	
A'pus	A'podis	Bird of Paradise	
*Aqua'rius	Aqua'rii	Water Carrier	4
*Aq'uila	Aq'uilae	Eagle	3, 4
*A'ra	A'rae	Altar	6
*A'ries	Ari'etis	Ram	4, 5
*Auri'ga	Auri'gae	Charioteer	5
*Boö'tes	Boö'tis	Herdsman	2, 3
Cae'lum	Cae'li	Graving Tool	
Camelopar'dalis	Camelopar'dalis	Giraffe	
*Can'cer	Can'cri	Crab	2, 5
Ca'nes Vena'tici	Ca'num Venatico'rum	Hunting Dogs	2
*Ca'nis Ma'jor	Ca'nis Majo'ris	Larger Dog	5
*Ca'nis Mi'nor	Ca'nis Mino'ris	Smaller Dog	5
*Capricor'nus	Capricor'ni	Sea-Goat	4
†Cari'na	Cari'nae	Keel	6
*Cassiope'ia	Cassiope'iae	Cassiopeia	1, 4
*Centau'rus	Centau'ri	Centaur	2, 6
*Ce'pheus	Ce'phei	Cepheus	1, 4
*Ce'tus	Ce'ti	Whale	4, 5
Chamae'leon	Chamaeleon'tis	Chameleon	
Cir'cinus	Cir'cini	Compasses	
Colum'ba	Colum'bae	Dove	5
Co'ma Bereni'ces	Co'mae Bereni'ces	Berenice's Hair	2
*Coro'na Austra'lis	Coro'nae Austra'lis	Southern Crown	
*Coro'na Borea'lis	Coro'nae Borea'lis	Northern Crown	3
*Cor'vus	Cor'vi	Crow	2
*Cra'ter	Crater'is	Cup	2
Crux	Cru'cis	Cross	6
*Cyg'nus	Cyg'ni	Swan	3, 4
*Delphi'nus	Delphi'ni	Dolphin	4
Dora'do	Dora'dus	Dorado	
*Dra'co	Draco'nis	Dragon	1, 3
*Equu'leus	Equu'lei	Little Horse	
*Erid'anus	Erid'ani	River	5, 6
For'nax	Forna'cis	Furnace	
*Gem'ini	Gemino'rum	Twins	5
Grus	Gru'is	Crane	4
*Her'cules	Her'culis	Hercules	3
Horolo'gium	Horolo'gii	Clock	
*Hy'dra	Hy'drae	Sea Serpent	2
Hy'drus	Hy'dri	Water Snake	6
In'dus	In'di	Indian	
Lacer'ta	Lacer'tae	Lizard	
*Le'o	Leo'nis	Lion	2

Table 11·I Names of the Constellations—*Continued*

Latin Name	Possessive	English Equivalent	Map
Le'o Mi'nor	Leo'nis Mino'ris	Smaller Lion	
*Le'pus	Le'poris	Hare	5
*Li'bra	Li'brae	Scales	3
*Lu'pus	Lu'pi	Wolf	3
Lynx	Lyn'cis	Lynx	
*Ly'ra	Ly'rae	Lyre	3, 4
Men'sa	Men'sae	Table Mountain	
Microsco'pium	Microsco'pii	Microscope	
Monoc'eros	Monocero'tis	Unicorn	
Mus'ca	Mus'cae	Fly	6
Nor'ma	Nor'mae	Level	
Oc'tans	Octan'tis	Octant	
*Ophiu'chus	Ophiu'chi	Serpent Holder	3
*Ori'on	Orio'nis	Orion	5
Pa'vo	Pavo'nis	Peacock	6
*Peg'asus	Peg'asi	Pegasus	4
*Per'seus	Per'sei	Perseus	4, 5
Phoe'nix	Phoeni'cis	Phoenix	4
Pic'tor	Picto'ris	Easel	
*Pis'ces	Pis'cium	Fishes	4
*Pis'cis Austri'nus	Pis'cis Austri'ni	Southern Fish	4
†Pup'pis	Pup'pis	Stern	5
†Pyx'is	Pyx'idis	Mariner's Compass	
Retic'ulum	Retic'uli	Net	
*Sagit'ta	Sagit'tae	Arrow	3, 4
*Sagitta'rius	Sagitta'rii	Archer	3
*Scor'pius	Scor'pii	Scorpion	3
Sculp'tor	Sculpto'ris	Sculptor's Apparatus	4
Scu'tum	Scu'ti	Shield	
*Ser'pens	Serpen'tis	Serpent	3
Sex'tans	Sextan'tis	Sextant	
*Tau'rus	Tau'ri	Bull	5
Telesco'pium	Telesco'pii	Telescope	
*Trian'gulum	Trian'guli	Triangle	4, 5
Trian'gulum Austra'le	Trian'guli Austra'lis	Southern Triangle	6
Tuca'na	Tuca'nae	Toucan	6
*Ur'sa Ma'jor	Ur'sae Majo'ris	Larger Bear	1, 2
*Ur'sa Mi'nor	Ur'sae Mino'ris	Smaller Bear	1, 3
†Ve'la	Velo'rum	Sails	2, 6
*Vir'go	Vir'ginis	Virgin	2
Vo'lans	Volan'tis	Flying Fish	
Vulpec'ula	Vulpec'ulae	Fox	

* One of the 48 constellations recognized by Ptolemy.

† Carina, Puppis, Pyxis, and Vela once formed the single Ptolemaic constellation Argo Navis.

guished by their positions in the imagined figures of heroes and animals. One star was the "mouth of the Fish"; another was the "tail of the Bird." Transcribed later into the Arabic, some of these expressions finally degenerated into single words. Betelgeuse, the name of the bright red star in Orion, was originally three words meaning the "armpit of the Central One."

11·4. Designations of the Stars by Letters. The plan of designating the brighter stars by letters was introduced by Bayer, a Bavarian attorney, in 1603. In a general way, the stars of each constellation are denoted by small letters of the Greek alphabet in order of their brightness, and the Roman alphabet is drawn upon for further letters. Where there are several stars of nearly the same brightness in the constellation, they are likely to be lettered in order from head to foot of the legendary creature. The full name of a star in the Bayer system is the letter followed by the possessive of the Latin name of the constellation. Thus Capella, the brightest star in Auriga, is α Aurigae. The letters for some of the brighter stars are shown in the maps that follow.

Some of the fainter stars are known by their numbers according to a plan of numbering the stars in each constellation in order of right ascension. The star 61 Cygni is an example. Most faint stars, however, are designated only by their running numbers in one of the many catalogs to which the astronomer can turn for information as to their positions, brightness, and other features.

11·5. The Map of the Northern Sky. The six maps in this chapter show all parts of the celestial sphere. They are designed particularly for an observer in latitude 40° N, but are useful anywhere in middle northern latitudes. In order to avoid confusion, the many stars only faintly visible to the naked eye are not included, the names of inconspicuous constellations are generally omitted, and the boundaries between the constellations do not appear in the maps.

Map 1 shows the region of the heavens within 40° from the north celestial pole. The pole is at the center, closely marked by Polaris at the end of the Little Dipper's handle. Hour circles appear in this projection as straight lines radiating from the center; they are marked around the circumference of the map in hours of right ascension. The concentric circles are circles of equal declination at intervals of 10°; their declinations are shown on the vertical line.

This map is to be held toward the north. When it is turned so that the present month is at the top, the map represents the posi-

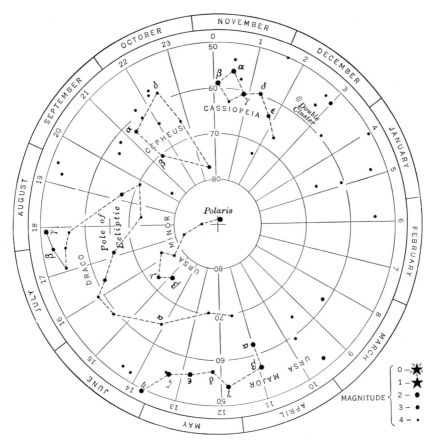

Map 1. The Northern Constellations.

tions of the northern constellations at 9 o'clock in the evening, standard time, or, more exactly, local mean time if the correct part of the month is at the top. The hour circle that is then vertically under the date coincides with the celestial meridian at this time of night on this date. For a different time of night the map is to be turned from the 9 o'clock position through the proper number of hours, clockwise for an earlier time and counterclockwise for a later time.

If we wish, for example, to identify the northern constellations at 9 o'clock in the evening on August 7, the map should be turned so that this date is at the top (at about the 18-hour circle). The Great Dipper is now bowl-down in the northwest, Cassiopeia is opposite it in the northeast, and so on. These northern constellations appear again in the maps for the different seasons. On all the maps the brightness of the stars is indicated by symbols which represent their approximate magnitudes (12·18).

11·6. Directions in the Sky. North in the sky is toward the north celestial pole; south is toward the opposite pole. East to west is the direction in which the stars seem to circle daily. If these rules are remembered, there can be no confusion about directions in the sky.

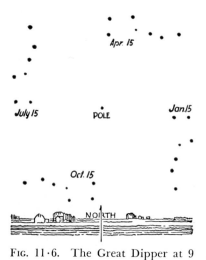

FIG. 11·6. The Great Dipper at 9 O'clock in the Evening at Different Seasons.

The position of a star is clearly described when its directions from other stars are given in this way. Its position is also perfectly definite if we say how it is related to two or more other stars; perhaps the star completes an equal-sided triangle with two other stars already identified, or it may be in line with them. We have noticed how a line through the pointer stars of the Great Dipper leads to the pole star. Such directions remain unaltered through the day and year.

Directions relative to the horizon, however, change as the stars go around the pole. From a star above the pole, north is down and west is to the left; from a star below the pole, north is up and west is to the right. Notice how the Great Dipper changes its position relative to the horizon during the night or from night to night as the seasons progress (Fig. 11·6). Along in the winter this figure of 7 stars stands on its handle in the northeast at 9 o'clock. In spring it appears inverted above the pole. In summer the Dipper is seen descending bowl-down in the northwest, and in autumn it is right side up under the pole, where it may be lost to view for a time.

11·7. Star Maps for the Four Seasons. Maps 2, 3, 4, and 5 show the constellations which cross the meridian at 9 o'clock in the evening during each of the 4 seasons, all the way from the north celestial pole to the south horizon of latitude 40° N. The pole is near the top of each map. Hour circles radiating from the pole are marked in hours of right ascension near the bottom of the map, and circles of equal declination go around the pole.

We select the map for the present season and hold it toward the south. The hour circle above the date of observation is along the celestial meridian at 9 o'clock in the evening on that date. Accordingly, the central vertical line in each of the 4 maps represents successively the positions of the meridian at 9 o'clock on April 21, July 21, October 21, and January 21. Remembering that the daily motions of the stars are from left to right for these maps and that a star comes to the meridian 2 hours earlier from month to month, we can locate the meridian in the maps for other times and dates.

Thus the maps are arranged to show what stars are crossing the celestial meridian at a particular time of the day and year. Any one of these stars can be identified in the sky if its distance from the zenith is also known at that time. The rule for finding the zenith distance is derived from Fig. 2·13: The zenith distance of a star at upper transit equals the observer's latitude minus the star's declination. If the distance is positive, the star is south of the zenith; if it is negative, the star is north of the zenith.

The zenith at the place of observation is on the circle having the same declination as the latitude of the place. As we are facing south, it would be necessary to lean backwards to view the constellations in the upper parts of the maps. The northern constellations, however, are shown more conveniently in Map 1. They are repeated in the seasonal maps to display more clearly how they are related to the constellations farther south.

The following examples illustrate the use of the maps.

1. Read from Map 2 the right ascension and declination of the star Regulus.
Answer: Right ascension 10^h 6^m, declination 12° N.

2. On June 20, 1960, the planet Jupiter was in right ascension 17^h 55^m, declination 24° S. What was its position among the stars (Map 3)?
Answer: In Sagittarius, west of the handle of the Milk Dipper.

3. On what date does the star Antares (Map 3) cross the meridian at 9 o'clock in the evening, standard time? What is then its distance from the zenith as observed in latitude 40° N?
Answer: July 12. The zenith distance is 66°, south.

4. On what date does Orion (Map 5) rise at 9 P.M.?

Answer: November 1. Because Orion is near the celestial equator, it rises 6 hours earlier than the time of its meridian crossing, which is 9 P.M. on February 1. Thus Orion rises at 3 P.M. on February 1, and at 9 P.M. on November 1.

STARS OF SPRING (MAP 2)

The star maps are useful for identifying the prominent constellations in the sky and also for reference during the reading of the book. Our brief inspection of the seasonal maps begins with the stars of spring, which are near the celestial meridian in the early evenings of this season.

11·8. Ursa Major. In the early evenings of spring the Great Dipper appears inverted above the pole. This figure of 7 bright stars is

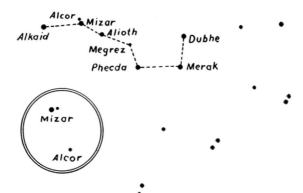

Fig. 11·8. Ursa Major. *Insert:* Mizar and Alcor viewed with an inverting telescope.

part of the large constellation Ursa Major, the Larger Bear, which extends for some distance to the west and south of the bowl of the Dipper; pairs of stars of nearly equal separations (Fig. 11·8) mark 3 paws of the ancient creature. Mizar, at the bend in the handle, has a fainter companion easily visible to the naked eye. With even a small telescope Mizar itself is revealed as a pair of stars.

Following the line of the Pointers northward we come to Polaris, the north star or pole star, less than 1° from the celestial pole. This useful star marks the end of the handle of the Little Dipper, the characteristic figure of Ursa Minor.

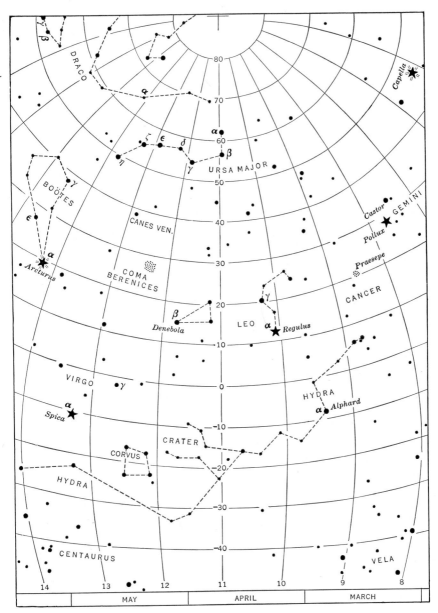

MAP 2. Stars of Spring.

11·9. Leo is peculiarly associated with the spring season.   Its familiar Sickle appears in the east in the early evening as spring approaches, and it becomes the dominant figure in the south as this season advances.   The bright star Regulus marks the end of the handle of the sickle-figure, which with the right triangle to the east is the distinguishing feature of this constellation of the zodiac.

To the east of Leo is the dim Cancer of the zodiac with its Praesepe star cluster.   To the west is the larger zodiacal constella-

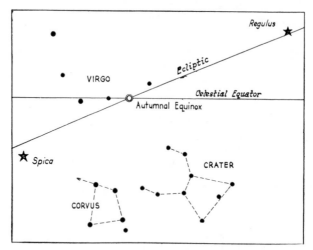

FIG. 11·9.   The Position of the Autumnal Equinox.

tion Virgo containing the bright star Spica.   The course of the ecliptic here is very nearly the line from the Praesepe cluster through Regulus and Spica.   Three fifths of the way from Regulus to Spica it crosses the celestial equator at the autumnal equinox.   The 4-sided figure of Corvus in this region is likely to attract attention. When Corvus is at upper transit, at 9 o'clock in the evening about the middle of May, the Southern Cross is on the meridian 40° to the south, where it is invisible from all except the extreme southern part of the United States.

STARS OF SUMMER (MAP 3)

A procession of familiar constellations, from Boötes to Cygnus, marches through the zenith in the evenings of summer in middle northern latitudes.   A fine region of the Milky Way, which we

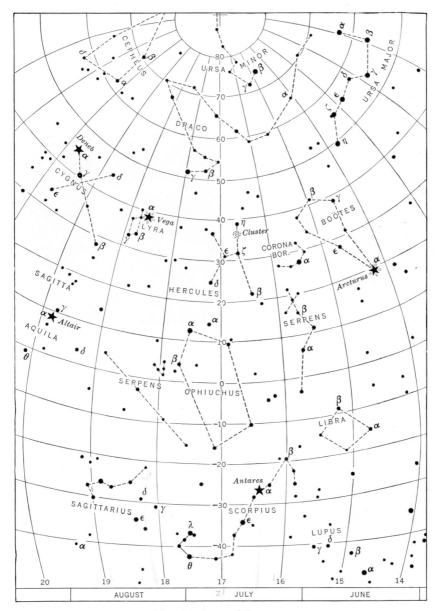

MAP 3. Stars of Summer.

examine in a later chapter, extends from Cygnus past Aquila down to Scorpius and Sagittarius in the south.

11·10. From Boötes to Lyra. Boötes is overhead when the stars come out at the beginning of summer. Its stars outline the figure of a large kite with the brilliant Arcturus at the point where the tail is attached. This somewhat reddish star is pointed out by

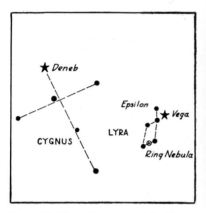

FIG. 11·10.   Cygnus and Lyra. Showing the positions of the double-double Epsilon Lyrae and the Ring nebula.

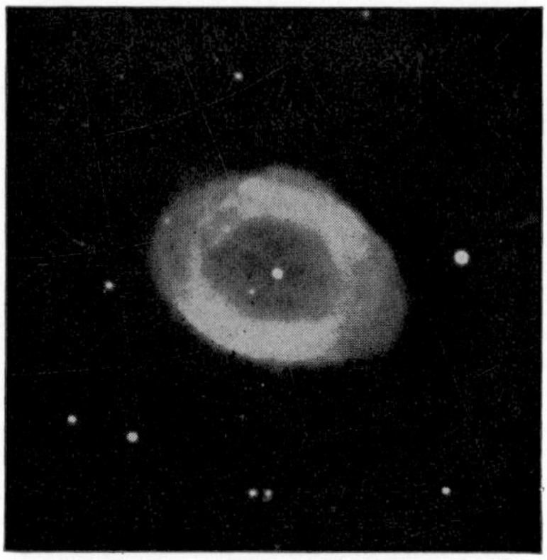

FIG. 11·10A. Ring Nebula in Lyra. (*Dominion Astrophysical Observatory photograph*)

following the curve of the Great Dipper's handle around past its end. Arcturus' only peers in the whole northern celestial hemisphere are blue Vega and yellow Capella.

Eastward from the kite-figure and beyond the semicircle of Corona Borealis, the Northern Crown, we find Hercules, which is passing overhead at nightfall in midsummer. Some of its brighter stars may seem to suggest the figure of a rather large butterfly that is flying toward the west. The great cluster in Hercules, scarcely visible to the naked eye, is situated two thirds of the way from the imagined butterfly's head along the west edge of the northern wing. Farther east on the line from the Crown through Hercules we come to Lyra. The figure here is a small parallelogram with a triangle attached at its northernmost point. Vega marks a vertex of the triangle. The star at the north point of the triangle is the "double-double" Epsilon Lyrae. It is visible as two stars to the unaided eye, but is more easily seen with binoculars; each star is again divided into two with the telescope. The Ring nebula in Lyra (Fig. 11·10), visible only with the telescope, is about midway between the two stars in the southern side of the parallelogram.

11·11. Scorpius and Sagittarius. The formidable figure of Scorpius, the Scorpion of the zodiac, dominates the southern sky at nightfall in early summer. Its bright Antares is a red supergiant star enormously larger than the sun.

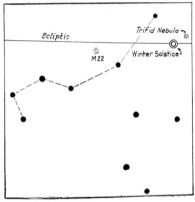 

FIG. 11·11. Milk Dipper of Sagittarius. Showing the position of the winter solstice.

FIG. 11·11A. Trifid Nebula in Sagittarius. (*Mount Wilson Observatory photograph*)

Directly east of Antares, 6 stars of the zodiacal constellation Sagittarius outline the Milk Dipper, so named because it is in the Milky Way. In this direction we look toward the center of our galaxy. The great star cloud of Sagittarius is an outlying portion of the galactic central region that is mainly obscured by intervening heavy clouds of cosmic dust. The Trifid nebula and the globular star cluster M 22 are some of the other features of this spectacular tract of the heavens. The place of the winter solstice is also near the handle of the Milk Dipper.

STARS OF AUTUMN (MAP 4)

Cassiopeia comes up high in the north in autumn skies. The Northern Cross is overhead early in the season and, as it moves along, the Square of Pegasus becomes the dominant figure. Dim watery constellations spread across in the south, having only the

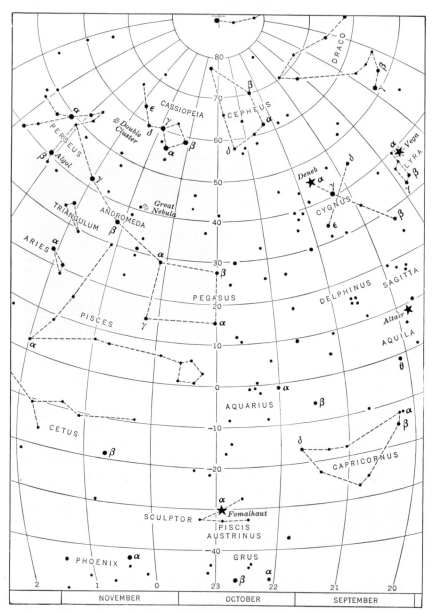

MAP 4. Stars of Autumn.

star Fomalhaut to attract attention except when bright planets appear there as well.

11·12. The Northern Cross is overhead at nightfall in the early autumn in middle northern latitudes. This attractive figure, set in a fine region of the Milky Way (Fig. 11·12), is the characteristic feature of Cygnus, the Swan. Its brightest star, Deneb, marks the

FIG. 11·12. The Northern Cross in the Milky Way. Beta Cygni at the foot of the Cross is out of picture at the lower right. (*Photographed by F. E. Ross, Yerkes Observatory*)

northern end of the longer axis of the Cross. Albireo (Beta Cygni) decorates the southern end of this axis; it appears double with even a small telescope, a reddish star with a fainter blue companion. The Northern Cross shows the direction toward which the sun with its planetary system is moving in the rotation of our galaxy.

11·13. The Square of Pegasus is peculiarly associated with our autumn skies. As this season approaches, we see it in the east in the early evening balanced on one corner. It crosses the meridian

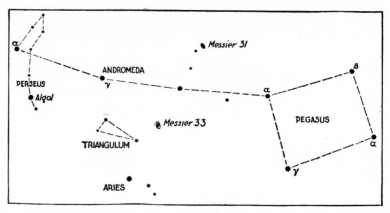

Fig. 11·13. Region of the Square of Pegasus. Showing the positions of the spiral galaxies M 31 and M 33.

at 9 o'clock about the 1st of November. Four rather bright stars mark the corners of the large square which is the characteristic figure of Pegasus; they are Alpha, Beta, and Gamma Pegasi, and in the northeast corner the Alpha star of Andromeda. If we imagine that the Square of Pegasus is the bowl of a very large dipper-figure, we find its handle extending toward the northeast (Fig. 11·13); its first three stars are the brightest of Andromeda. A feature of this constellation is Messier 31, which is only faintly visible to the naked eye but is actually a spiral galaxy larger than our own. It is denoted in Map 4 by its older name, the "Great Nebula" in Andromeda. Another galaxy is marked in the figure in the neighboring constellation Triangulum.

Southeast of the Square two streams of faint stars represent the ribbons with which the Fishes are tied. This dim constellation Pisces of the zodiac contains the zodiacal sign Aries, which has moved westward from its own constellation. Here we find the "first of Aries," or vernal equinox (Fig. 11·13A). The line of the eastern side of the Square prolonged as far again to the south leads

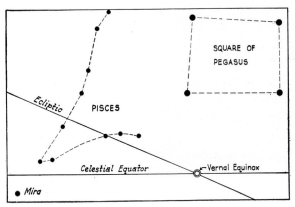

FIG. 11·13A. The Position of the Vernal Equinox.

to this important point of the celestial sphere. The red variable star Mira shown in this figure is in the adjoining constellation Cetus.

STARS OF WINTER (MAP 5)

The bright winter scene is grouped around Orion, its most conspicuous figure. The zodiac is farthest north here; Taurus and Gemini have between them the position of the summer solstice.

11·14. Taurus contains two bright star clusters. The Pleiades cluster looks something like a short-handled dipper (Fig. 11·14). Seven of its stars are clearly visible to the naked eye, and two or three others twinkle into view. The conspicuous feature of the larger, Hyades cluster is in the form of the letter V which, including the bright star Aldebaran, represents the head of Taurus. At the tips of the horns are two fairly bright stars, the northern one of which is needed to complete the muffin-figure of Auriga; its brilliant Capella is near the zenith at 9 o'clock toward the end of January.

Gemini has an oblong figure. The heads of these Twins of the zodiac are marked by the bright stars Castor and Pollux. The position of the summer solstice (Fig. 11·14A) is between their feet and

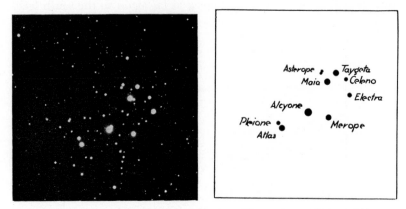

FIG. 11·14.   The Pleiades.   (*Yerkes Observatory photograph*)

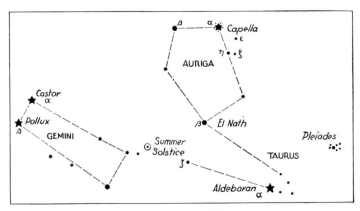

FIG. 11·14A.   Gemini, Auriga, and Taurus.   Showing the position of the summer solstice.

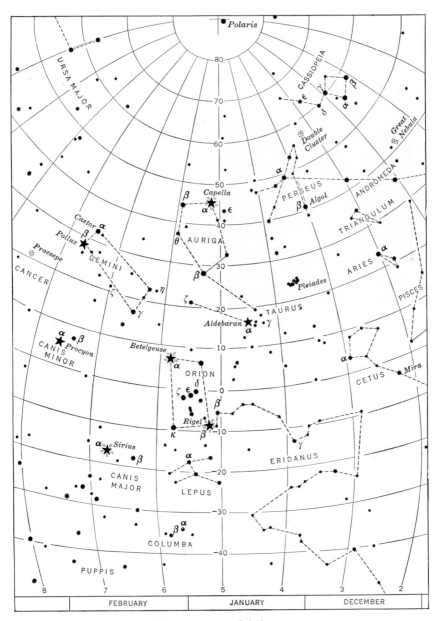

MAP 5.   Stars of Winter.

the horns of Taurus. The Milky Way sweeps down from Auriga
and Taurus past the feet of the Twins and on to the south horizon.

11·15. Orion and His Dogs. Orion, the brightest constellation,
is peculiarly associated with the winter. Its oblong figure rises in
the early evening as winter approaches, appears in the south at

 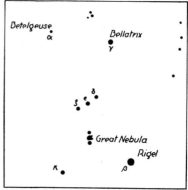

Fig. 11·15.   Orion Tangled in Nebulae.   Showing the position of the
Great Nebula.   (*Mount Wilson Observatory photograph*)

9 o'clock around the 1st of February, and is setting in the twilight
as spring advances.

This bright region of the heavens inspired a lively scene in the
old celestial picture book. Orion, a mighty hunter accompanied
by his dogs, stands with uplifted club awaiting the charging Taurus.
Red Betelgeuse glows below his shoulder. Blue Rigel diagonally
across the figure is somewhat the brighter of the two. Three stars
near the center of the rectangle mark Orion's belt, and three fainter
ones in line to the south (Fig. 11·15) represent his sword. The
middle star of the three appears through the telescope as a trapezium of stars surrounded by the foggy glow of the great nebula in
Orion.

The stars of Orion's belt are useful pointers. The line joining
them directs the eye northwestward to the Hyades and southeast-
ward to Sirius, the "Dog Star," the brightest star in the heavens and
one of the nearest. Sirius, Betelgeuse, and a third bright star across
the Milky Way form a nearly equal-sided triangle. The third one
is Procyon, the "Little Dog Star."

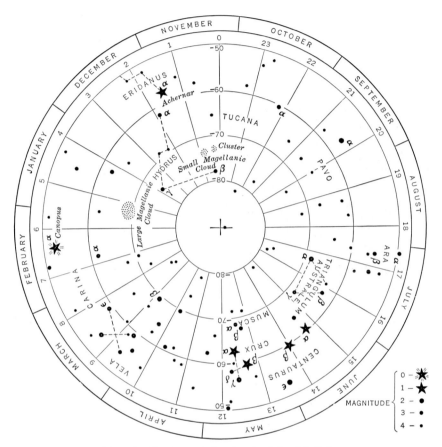

Map 6.   Region of the South Celestial Pole.

TABLE 11·II   GREEK ALPHABET (SMALL LETTERS)

α alpha	ι iota	ρ rho
β beta	κ kappa	σ sigma
γ gamma	λ lambda	τ tau
δ delta	μ mu	υ upsilon
ε epsilon	ν nu	φ phi
ζ zeta	ξ xi	χ chi
η eta	ο omicron	ψ psi
θ theta	π pi	ω omega

THE SOUTHERN CONSTELLATIONS (MAP 6)

11·16. The Region of the South Celestial Pole. Map 6 shows the part of the heavens that does not come up into view in latitude 40° N. It contains the Southern Cross, the two Magellanic Clouds, a number of brilliant stars, and a fine region of the Milky Way.

Crux, the Southern Cross, is a small figure of 4 stars, which resembles a kite fully as much as a cross. It becomes entirely visible south of latitude 28° N. Its brightest star, Alpha Crucis, is about as bright as Aldebaran. The Magellanic Clouds, companions of our spiral galaxy, do not rise anywhere in the United States. From more southern latitudes they are clearly visible to the unaided eye. Canopus, almost directly south of Sirius, is second to it in brightness. Alpha Centauri is third in order of brightness among all the stars, and is nearest of all to the sun.

The south celestial pole is situated in the dim constellation Octans. There is not a star as bright as Polaris within 20° from this point. Sigma Octantis, a star barely visible to the naked eye, is 50′ from the pole.

QUESTIONS ON CHAPTER 11

1. Define the term "constellation" in two ways. Take the constellation Orion as an example.

2. Three ways of designating individual stars are represented by the following examples: (a) Antares; (b) Alpha Tauri; (c) 61 Cygni. Explain.

3. Why are the names of the months placed as they are in Map 1? Notice that September 21 and right ascension 21 hours are together.

4. About what date is the bowl of the Little Dipper (Map 1) directly above the pole at 9 o'clock in the evening, standard time?

5. Precisely where would we look for the star Spica (Map 2) at 9 P.M. on May 25?

6. Describe the characteristic figures formed by the stars of Boötes; Leo; Cygnus; Pegasus; Orion.

7. Name the two brightest stars of the early evenings of summer; the four brightest stars of winter.

8. On what date does the great cluster in Hercules (Map 3) pass near the zenith at 9 P.M.?

9. Orion and Auriga (Map 5) cross the meridian at the same time. Do they also rise and set at the same time? Explain.

10. At the opposition of November 16, 1958, Mars was in right ascension $3^h 25^m$, declination $+19°$. How was it situated relative to the Pleiades and Hyades at that time?

11. For an observer in the southern hemisphere the south celestial pole

is the elevated one. On what date does the Southern Cross appear directly above that pole?

12. Name the constellation containing: (a) the Milk Dipper; (b) the brightest star; (c) the Praesepe cluster; (d) the Ring nebula; (e) the eclipsing star Algol; (f) the star Canopus.

REFERENCES

Allen, Richard H., *Star-Names and Their Meanings*. Stechert, New York, 1899.

Baker, Robert H., *Introducing the Constellations*. Revised edition. The Viking Press, New York, 1957.

Baker, Robert H., *When the Stars Come Out*. Revised edition. The Viking Press, New York, 1954.

Mayall, Newton, Margaret Mayall, and Jerome Wyckoff, *The Sky Observer's Guide*. Golden Press, New York, 1959.

Norton, Arthur P., *A Star Atlas*. Fourteenth edition, 1959. Also the simpler *Popular Star Atlas*. Sky Publishing Corp. Harvard Observatory, Cambridge, Mass.

Olcott, William T., *Field Book of Stars*. Revised by Newton Mayall and Margaret L. Mayall. G. P. Putnam's Sons, New York, 1954.

12

THE STARS AROUND US

DISTANCES OF THE STARS – THE STARS IN MOTION –
STELLAR SPECTRA – MAGNITUDES OF THE STARS

The distances of the nearer stars are shown by the amounts of their slightly altered directions as the earth revolves around the sun. The motions of the stars are revealed by their progress against the background of more remote stars and by displacements of the lines in their spectra. Stars in the sun's neighborhood are often bright enough to permit the study and classification of their spectra. With such data of observation, including the relative brightness, the stars may be compared with one another and with the sun.

DISTANCES OF THE STARS

The distance of a celestial object may be found by observing its parallax, which has been defined as the difference between the directions of the object as viewed from two different places a known distance apart. The moon's parallax (6·2) measured from widely separated stations on the earth is quite large enough for the purpose. The difference between the directions of even the nearest star, however, observed from opposite points on the earth is not greater than the width of a period on this page if it were viewed from a distance of a thousand miles. To detect the parallaxes of stars we require the far greater separation of points of observation afforded by the earth's revolution around the sun.

12·1. Parallaxes of the Stars. The earth's revolution causes apparent slight oscillations of the nearer stars (Fig. 12·1). The extent of the displacement for a particular star is found by comparing its positions in a series of photographs taken 6 months apart; the positions are determined with reference to other stars that appear nearby but are likely to be too far from us to be considerably displaced. Because part of the observed displacement may be caused by the movement of the star itself, it is necessary to repeat the photographs

234

at half-year intervals until the annual parallax oscillation can be disentangled from the straight-line motion of the star.

The *parallax* of a star, in the usual meaning of the term, is its heliocentric parallax. It is the greatest difference between the star's directions from the earth and sun during the year, with slight cor-

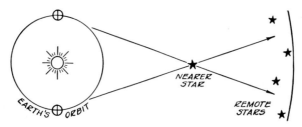

Fig. 12·1. The Parallax of a Star. As the earth revolves around the sun, the nearer star appears to oscillate relative to the more remote stars.

rection to keep the earth at its average distance from the sun, and is about half the greatest parallax displacement of the star. When the parallax has been measured, the star's distance can be calculated.

12·2. Distances in Light Years and Parsecs. The distance of a star in miles is related to its parallax, p'', by the formula:

$$\text{Distance in miles} = (206{,}265''/p'') \times 92{,}900{,}000,$$

where the numbers are the values of the radian and the earth's mean distance from the sun. The distances in miles are so great that

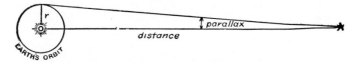

Fig. 12·2. Heliocentric Parallax of a Star.

larger units for expressing them are generally preferred. These are the light year and the parsec.

The *light year* is the distance traversed by light in 1 year. This distance is found by multiplying the speed of light, 186,300 miles a second, by $31\frac{1}{2}$ million, about the number of seconds in a year. One light year equals 5.88 million million miles, or 5.88×10^{12} miles. A star's distance in light years is accordingly its distance in miles divided by this value of the light year; it is:

$$\text{Distance in light years} = 3''.26/p''.$$

The *parsec* is the distance at which a star would have a *pa*rallax of 1 *sec*ond. A star's distance in parsecs is $1/p''$, the reciprocal of its parallax in seconds. Thus 1 parsec equals 3.26 light years.

As an example, consider the bright star Capella, having a parallax of $0''.073$. Its distance in light years is $3.26/0.073 = 45$ light years, and in parsecs is $1.0/0.073 = 13.7$ parsecs. Its distance in miles is $45 \times 5.88 \times 10^{12} = $ about 260 million million miles.

The sun's mean distance from the earth in terms of the speed of light is found by dividing 92,900,000 miles by 186,300 miles a second; it is $498\frac{1}{2}$ light seconds, or 8.3 light minutes. The moon's distance from the earth is 1.3 light seconds; thus the echo of a radar pulse directed to the moon returns 2.6 seconds after the pulse is sent. The average distance of Pluto from the sun is $5\frac{1}{2}$ light hours.

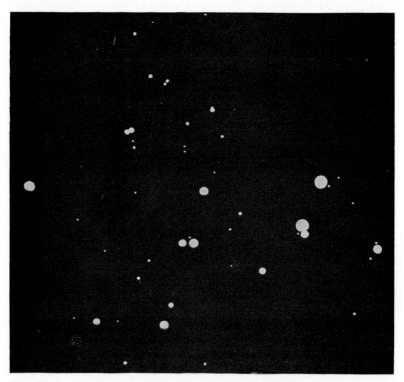

FIG. 12·3. Stars in the Sun's Neighborhood. Photograph of a model constructed at the University of Wisconsin by students in the elementary course. The sun is at the center. Alpha Centauri is below it, and Sirius and Procyon are the largest stars at the right. (*Washburn Observatory photograph*)

12·3. The Nearest Stars. The sun's nearest neighbor among the stars is the bright double star Alpha Centauri. The two stars have a faint companion situated about 2° from them; it is known as "Proxima," because it seems to be slightly nearer us than they are. The parallax of these stars is 0″.760, so that their distance is 4.3 light years, or about 25 million million miles. If the size of the sun is represented by a period on this page, Alpha Centauri would be shown on this scale by two similar dots 5 miles away. This is a fair sample of the wide separation of the stars around us.

More than two dozen stars are known to be within 12 light years from the sun. Although the bright stars Alpha Centauri, Sirius, and Procyon are included in this list, the majority of the nearest stars are too faint to be seen without a telescope. We conclude that the stars differ greatly in intrinsic brightness, so that a bright star in our skies may not be nearer than a faint one.

The direct method of determining the distances of stars by observing their parallaxes is limited to the nearer ones. At the distance of 300 light years, which is only a step into space, the parallaxes become too small to be measured reliably. Ways of finding the distances of more remote stars will be described later.

THE STARS IN MOTION

The motions of the stars in different directions relative to the sun are shown by the very gradual changes in their places in the heavens and by Doppler displacements of their spectral lines. The sun is also moving among the stars around it. Like the sun, the stars are rotating on their axes.

12·4. Proper Motions of the Stars. Edmund Halley, whose name a famous comet bears, was the first, in 1718, to explain that the stars are not stationary. He observed that Sirius and some other bright stars had drifted as much as the apparent width of the moon from the places assigned them in Ptolemy's early catalog. Meanwhile, the proper motions of all lucid stars and of many fainter ones have become known by comparison of the records of their places at different times suitably far apart.

The *proper motion* of a star is the angular rate of its change of place in the heavens. This change becomes so slow at greater distances from us that the remote stars can serve as landmarks to show the progress of the nearer stars. Barnard's star (Fig. 12·4) has the

largest proper motion. Named after the astronomer who first observed its swift flight, this faint star in Ophiuchus moves among its
neighbors in the sky at the rate of 10″.3 a year, or as far as the apparent width of the moon in 175 years. If all the stars were moving
as fast as this and at random, the forms of the constellations would
be altered appreciably during a lifetime. W. J. Luyten reports that
the known motions of only 330 stars exceed 1″ a year and that the
average for all naked-eye stars is not greater than 0″.1 a year. In

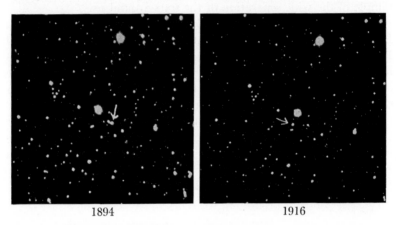

1894   1916

Fig. 12·4. Proper Motion of Barnard's Star. In the interval of 22 years
between the two photographs, the star had moved an eighth of the moon's
apparent diameter. (*Yerkes Observatory photographs*)

the course of a century the progress of very few stars is enough to
be detected without a telescope.

12·5. Radial Velocities of the Stars. The proper motion of a star
tells us nothing of its movement toward or away from us. The
radial velocity, or velocity in the line of sight, is revealed by the
Doppler effect (5·14) in its spectrum. If the lines are displaced
toward the violet end of the spectrum, the star is approaching us;
if they are displaced toward the red end, the star is receding from
us. The amount of the displacement is proportional to the speed
of approach or recession.

The spectra of two stars are shown in Fig. 12·5 with the bright
lines of the iron arc above and below them. Dark lines in the upper
spectrum are displaced to the violet (left); the star is approaching
us at the rate of 58 miles a second. The same dark lines in the
lower spectrum are displaced to the red (right); the star is receding
at the rate of 62 miles a second. These are unusually swift motions.

Fig. 12·5. Doppler Displacements in Stellar Spectra. In the upper spectrum the displacement of the dark lines to the violet (left) shows that the star is approaching the earth. In the lower spectrum the displacement to the red (right) shows that the star is receding from us. (*David Dunlap Observatory photographs*)

The radial velocities of most stars in the sun's neighborhood do not exceed 20 miles a second.

12·6. The Sun's Motion among the stars in our neighborhood is indicated by the common drift of these stars in the opposite direction in addition to their individual motions. The stars are spreading from the standard *apex of the sun's way* (Fig. 12·6), the point in the heavens toward which the sun's motion is directed, and are closing in toward the *antapex,* the opposite point. This apparent drift of the celestial scenery may be observed by examining the proper motions of many stars in various parts of the heavens. It is also observed in the radial velocities, which have their greatest values of approach in the region of the apex and of recession around the antapex; these show the speed of the solar motion as well.

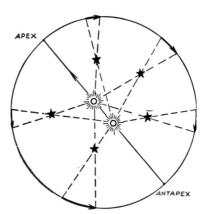

Fig. 12·6. Apparent Drift of Stars Away from the Apex of the Sun's Way.

Relative to the stars around it, the sun with its family of planets is moving at the rate of 12 miles a second toward a point in the constellation Hercules, in right ascension $18^h 0^m$ and declination $+30°$, about $10°$ southwest of the bright star Vega. When the drift of fainter stars is included, the apex shifts toward Cygnus, toward which the sun's motion is directed in the rotation of the galaxy $(17 \cdot 10)$.

12·7. Rotations of the Stars. Since the pioneer work of Otto Struve and C. T. Elvey at Yerkes Observatory, about 1930, the rotations of stars have been studied extensively by means of

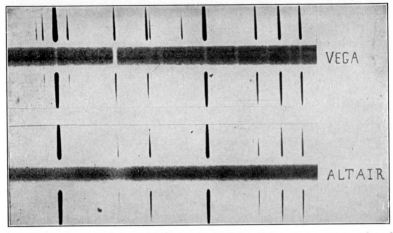

Fɪɢ. 12·7. Spectra of Vega and Altair. These are negatives. The widened lines in the spectrum of Altair show the rapid rotation of this star. *(Yerkes Observatory photographs)*

the widening of the lines of their spectra. Except where the axis of rotation is directed toward the earth, the starlight comes from a source that is partly approaching and partly receding from the earth. Thus the lines are widened by the Doppler effect by an amount that depends on the speed of the rotation and the direction of the axis.

Blue stars of the main sequence are likely to have high speeds of rotation, some exceeding 200 miles a second at their equators. As an example, note the wide lines in the spectrum of Altair (Fig. 12·7); the period of rotation of this star is 6 hours, as compared with about a month in the case of the sun. The narrower lines in the spectrum of Vega, also a blue star, suggest that its axis is directed more nearly toward us.

Yellow and red stars of the sequence rotate more slowly, except where they belong to close binary systems; perhaps much of the original spins of the single stars now appear in the revolutions of their planets. Giant stars generally have slower rotations than corresponding main-sequence stars. Conservation of their angular momentum required them to rotate more slowly as they expanded in their evolutions from the main sequence to the giant stage.

12·8. Magnetism of Stars. The Zeeman effect (10·8) in stellar spectra was discovered by H. W. Babcock at the Mount Wilson Observatory in 1946. His catalog of 1958 lists 89 stars definitely showing this evidence of magnetism, and many other stars that probably show this effect. The majority are stars of type A (12·16), which have in their spectra narrow and unusually intense lines of metals such as chromium and strontium, and of rare earths such as europium. They are presumed to be rapidly rotating stars viewed pole-on.

The magnetic fields vary in strength, and some show periodic reversals of polarity. As an example, the polar magnetic field of the star α^2 Canum Ven. ranges in cycles of $5\frac{1}{2}$ days between extremes of $+5000$ and -4000 gauss, values that are comparable with the strongest magnetic fields of sunspots. At the first extreme the lines in the spectra of the metals have their greatest intensity, and at the second extreme the lines of the rare earths are the most intense. The explanation is proposed that these are effects of oscillations in the outer layers of the stars analogous to those in the magnetic cycle of sunspots.

STELLAR SPECTRA

The spectra of the stars are characterized by patterns of dark lines, and in some cases of bright lines as well, on otherwise continuous bright backgrounds. The patterns are different for stars of different surface temperatures. This topic is introduced by a brief account of the atoms of chemical elements in the stars and their relation to the radiations they absorb and emit.

12·9. Constituents of Atoms. Atoms are composed essentially of electrons, protons, and neutrons. The *electron* is the lightest of these constituents and it carries unit negative charge of electricity. The *proton* is 1836 times as heavy as the electron and carries unit positive charge. The *neutron* has about the same mass as the proton and is electrically neutral.

The *atom* consists of a nucleus surrounded by electrons. The nucleus ranges from a single proton in the ordinary hydrogen atom to an increasingly complex group of protons and neutrons in the heavier chemical elements. Each added proton contributes one unit to the positive charge on the nucleus. In the normal atom the nucleus is surrounded by negatively charged electrons equal in number to the protons, so that the atom as a whole is electrically neutral.

12·10. The Chemical Elements. Table 12·I lists the names, symbols, atomic numbers, and atomic weights of the 26 lighter elements, from hydrogen to iron.

TABLE 12·I   THE LIGHTER CHEMICAL ELEMENTS

Element	Symbol	Atomic Number	Atomic Weight	Element	Symbol	Atomic Number	Atomic Weight
Hydrogen	H	1	1.0080	Silicon	Si	14	28.0
Helium	He	2	4.003	Phosphorus	P	15	30.975
Lithium	Li	3	6.940	Sulfur	S	16	32.066
Beryllium	Be	4	9.013	Chlorine	Cl	17	35.457
Boron	B	5	10.82	Argon	A	18	39.944
Carbon	C	6	12.01	Potassium	K	19	39.100
Nitrogen	N	7	14.008	Calcium	Ca	20	40.08
Oxygen	O	8	16.0000	Scandium	Sc	21	44.96
Fluorine	F	9	19.00	Titanium	Ti	22	47.90
Neon	Ne	10	20.183	Vanadium	V	23	50.95
Sodium	Na	11	22.99	Chromium	Cr	24	52.01
Magnesium	Mg	12	24.32	Manganese	Mn	25	54.94
Aluminum	Al	13	26.98	Iron	Fe	26	55.85

The *atomic number* of an element is the number of protons in the nucleus and also the number of electrons around the nucleus of the normal atom. All atoms having the same atomic number belong to the same chemical element. Of the 102 recognized elements, those beyond uranium, number 92, were first identified in the radiation laboratories.

The *atomic weight* is the relative mass of the atom; the unit employed in the table is one sixteenth the mass of the average oxygen atom, taken as 16.0000. The weights given here are generally the averages for two or more different kinds of atoms, or *isotopes,* of the same element having different numbers of neutrons in their nuclei.

Hydrogen comprises about 93 per cent of all the atoms and 76 per cent of all the mass of material in the stars. Helium is second with about 7 per cent of the atoms and 23 per cent of the mass. All the other elements together contribute only a little more than 1 per cent to the mass of the stars.

12·11. Model of the Hydrogen Atom. The ordinary hydrogen atom consists of one proton attended by a single electron. In the conventional model proposed by the physicist Niels Bohr in 1913,

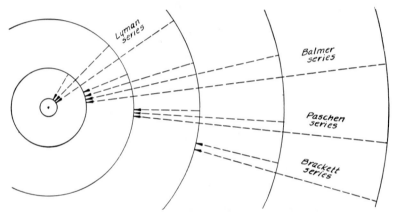

Fig. 12·11. Conventional Representation of the Hydrogen Atom. Possible orbits of the electron around the nucleus are shown as circles.

the electron revolves around the proton in one of a number of permitted orbits. The atom can absorb energy, as from light that strikes it, only in the precise amount required to raise the electron against the electrical attraction of the oppositely charged proton to one of the outer orbits. Such absorption produces a dark line at the appropriate wavelength in the spectrum of the light.

Although one hydrogen atom with its single electron absorbs only one dark line at a time, the many atoms in the atmosphere of a star can produce together the series of all permitted lines. The particular series where the electrons are raised from the second orbit of the Bohr model (Fig. 12·11) is known as the *Balmer series.* Its first line, $H\alpha$, is in the red region of the spectrum and its second line, $H\beta$, is in the blue-green. From there the lines continue with dimin-

ishing spaces between them to a head in the ultraviolet.   More than
30 lines of the Balmer series are recognized in the spectra of blue
stars.

The Lyman series, based on the innermost Bohr orbit, is a similar
array of lines in the far ultraviolet; it is recorded as a series of
bright lines in the spectrum of the sun photographed from rockets.
The Paschen series and others are in the infrared.

12·12. Atomic Models of Other Elements.   Each step in the succession of elements heavier than hydrogen adds one proton in the
nucleus of the atom and one electron in the superstructure.   Thus

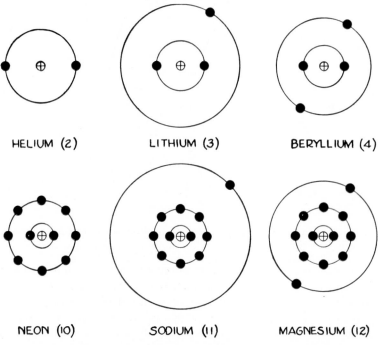

HELIUM (2)   LITHIUM (3)   BERYLLIUM (4)

NEON (10)   SODIUM (11)   MAGNESIUM (12)

Fig. 12·12.   Electron Structures of Some Lighter Atoms.

the normal helium atom has two protons and electrons, and lithium
has three.   The electrons of the growing population take their
places systematically in *shells*, which are the same as the Bohr orbits.
The shells are filled in order of distance from the nucleus by $2n^2$
electrons in each, where n is the number of the Bohr orbit.   Thus
the first shell is filled by 2 electrons, the second by 8 electrons, and

so on. A filled shell will not receive more electrons and is reluctant to release any that it possesses.

The electron structures of a few normal atoms are shown in Fig. 12·12. The helium atom has its two electrons locked in its filled innermost shell, which is not easily broken. The neon atom has two filled shells and is also relatively inactive. The lithium and sodium atoms each have in an outer shell a single electron that can be readily removed. These few examples will suggest that atoms of the different chemical elements in the atmospheres of stars in the same conditions may not be equally effective in producing lines in their spectra. We see presently that the different patterns of lines in stellar spectra are determined mainly by the different temperatures of the stars.

12·13. Neutral and Ionized Atoms. The *neutral atom* has its full quota of electrons. The *normal atom* has its electrons at the lowest possible levels, as in Fig. 12·12, whereas the *excited atom* has absorbed energy to raise one or more electrons to higher levels.

The *ionized atom* has lost one or more electrons. It has absorbed enough energy to expel these electrons beyond its outermost orbit. They have become *free electrons,* free to move independently until they are captured by other ionized atoms. The singly ionized atom has lost a single electron and thereby has acquired a single unit positive charge of electricity. The doubly ionized atom has an excess of two positive charges. Each successive ionization makes the atom more difficult to excite or to ionize further.

12·14. Thermal Excitation and Ionization. Atoms of gases in the atmosphere of a star may be excited or ionized by the star's radiation or by energy imparted by collisions with other atoms. The latter is *thermal excitation and ionization.* Its extent is greater (1) as the temperature of the gas and thus the violence of the atomic collisions is greater; and for a particular temperature (2) as the electron is more loosely held by the atom.

The energy required to ionize an atom is pictured in terms of an electron colliding with the atom, as a number of *electron volts;* it is equivalent to the energy an electron acquires when it is accelerated across a difference of a specified number of volts. For a few elements represented by prominent lines in stellar spectra, the ionization numbers of neutral atoms are: sodium, 5.1; calcium, 6.1; iron, 7.8;

hydrogen, 13.5; helium, 24.5. The corresponding numbers are smaller for excitation and larger for higher stages of ionization. With this introduction it is in order to describe and interpret the classification of stellar spectra.

12·15. Photographs of Stellar Spectra are taken generally in two different ways. One method employs the *slit spectroscope* at the focus of the telescope. It permits wider separation of the spectrum

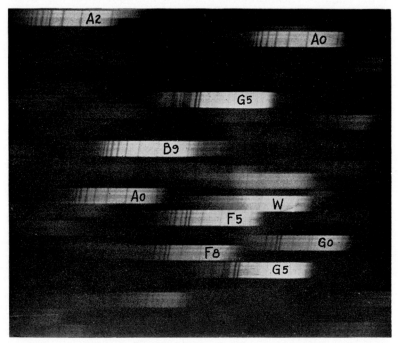

Fig. 12·15.   Objective Prism Spectra of Stars in a Region of Cepheus.
(*Warner and Swasey Observatory photograph*)

lines and the recording of a laboratory spectrum adjacent to the star's spectrum (Fig. 12·5). This method is accordingly useful for measuring wavelengths and Doppler shifts of the lines; but it is time-consuming because it gives the spectrum of only one star at a time.

In the second method a large prism of small angle is placed in front of the telescope objective, so that the whole apparatus becomes a spectroscope without slit or collimator. A single photograph shows the spectra of all stars of suitable brightness in the field of view of the telescope. This *objective prism* type is useful in qualitative studies of many stars, as in the classification of stellar spectra.

Studies of stellar spectra in objective prism photographs were in progress at Harvard Observatory as early as 1885. A result of these studies is the *Henry Draper Catalogue,* mainly the work of Annie J. Cannon, which with its extensions lists the positions, magnitudes, and spectral types of 400,000 stars. The Harvard types, together with the more recent luminosity classes (12·24), remain the criteria in the present classification of stellar spectra.

12·16. Types of Stellar Spectra. The Harvard classification arrays the majority of the stars in a single continuous sequence with respect to the patterns of lines in their spectra. Seven divisions of the sequence are the principal spectral types. These are designated by the letters O, B, A, F, G, K, and M, and are subdivided on the decimal system. Thus an A5 star is halfway between A0 and F0. Some features of the principal types, as they appear in the violet and blue regions of the spectrum, are the following:

Type O. Lines of ionized helium, oxygen, and nitrogen are prominent in the spectra of these very hot stars along with lines of hydrogen.

Type B. Lines of neutral helium are most intense at B2 and then fade, until at B9 they have practically vanished. Hydrogen lines increase in strength through the subdivisions. Examples are Spica and Rigel.

Type A. Hydrogen lines attain their greatest strength at A2 and then decline through the remainder of the sequence. Examples are Sirius and Vega. Thus far the stars are blue.

Type F. Lines of metals are increasing in strength, notably the Fraunhofer H and K of ionized calcium. These are yellowish stars. Examples are Canopus and Procyon.

Type G. Metallic lines are numerous and conspicuous in the spectra of these yellow stars. The sun and Capella belong to this type.

Type K. Lines of metals surpass the hydrogen lines in strength. Bands of cyanogen and other molecules are becoming conspicuous. These cooler stars are reddish. Examples are Arcturus and Aldebaran.

Type M. Bands of titanium oxide become stronger up to their maximum at M7. Vanadium oxide bands strengthen in the still

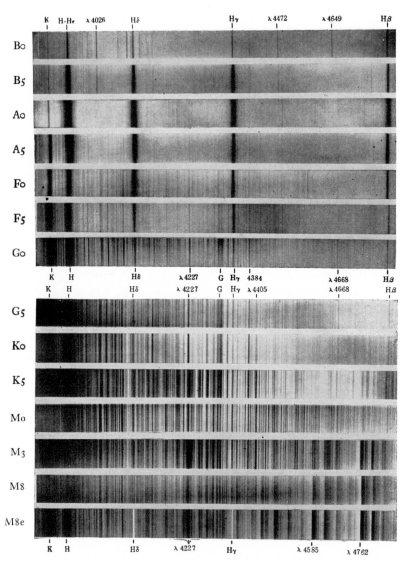

F𝐼𝐺. 12·17. Sequence of Stellar Spectra. Types B to M, in the Violet
and Blue. (*Photographed at the University of Michigan Observatory*)

cooler divisions of these red stars. Examples are Betelgeuse and Antares.

Four additional and less populous types branch off near the ends of the sequence. *Type W* near the blue end comprises the Wolf-Rayet stars, having broad bright lines in their spectra. Near the red end, *types R* and *N* show molecular bands of carbon and carbon compounds, and *type S* has conspicuous bands of zirconium oxide.

12·17. The Sequence of Stellar Spectra (Fig. 12·17) is in order of increasing redness, and therefore of diminishing surface brightness of the stars. The progression in the line patterns is not caused mainly by difference of chemical composition; helium is not more abundant in B stars, nor is hydrogen in A stars. The lines of the different chemical elements become strongest at temperatures where their atoms in the stellar atmospheres are most active in absorbing the starlight.

The compact neutral helium atoms imprint their dark lines at the high temperatures of B stars. Hydrogen is most active at the more moderate temperatures of A stars, although the great abundance of this element makes its lines visible throughout the sequence. Neutral atoms of the metals are more easily excited, so that their lines are strongest in the spectra of the cooler yellow and red stars. At higher temperatures the atoms of metals are ionized and have their stronger lines in other regions of the spectrum. Atoms can assemble into molecules in the relatively cool atmospheres of red stars; bands of titanium oxide are conspicuous in the spectra of M stars in the figure.

MAGNITUDES OF THE STARS

In his star catalog of 18 centuries ago, Ptolemy gave estimates of brightness of the stars to aid in their identification. For these estimates the stars were divided into six classes, or *magnitudes,* in order of brightness. The brightest stars were assigned to the 1st magnitude. Somewhat less bright stars, such as the pole star, were of the 2nd magnitude. Each succeeding class contained fainter stars than the one before, until the 6th magnitude remained for stars barely visible to the unaided eye.

The original magnitudes of the lucid stars continued in use up to recent times, and the plan was extended somewhat arbitrarily to include fainter stars brought into view with telescopes. The present precise plan of magnitudes was proposed in 1856, when the brightness of stars had begun to be determined more accurately and was becoming an important factor in astronomical inquiries.

12·18. Apparent Magnitudes.   Two stars differ in the modern plan by exactly 1 magnitude if their ratio of brightness is the number whose logarithm is 0.4; this ratio is the number 2.512.   Thus a star of magnitude 2.0 is about 2½ times as bright as a star of magnitude 3.0, more than 6 times as bright as one of magnitude 4.0, and so on.   Stars down to the 19th magnitude are visible with the 200-inch Palomar telescope, and stars almost as faint as magnitude 24 can be photographed with this telescope.

Because the very brightest of the original 1st-magnitude stars are visually more than 2½ times as bright as a standard star of magnitude 1.0, such as Spica, these are now promoted to brighter magnitudes.   The magnitude of Vega is 0.0 and that of Sirius is minus 1.4.

These *apparent magnitudes* refer to the observed brightness of stars.   They may be determined to hundredths of a magnitude in photographs and to thousandths by the more precise photoelectric methods.

12·19. Magnitudes in Different Colors.   The *visual magnitude* of a star refers to its brightness as observed with the eye, which is most sensitive to yellow light.   The *photographic magnitude* refers to the star's brightness as recorded in a blue-sensitive photograph.   The magnitudes differ in the two cases by an amount that depends on the color of the star.   Note in Fig. 12·19 how much fainter, as indicated by its smaller image, a red star appears as photographed in blue than in yellow light.

Present studies often require the magnitudes of a star in several colors.   The magnitudes may be measured in photographs with suitably stained plates exposed behind filters that transmit the light of different regions of the spectrum, or more precisely with the photoelectric cell and filters.   The magnitudes are generally measured around specified wavelengths in the ultraviolet, blue, visual or yellow, red, and infrared, and are denoted by the letters U, B, V, R, and I.   The magnitudes of standard stars are being carefully determined in the different colors, so that all investigators may keep to the same color systems.

The *color index* of a star is the difference of its magnitudes in two selected colors. Its value is given most often as the difference, $B - V$, between the blue and visual magnitudes. The color index is then a numerical expression of the star's color. Taken as zero for stars of spectral type A0, it is accordingly negative for the bluest stars and attains a positive value of 2 magnitudes or more for the

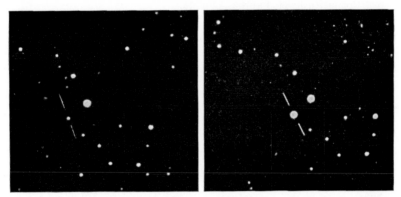

FIG. 12·19. A Red Star Appears Fainter in Blue (left) than in Yellow Light (right). (*Yerkes Observatory photographs*)

reddest ones. The observed color index of a star may exceed the normal index for the particular spectral type because of reddening of the starlight by intervening cosmic dust.

12·20. The Brightest Stars. The 22 stars listed in Table 12·II are brighter than apparent visual magnitude +1.5 and are sometimes called "stars of the first magnitude," although they range through nearly 3 magnitudes. The visual (V) and photographic (B) magnitudes were measured photoelectrically with filters by H. L. Johnson. The colors are shown by the color indexes, the differences $B - V$, which can be read from the table. The bluest stars, having the largest negative color indexes, are Alpha and Beta Crucis and Spica. The reddest are Betelgeuse and Antares, which have the largest positive indexes. The spectral types and luminosity classes are on the Morgan-Keenan system (12·24); where the star is double, they refer to the brighter star of the pair.

The brightest stars have a considerable range in distance from us, as the parallaxes in the table show. Alpha Centauri, Sirius, and Procyon are among the nearest stars. Rigel, Betelgeuse, and Deneb are the most remote in the list; they are evidently very luminous

to shine so brightly in our skies. The significance of the last column
of the table is explained in the following section.

Sixteen of the brightest stars are visible in their seasons throughout the United States. The remaining six become visible south of
the following north latitudes: Canopus, 38°; Achernar, 33°; Alpha
and Beta Centauri and Beta Crucis, 30°; Alpha Crucis, 28°, or
about the latitude of Tampa, Florida.

12·21. Absolute Magnitudes. The apparent magnitude of a star
relates to its observed brightness. This depends on the star's in-

TABLE 12·II   THE BRIGHTEST STARS

Name	Spectrum	Apparent Visual Magnitude	Apparent Photographic Magnitude	Parallax	Absolute Visual Magnitude
Sirius	A1 V	−1.43	−1.43	0″.379	+1.5
Canopus	F0 Ia	−0.73	−0.58	.018	−4.4
d α Centauri	G2 V	−0.27	+0.39	.760	+4.1
Arcturus	K2 III	−0.06	+1.17	.090	−0.3
Vega	A0 V	+0.04	+0.04	.123	+0.5
Capella	(G0)	0.09	0.89	.073	−0.6
Rigel	B8 Ia	0.15	0.11	.005	−6.4
Procyon	F5 IV	0.37	0.78	.288	+2.7
Achernar	B3 V	0.53	0.37	.023	−2.7
dβ Centauri	B0 V	0.66	0.45	.016	−3.3
v Betelgeuse	M2 I	0.7	2.6	.005	−5.8
Altair	A7 IV	0.80	1.02	.198	+2.3
v Aldebaran	K5 III	0.85	2.37	.048	−0.7
d α Crucis	B0 V	0.87	0.63	.015	−3.2
dv Antares	M1 Ib	0.98	2.78	.019	−2.6
Spica	B1 V	1.00	0.77	.021	−2.4
Fomalhaut	A3 V	1.16	1.25	.144	+2.0
Pollux	K0 III	1.16	2.17	.093	+1.0
Deneb	A2 Ia	1.26	1.35	.006	−4.8
β Crucis	B0 IV	1.31	1.08	(.011)	−3.5
Regulus	B7 V	1.36	1.25	.039	−0.7
ε Can. Maj.	B2 II	1.49	1.32	(.012)	−3.1

d Visual double star with brightness difference less than 5 magnitudes; combined
magnitudes are given.

v Variable star. Visual magnitude range for Betelgeuse, 0.4 to 1.0; Aldebaran,
0.75 to 0.95; Antares, 0.90 to 1.06.

trinsic brightness, or *luminosity,* and its distance from us. One star may appear brighter than another only because it is the nearer of the two; thus Sirius appears brighter than Betelgeuse, although the latter is actually many times the more luminous. In order to rank the stars fairly with respect to luminosity, it is necessary to calculate how bright they would appear if they were all at the same distance. By agreement the standard distance is 10 parsecs, at which the parallax is 0″.1.

The *absolute magnitude* is the magnitude a star would have at the distance of 10 parsecs, or 32.6 light years. The relation is:

$$M = m + 5 - 5 \log r,$$

where M is the absolute magnitude and m is the apparent magnitude at the distance r in parsecs. The absolute magnitude has the same character as the apparent magnitude from which it is derived, whether visual, photographic, or some other kind.

The sun's absolute visual magnitude is $+4.8$. At the moderate distance of 32.6 light years the sun would appear as a star only faintly visible to the unaided eye. Note in the last column of Table 12·II that the apparently brightest stars are all intrinsically brighter than the sun.

12·22. Stars of the Main Sequence. When the spectral types of stars around us are plotted with respect to the absolute magnitudes of these stars, as in Fig. 12·22, the majority of the points are arrayed in a band running diagonally across the diagram. This band is known as the *main sequence.* The middle line of the band drops from about absolute magnitude -3 for blue stars to fainter than $+10$ for red stars.

The sun, a yellow star of class G2 and absolute visual magnitude $+4.8$, is a main-sequence star, as we see. Blue stars of the sequence are more luminous than the sun because they are hotter and larger. Red stars of the sequence are less luminous than the sun because they are cooler and smaller. Remembering that the sun at the standard distance of 32.6 light years would be only faintly visible to the unaided eye, we understand why the red stars of the sequence are generally invisible without a telescope.

12·23. Giant and Dwarf Stars. Since its introduction, in 1913, by H. N. Russell, the spectrum–absolute magnitude diagram, often known as the H-R diagram, or the similar color-magnitude diagram

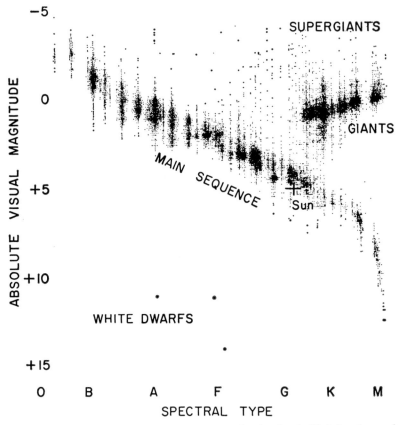

F<small>IG</small>. 12·22. Absolute Magnitudes of Stars in the Sun's Vicinity Arrayed with Respect to Their Spectral Types. The point at magnitude +4.8 and type G2 represents the sun. (*Diagram by W. Gyllenberg, Lund Observatory*)

has played a leading part in directing the studies of the stars. Ejnar Hertzsprung had previously drawn attention to a sharp distinction between red stars of high and low luminosity, and had named them giant and dwarf stars, respectively. The original term *dwarf stars* is commonly used today to denote main-sequence stars fainter than about absolute magnitude +1, but is not generally applied to the white dwarf stars.

Giant stars, such as Capella and Arcturus, are considerably more luminous than main-sequence stars of the same spectral type. They are giants in size as well as in brightness. All stars of the same type have the same order of surface temperature, and therefore of surface brightness per square mile. If one type M star, for example, greatly surpasses another in luminosity, its surface must contain many more square miles; its diameter must be much the greater. Giants in the sun's neighborhood are mainly red stars.

The dots near the top of Fig. 12·22 represent the very large and luminous *supergiants*. Those near the upper right corner denote the largest stars of all. The red star Betelgeuse is one of these; it has several hundred times the diameter of the sun. *Subgiants* are between the giants and the main sequence. *Subdwarfs* are somewhat below this sequence. Dots near the bottom of the diagram represent a few of the white dwarf stars (16·13), some of which are yellow and even reddish. These very faint stars are smaller than the larger planets.

12·24. Luminosity Classes of Stars. The surface temperatures and normal color indexes of stars at intervals along the spectral sequence are shown in Table 12·III. The temperatures, as assigned by P. C.

TABLE 12·III   EFFECTIVE TEMPERATURES AND COLOR INDEXES

Spec-trum	Tempera-ture	Color Index B − V	Spec-trum	Main Sequence		Giants	
				Tempera-ture	Color Index B − V	Tempera-ture	Color Index B − V
		mag.			mag.		mag.
05	50,000° K	....	F5	6,600° K	+0.44	6,470° K	......
B0	25,000	−0.32	G0	6,000	+0.60	5,300	......
B5	15,600	−0.16	G5	5,520	+0.68	4,650	......
A0	11,000	0.00	K0	5,120	+0.82	4,200	+1.01
A5	8,700	+0.15	K5	4,400	+1.18	3,550	+1.52
F0	7,600	+0.30	M0	3,600	+1.45	3,340	+1.56
F5	6,600	+0.44	M5	....	+1.69	2,710	......

Keenan and W. W. Morgan, are tied to an adopted temperature of 5730° K for the sun, type G2. Diminishing temperature is mainly responsible for the succession of spectral patterns, as has been said.

Note in the table that the temperatures of yellow and red giants are lower than those of main-sequence stars of the same spectral type. The reason is that the giant stars are the less dense, so that their atoms attain a particular degree of ionization at a lower temperature. Although the spectra of giants and main-sequence stars of type K0, for example, are similar in general, particular features may be considerably different. Some lines become stronger and others weaker as the stars are more luminous. Thus a complete description of a star's spectrum is obtained by adding its luminosity class to its spectral type.

The *luminosity classes* of Morgan and Keenan are numbered in order beginning with the most luminous stars, which have the least dense atmospheres. The numeral I refers to supergiant stars, Ia for the more luminous and Ib for the less luminous supergiants; II refers to bright giants, III to normal giants, IV to subgiants, and V to main-sequence stars. Thus the two-dimensional designation in Table 12·II for Deneb is A2 Ia; Antares, M1 Ib; Epsilon Canis Majoris, B2 II; Aldebaran, K5 III; Procyon, F5 IV; Vega, A0 V.

QUESTIONS ON CHAPTER 12

1. Describe the parallax method of measuring the distances of stars. Why is it effective only for the nearer stars?

2. The parallax of Altair is 0".2. Show that the star's distance is 5 parsecs, or 16 light years, or about 100 million million miles.

3. Distinguish between the proper motion and radial velocity of a star. Explain how each is determined.

4. How is the sun's motion relative to stars around it revealed by the proper motions of these stars? by their radial velocities?

5. Explain that stars in rapid rotation have noticeably widened spectrum lines if the rotation axes are not nearly in the line of sight.

6. State the type of stellar spectrum in which the following features are prominent: (a) lines of neutral helium; (b) hydrogen lines; (c) lines of neutral metals; (d) molecular bands.

7. When the apparent magnitude of a star has been observed, explain that: (a) the absolute magnitude can be calculated if the star's distance is known, or (b) the distance can be calculated if the absolute magnitude is independently known.

8. What is gained by comparing the absolute magnitudes of stars rather than their apparent magnitudes?

9. The sun is a type G2 star of the main sequence. Explain.

10. Show that a giant star should be larger than a main-sequence star of about the same spectral type.

11. Note in Table 12·II that the photographic magnitudes of Spica (type B1) and Antares (type M1) differ considerably although the visual magnitudes are nearly the same. Explain.

12. Define: color index. Why does it have a greater positive value as the star is redder?

References

Goldberg, Leo, and Lawrence H. Aller, *Atoms, Stars and Nebulae.* Harvard University Press, Cambridge, 1943.

Hoyle, Fred, *Frontiers of Astronomy.* Harper and Brothers, New York, 1955.

van de Kamp, Peter, *Basic Astronomy.* The Macmillan Company, New York, 1952.

Whipple, Fred L., editor, *New Horizons in Astronomy.* Superintendent of Documents, U.S. Government Printing Office, Washington 25, D. C.

The Great Nebula near Eta Carinae *(Photograph with the Uppsala Schmidt telescope by Bart J. Bok, Mount Stromlo Observatory)*

13

DOUBLE AND VARIABLE STARS

BINARY STARS – ECLIPSING VARIABLES – PULSATING VARIABLES – ERUPTIVE VARIABLES

Binary stars are physically associated pairs of stars. In some pairs the components are far enough apart to be separated with a telescope; in other pairs the presence of the companions can be detected only with the spectroscope. Some spectroscopic binaries mutually eclipse as they revolve, so that they vary periodically in brightness. Many single stars are intrinsically variable in light because they are pulsating. The variations of large red stars are ascribed at least in part to their variable veiling by clouds rising high above them. Spectacular variations are exhibited by eruptive stars.

BINARY STARS

13·1. Visual Double Stars are single stars to the unaided eye that are separated into pairs with the telescope. Mizar, at the bend in the Great Dipper's handle (Fig. 11·8), was the first of these, in 1650,

| 1908 | 1915 | 1920 |

FIG. 13·1. Binary Star Krueger 60. Between 1908 and 1920 the double star, in the upper left corners, completed about a quarter of a revolution. See also Fig. 13·23. (*Yerkes Observatory photographs*)

to be reported casually; the only connection between the two stars of such pairs was believed to be that they chanced to have nearly the same direction from us. Castor, Beta Cygni, and Alpha Centauri were other early known examples. By 1803, William Herschel had determined from repeated observations that the two stars of Castor

were revolving around a common center between them. He then
made the distinction between "optical doubles" and "real doubles."
The latter, now called *visual binary stars*, are in the great majority.

A total of 40,000 visual binaries are recognized, mainly by the
common proper motions of the component stars.   About 2500
binaries have had time since their discoveries to show evidence of
orbital motion, and 10 per cent of these have progressed far enough
in their revolutions to permit reliable determinations of their orbits.
Pairs having the smallest separations, which are likely to go around
most rapidly, can be observed satisfactorily only with long-focus
telescopes.

The presence of additional stars in binary systems is not exceptional. Alpha Centauri is representative of a common type of triple
systems.   The double-double Epsilon Lyrae is a familiar example
of quadrupal systems.

13·2. The Apparent and the True Orbit.   The position of the
fainter star of a visual binary relative to the brighter star is denoted
by the position angle and distance.   The *position angle* is the angle

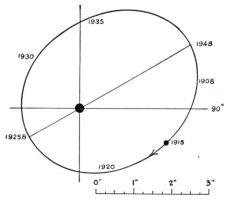

Fig. 13·2. Orbit of Krueger 60.   Relative apparent orbit of the fainter
star. Compare with Figs. 13·1 and 13·23.

at the brighter star between the directions of the fainter star and
the north celestial pole; it is reckoned in degrees from the north
around through the east.   The *distance* is the angular separation
of the two stars.   The position is measured micrometrically either
directly at the telescope or in a photograph where the separation is
wide enough.

When the recorded positions have extended through a consider-able part of the period, the relative *apparent orbit* of the fainter star is an ellipse that best represents the observed positions and in which Kepler's law of areas (7·6) is maintained in the motion around the brighter star. The apparent ellipse is projected on the plane tangent to the sky, and from it the true ellipse having the brighter star at one focus is readily calculated.

The *elements* of the relative *true orbit* are the specifications of the true ellipse, such as its eccentricity, inclination to the plane of the sky, and angular size, or the linear size if the distance from us is also known. When the revolutions of both stars have been ob-served with reference to stars nearby in the photographs, the sepa-rate orbits can be determined; these differ from the relative orbit only in size.

13·3. Examples of Visual Binaries. Some characteristics of a few visual binaries are shown in Table 13·I, which is taken mainly from

TABLE 13·I   ORBITS OF VISUAL BINARIES

Name	Visual Magnitudes		Period P	Semi-Major Axis a	Eccen-tricity e	Parallax p	Masses m_1 m_2	
BD −8° 4352	10.1	10.3	1.7	0″.22		0″.157	(1.0)	
Delta Equulei	5.2	5.2	5.7	0 .26	0.39	.052	2.0	1.9
42 Comae	5.2	5.2	25.0	0 .66	.52	.058	(2.2)	
Procyon	0.4	10.6	40.6	4 .55	.31	.287	1.8	0.6
Krueger 60	9.8	11.5	44.6	2 .41	.41	.253	0.3	0.2
Sirius	−1.5	8.6	49.9	7 .62	.59	.379	2.3	1.0
Alpha Centauri	0.1	1.4	80.1	17 .66	.52	.760	1.1	0.9
Castor	2.0	2.8	380	5 .84	.37	.074	(3.4)	

a more extended table by P. van de Kamp. The first two binaries in the list have unusually short periods of revolution. The angular semi-major axis of an orbit may be converted to astronomical units by dividing the tabular value by the corresponding parallax. Thus the mean distance between the stars of the binary BD −8° 4352 is slightly more than the earth's distance from the sun, and that of the components of Castor is twice Pluto's distance from the sun.

The separate masses of the stars are given in terms of the sun's mass, except that the values in parentheses are the sums of the two masses.

13·4. The Companion of Sirius. One of the nearest stars, the brilliant Dog Star, Sirius, drifts in the heavens three fourths the apparent width of the moon in 1000 years. As early as 1844, F. W. Bessel at Königsberg discovered that it is pursuing a wavy course

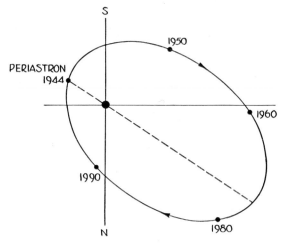

FIG. 13·4. Apparent Relative Orbit of the Companion of Sirius. The stars were least separated in 1944.

instead of having the uniform motion of a single star. He concluded that Sirius is mutually revolving with a traveling companion; and its orbit with the still unseen companion was derived in 1851.

The companion was first seen, in 1862, by the American optician Alvan Clark, who was testing a new lens, now the objective of the 18½-inch telescope at the Dearborn Observatory. The companion revolves in a period of 50 years and in an orbit of rather high eccentricity (Fig. 13·4). Despite the glare of Sirius, the companion is clearly visible with large telescopes except when the two stars are the least separated. The latest periastron passage occurred in 1944 and the widest separation will come next in 1969. The companion of Sirius was among the first to be known of the white dwarf stars (12·23).

The companion of Procyon was likewise discovered by Bessel from its gravitational effect on the proper motion of the bright star; it was first observed with the telescope in 1896. A recent similar case is the companion of the faint red star Ross 614, which was detected by S. L. Lippincott at Sproul Observatory and was later seen and photographed by Walter Baade with the 200-inch telescope.

Unseen companions of other stars have been detected by irregularities they cause in the revolutions of binary stars. An example is the binary 61 Cygni, studied by K. Aa. Strand. Here the two visible members revolve in a period of 720 years, while an invisible companion revolves around one of them once in nearly 5 years.

13·5. Masses of Binary Stars. The combined mass of a visual binary can be evaluated when the orbit of the binary has been determined. The method is another application of the general statement of Kepler's harmonic law, by means of which we have already seen (7·12) that the combined mass of a planet and its satellite can be found. Let one pair of mutually revolving bodies considered in this law be the stars of the binary, and let the second pair be the sun and the earth. Where the units of measurement are the sun's mass (the mass of the earth is negligible in comparison), the earth's mean distance from the sun, and the sidereal year, the law becomes:

$$m_1 + m_2 = a^3/P^2 p^3,$$

where $m_1 + m_2$ is the sum of the masses of the two stars in terms of the sun's mass, a is the semi-major axis of the relative orbit in seconds of arc, P is the period of revolution in sidereal years, and p is the parallax of the binary in seconds. Thus with the specified units the combined mass of the pair of stars equals the cube of their linear mean distance apart (13·3) divided by the square of the period of revolution.

As an example of the use of the above relation, the sum of the masses of the binary Alpha Centauri is calculated from the data of Table 13·I as follows: $m_1 + m_2 = (17.66)^3/(80.1)^2(.760)^3 = 2.0$. Thus the combined mass of Alpha Centauri is twice the sun's mass.

The sum of the masses is all that can be determined from the relative orbit. When, however, the revolutions of both stars have been observed, the individual masses become known; for the ratio of the masses is inversely proportional to the ratio of the distances of the two stars at any time from the common center around which they revolve.

13·6. The Mass-Luminosity Relation. Studies of binary stars led to the discovery by A. S. Eddington in 1924 of a relation between the masses and luminosities of stars in general. The more massive the star, the greater is its absolute brightness. The relation is shown by the broken line of Fig. 13·6, where the logarithm of the mass in terms of the sun's mass is plotted with respect to the star's

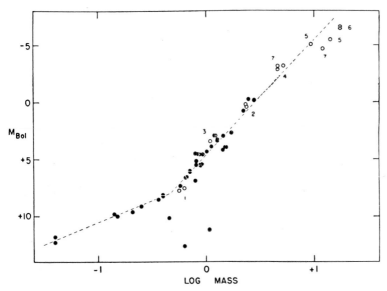

Fig. 13·6. Mass-Luminosity Relation for Stars of Visual Binaries (filled circles) and Spectroscopic Binaries (open circles). The three points below the curve represent white dwarf stars. (*Diagram by K. Aa. Strand*)

absolute bolometric magnitude. *Bolometric magnitude* refers to the star's radiation in all wavelengths with allowance for its absorption by the earth's atmosphere.

The mass of a single star may be read from the curve if the bolometric magnitude is known and if the star is of a type that conforms to the relation. Among special kinds of stars that do not conform are the white dwarf stars, which are much fainter than main-sequence stars of equal mass.

13·7. Spectroscopic Binaries are mutually revolving pairs that appear as single stars with the telescope. They are recognized by the periodic oscillations of the lines in their spectra, the Doppler effect as the two stars alternately approach and recede from us in their revolutions. Where the two stars of a binary differ in brightness by as much as one magnitude, only the spectrum of the brighter star is likely to be observed. Capella and Spica are examples of spectroscopic binaries among the brightest stars.

FIG. 13·7. Spectrum of Mizar. The spectrum lines of the two components of the binary are separated in the upper photograph and superposed in the lower one. (*Yerkes Observatory photographs*)

The brighter star of Mizar's visual pair was the first spectroscopic binary to be detected. In the early studies of stellar spectra at Harvard Observatory it was noticed, in 1889, that the dark lines in the spectrum of this star were double in some photographs and single in others.

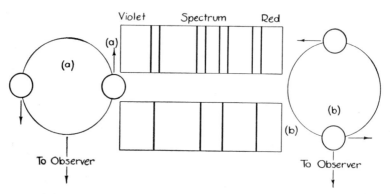

FIG. 13·7A. Doppler Displacements in the Spectrum of Mizar. (a) When one star approaches and the other recedes from us, the lines are double. (b) When both stars move across the line of sight, the lines are superposed.

When the displacements of the lines in the spectrum of a binary have been measured at intervals throughout the period of revolution, the *velocity curve* can be drawn to show how the radial velocity varies during the period. From this curve it is possible to determine the orbit projected on a plane through the line of sight. The inclination of the true orbit to this plane is not determined from the spectrum; it may be derived from the light curve when the pair is also an eclipsing binary.

ECLIPSING VARIABLES

13·8. Variable Stars are stars that vary in brightness. Their fluctuations in light are studied by comparing their magnitudes repeatedly with those of stars having constant brightness. The comparisons are often made in photographs taken at different times, or with the photoelectric cell where the highest precision is required.

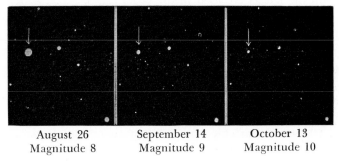

August 26   September 14   October 13
Magnitude 8   Magnitude 9   Magnitude 10

Fig. 13·8. Variation in Brightness of the Recurrent Nova RS Ophiuchi in 1933. (*Photographed by F. Quénisset*)

The *light curve* shows how the magnitude of the star varies with time. If the same variation is repeated periodically, the *elements* of the light variation can be derived; these are the *epoch*, the time of a well-defined place on the curve such as maximum brightness, and the *period* of the variation. The curve for a single cycle may then be defined more precisely by plotting all the observed magnitudes with respect to *phase*, the interval of time expressed either in days or in fractions of the period since the epoch preceding the time of each observation.

As an example, the elements of the variable star Eta Aquilae are recorded as: Maximum brightness $= 2,414,827.15 + 7^d.1767 \cdot E$, where the first number is the epoch expressed in Julian days and the second is the period in days. In order to predict the times of subsequent maxima we have simply to multiply the period by $E = 1, 2,$ . . . and to add the products to the original epoch. The *Julian date* is the number of days that have elapsed since Greenwich mean noon of an arbitrary zero day. It is a convenient device often used to avoid the complexity of the calendar system. The Julian dates are tabulated for each year in the *American Ephemeris and Nautical Almanac*. J.D. 2,436,934.5 corresponds to January 1, 1960, at Greenwich mean midnight.

13·9. The Designation of Variable Stars follows a plan that started simple enough but became complicated when the discoveries of these stars ran into thousands. Unless the star already has a number in the Bayer system (11·4), it is assigned a capital letter, or two, in the order in which its variability is recognized, followed by the possessive of the Latin name of its constellation. For each constellation the letters are used in the order: R, S, . . . , Z; RR, RS, . . . , RZ; SS, . . . , SZ; and so on until ZZ is reached. Subsequent variables are AA, AB, . . . , AZ; BB, . . . , BZ; etc. By the time QZ is reached (the letter J is not employed), 334 variable stars are so named in the constellation. Examples are R Leonis, SZ Herculis, and AC Cygni. Following QZ the designations are V 335, V 336, and so on; an example is V 335 Sagittarii.

13·10. Classes of Variable Stars. *The General Catalogue of Variable Stars,* prepared by B. V. Kukarkin, P. P. Parenago, and associates at the Sternberg Astronomical Institute, Moscow, gives the names, elements of the light variations, and other information about recognized variable stars in our galaxy. The second edition (1958) lists 14,708 variable stars. All variable stars, according to the *Catalogue,* may be divided into three main classes: eclipsing, pulsating, and eruptive variables, each of which is subdivided into several types.

13·11. Eclipsing Variable Stars are spectroscopic binaries having their orbits so nearly edgewise to the earth that the two stars mutually eclipse twice in the course of each revolution. They appear with the telescope as single stars that become fainter while the eclipses are in progress. The periods in which they revolve and fluctuate in brightness average 2 or 3 days; they range from 100 minutes for VV Puppis to 27 years in the very exceptional case of Epsilon Aurigae.

Algol is representative of eclipsing pairs in which the stars are nearly spherical. In pairs such as Beta Lyrae the stars are elongated one toward the other by mutual tidal action, so that additional variation in brightness is produced by the different presentations of the ellipsoidal stars to us, from end-on at the eclipses to broadside between eclipses. In short-period pairs of the W Ursae Majoris type the components are so nearly in contact that the tidal effect is extreme. The spectra of some eclipsing pairs reveal gas streams that issue from the two stars and swirl in the directions of their revolutions.

Combined photometric and spectroscopic observations of eclipsing stars lead to evaluations of their linear dimensions and masses—important data in studies of the constitution of stars.

13·12. Algol (Beta Persei) is a familiar example of eclipsing variable stars and was the first of these to be recognized, in 1783. In the severed head of Medusa, which Perseus carried in the old picture

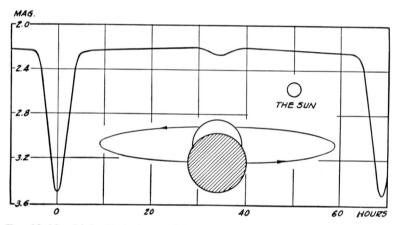

FIG. 13·12. Light Variation and System of Algol. The size of the sun is shown on the same scale. (*Determined by Joel Stebbins*)

book of the skies, this "Demon Star" winks in a way that might have seemed mysterious until the reason for its winking came to be understood. The brighter star of Algol revolves in a period of $2^d 21^h$ (Fig. 13·12) with a companion that is 20 per cent greater in diameter but 3 magnitudes the fainter of the two. Once in each revolution the companion passes in front of the brighter star, partially eclipsing it for nearly 10 hours. At the middle of this eclipse the light of the system is reduced to a third of its normal brightness.

The small drop in the light midway between the primary eclipses occurs when the companion is eclipsed by the brighter star. The light of the system rises slightly toward the secondary eclipse, because the hemisphere of the companion that is then turned toward us is made the more luminous by the light of the brighter star.

The diameter of the brighter star of Algol is 3 times the sun's diameter. The centers of the two stars are 13 million miles apart, or somewhat more than a third of Mercury's mean distance from the sun. The orbit is inclined 8° from the edgewise position.

PULSATING VARIABLES

Intrinsic variable stars fluctuate in brightness from causes inherent in the stars themselves and not because of eclipses. Some of these stars are variable because they are alternately contracting and expanding, becoming hotter and cooler in turn. Pulsating stars include prominently the cepheid and RR Lyrae variables.

13·13. Cepheid Variable Stars take their name from one of their earliest known examples, Delta Cephei. This star fluctuates reg-

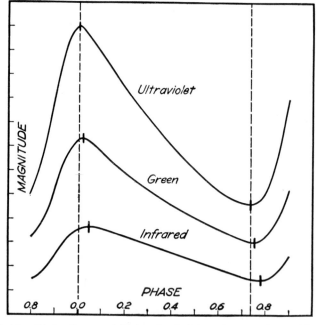

FIG. 13·13. Light Curve of Delta Cephei in Three Colors. The range of the light variation is less and the times of maximum and minimum brightness are later in the longer wavelengths. (*Determined photoelectrically by Joel Stebbins*)

ularly in cycles of $5^d 9^h$, brightening more rapidly than it fades (Fig. 13·13). The velocity curve is nearly the mirror image of the light curve. Near maximum brightness the spectrum lines are displaced farthest to the violet, showing that the gases in front of the star are approaching us in the pulsation at the greatest speed. Near minimum light the lines are displaced farthest to the red, showing that these gases are receding from us at the greatest speed; the star is then redder than at greatest brightness and its spectrum has changed to the pattern of a cooler star.

Cepheid variables are yellow supergiants; the more numerous *classical cepheids* resemble the prototype. Their periods range from a day to several weeks and are most frequent around 5 days. The visual range of the light variation is often around 1 magnitude. Those in our own galaxy congregate toward the Milky Way. Other examples are Eta Aquilae, Zeta Geminorum, and Polaris, which has an exceptionally small range of variation.

The *type II cepheids* have been recognized more frequently in the globular clusters and toward the center of the galaxy. Their periods are generally between 12 and 20 days. The light curves have broader maxima and are more nearly symmetrical. An example is W Virginis.

13·14. RR Lyrae Variables are named after one of their brightest examples; they are also known as cluster variables because they were first observed in large numbers in the globular clusters. They

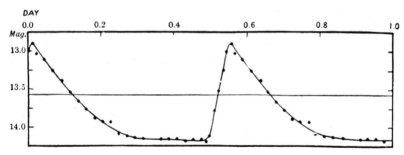

FIG. 13·14. Light Curve of an RR Lyrae Variable. The rapid rise to maximum light is characteristic of many variable stars of this type. (*Harvard Observatory diagram*)

are blue giants varying in brightness in periods around half a day and with ranges up to $1\frac{1}{2}$ magnitudes or more. The light curves of those stars with the shorter periods are likely to be almost symmetrical; at half a day the curves become abruptly asymmetrical with very steep upslopes and extreme ranges, effects that moderate as the periods are longer.

RR Lyrae variables are pulsating stars with some characteristics like those of the cepheids. Their spectrum lines oscillate in the period of the light variation and the stars are bluer at maximum than at minimum brightness. These stars are recognized in greater numbers than are the cepheids even though they are much the less luminous so that they cannot be observed as far away. Not one is visible to the unaided eye. Their brightest examples are the prototype and VZ Cancri, both of the 7th magnitude.

13·15. The Period-Luminosity Relation. The periods of cepheid variables are longer as the stars are more luminous. Originally established by Harlow Shapley in 1917, the relation was given a later form by Walter Baade in 1952. The former curve for the classical cepheids was then raised 1.5 magnitudes in the diagram and was replaced at the lower level by the curve for the type II cepheids. The horizontal line for the RR Lyrae variables was left unaltered. This stage in the development of the relation is represented with certain changes by the full lines of Fig. 13·15. The lines for the cepheids show how the logarithm of the period was then believed to vary with the median absolute magnitude of the star. The *median magnitude* is the average of the brightest and faintest magnitudes. The bands around these lines in the figure illustrate a more recent version of the relation.

The way for this revision of the period-luminosity relation was prepared by H. C. Arp's measures of cepheids in the Small Magellanic Cloud. Arp found that the relation must be represented by a band at least 1 magnitude wide rather than by a simple curve. Allan Sandage supplied the reason for the band. From a relation already known between the period and mean density, he deduced that the absolute magnitude of a cepheid depends not only on the period of its pulsation but also on the star's mean surface temperature, or color. This would apply to all pulsating stars. The next step began with J. B. Irwin's discovery of two cepheids in galactic clusters and the later finding of a few additional cases. Accurate distances and colors of cepheids that can be obtained in these clusters seem to sustain the revised relation.

When the period and mean color of a cepheid of either type is observed, the star's median absolute magnitude can be read from the appropriate diagram. When the median apparent magnitude is also observed, the star's distance, r, in parsecs may be calculated by the formula $(12 \cdot 21)$: $\log r = (m - M + 5)/5$. For the RR Lyrae

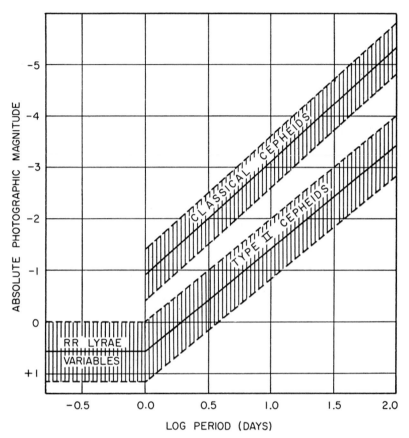

FIG. $13 \cdot 15$. Period-Luminosity Relation for Cepheids. (*From preliminary data supplied by H. C. Arp*)

variables the median magnitudes are independent of the period and the value of M, formerly taken as zero, has now become $+0.6$ in the average. The amount of the spread depending on the surface temperature is uncertain. All such distances require correction where cosmic dust intervenes $(14 \cdot 11)$.

Because of their high luminosity, cepheid variables are useful as distance indicators for the nearer exterior galaxies, whereas the less luminous RR Lyrae variables are employed generally for distances of objects in our own galaxy.

13·16. Mira-Type Variables. Many red supergiant and giant stars are variable in brightness in roughly periodic manner. The periods range from a few months to more than 2 years. The visual variation averages 5 magnitudes and may exceed 10 magnitudes in the extreme case of Chi Cygni (Fig. 13·16); yet the total radiation, as measured by the heating of a thermocouple at the focus of a telescope, varies only about 1 magnitude. These *Mira-type*, or *long-*

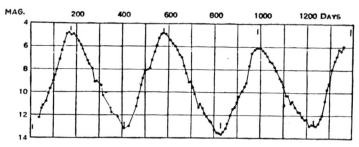

F<small>IG</small>. 13·16. Light Curve of the Mira-Type Variable Chi Cygni. (*Determined by the American Association of Variable Star Observers*)

period variables, are often regarded as pulsating stars and are so classified in the *General Catalogue.*

In addition to the dark lines and bands that characterize the spectra of red stars, these spectra show bright lines at certain phases, particularly lines of hydrogen. They are likely to be somewhat displaced to the violet at the maximum brightness of the stars; but a one-way shifting of the lines and not an oscillation is suggested.

13·17. Mira (Omicron Ceti) is the best known and at times the brightest of these variables. It was in fact the first variable star to be recognized aside from a few novae, and was accordingly called *stella mira.* This red supergiant is at least 10 times as massive as the sun, and its diameter is 300 times the sun's diameter. The average period of the light variation is 330 days. The greatest brightness in the different cycles ranges generally from the 3rd to the 5th visual magnitude and the least brightness from the 8th to the 10th magnitude, where the star is accordingly invisible to the unaided eye.

There is considerable doubt that the fluctuation of Mira is caused mainly or even at all by pulsation. P. W. Merrill has expressed his preference for a main hypothesis of successive "hot fronts" that move outward from below the photosphere and disappear at the upper-most levels of the atmosphere. Here the dissipating waves may cause the gases to condense into droplets, which veil the photosphere until they finally evaporate.

13·18. Irregular and Semiregular Variables. Many red supergiants and giants vary irregularly in narrower limits often not exceeding half a magnitude. Betelgeuse is the brightest of the irregular variables.

The red supergiant Alpha Herculis is another example. This star varies between visual magnitudes 3.0 and 4.0 in irregular cycles of several months' duration. Its distance is 500 light years and its diameter is several hundred times the sun's diameter. This star is surrounded by an expanding shell of patchy clouds, according to A. J. Deutsch, which rise to heights above the surface of at least 700 times the earth's distance from the sun. At very high levels they become clouds of solid particles, which disappear by dilution as they move outward and are replaced by other clouds. Their par-tial veiling of the photosphere is believed to cause the variability of Alpha Herculis and other large red stars.

RV Tauri stars are semiregular yellow and reddish supergiants that form a sort of connecting link between the cepheids and the Mira-type variables. Other types of semiregular variables having small memberships are recognized.

ERUPTIVE VARIABLES

Eruptive, or explosive, variable stars include novae, supernovae, and recurrent novae. Other types are flare stars and T Tauri stars (16·2).

13·19. Novae are stars that rise abruptly from relative obscurity and gradually decline to their former faintness. They are designated either by the word Nova followed by the possessive of the constella-tion name and the year of the outburst, or more recently by letters along with other variable stars. Thus Nova Herculis 1934 is also known as DQ Herculis.

A nova as bright as Venus at greatest brilliancy appeared in Cassiopeia in November, 1572, and was observed by Tycho Brahe until it became invisible to the unaided eye in the spring of 1574. "Kepler's star," in Ophiuchus in 1604, rivaled Jupiter in brightness, and a nova of 1054 in Taurus was reported to have been as bright as Jupiter. These three were of the unusually spectacular type known as supernovae (18·13). Nova Aquilae 1918, the brightest of the present century, rose to the brilliance of Sirius. Such bright ones are exceptional. The majority of the 150 recorded novae in our galaxy did not become visible without the telescope.

13·20. Outbursts of Novae. Before the outburst a nova is smaller and denser than the sun. We think of it as a semidegenerate star that is collapsing to become a white dwarf. When more energy is

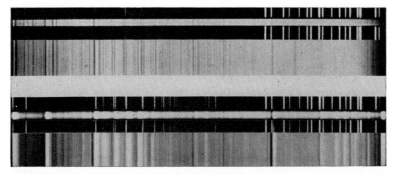

Fig. 13·20. Spectrum of Nova Herculis 1934. Before (above) and after (below) its greatest brightness. The widened spectrum appears below in each case. (*Lick Observatory photographs*)

liberated by the contraction than the small surface can radiate, the star blows off the excess energy along with a small fraction of its gaseous material in a succession of violent explosions. The total mass of material ejected is about 1/10,000 of the star's mass. Clouds of gas emerge with speeds that have exceeded 3000 miles a second, as shown by the Doppler shifts of the spectrum lines. With the growing volume of these hot gases the star may rise 12 magnitudes, or about 60,000 times in brightness.

The gas clouds are opaque at first, as D. B. McLaughlin has explained. The dark spectrum lines are displaced strongly to the violet, giving the illusion that the whole star is swelling enormously. Soon after maximum light the spreading gas clouds become more nearly transparent. Bright undisplaced lines then appear in the spectrum (Fig. 13·20), much broadened because the light then comes from parts of the gas that are approaching and other parts that are receding from us in the expansion. The broad bright lines are bordered at the violet edges by narrow dark lines absorbed as before by the gas immediately in front of the star.

When the envelope has become still more tenuous, the spectrum of the nova changes to the bright-line pattern of an emission nebula, except that the lines are wider. Meanwhile, the brightness fades as the envelope is dissipated by its expansion, until the star returns to its original status. As an example, Nova Aquilae 1918 is now a faintly luminous white star having one fourth the diameter and 70 times the density of the sun.

13·21. Expanding Envelopes Around Novae. The envelopes produced by explosions of novae have sometimes become large enough to be observed directly with the telescope. Nova Aquilae 1918 had a spherical envelope; the envelope began to be visible 4 months after the outburst and increased in radius at the rate of 1″ a year, which at its distance of 1200 light years corresponded to an increase

Fig. 13·21. Crab Nebula, M 1, in Taurus. The nebula is expanding from the site of a supernova. (*Palomar Observatory photograph*)

of 1000 miles a second. In 1940, the vanishing envelope had a radius exceeding 5000 times the earth's distance from the sun. The envelope around Nova Herculis 1934 was ellipsoidal.

The envelopes around normal novae have generally disappeared after a few years. Their short durations and rapid expansions contrast with the longer lives and slower expansions of the planetary nebulae (14·7), which they otherwise resemble. The Crab nebula in Taurus (Fig. 13·21) differs from both in having long duration and also rapid expansion. Now increasing in radius at the rate of 60 million miles a day, this nebula has been spreading for more than 900 years from the site of the supernova of 1054.

13·22. Recurrent Novae, which have two or more recorded outbursts, differ from normal novae only in their more moderate rise in brightness (around 7 magnitudes) and their more rapid decline.

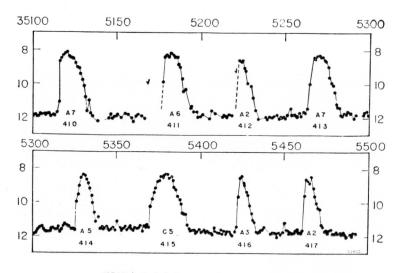

MEAN LIGHT CURVE OF SS CYGNI, 1955

Fig. 13·22. Light Curve of SS Cygni in 1955. Numbers at the top are Julian days 2,435,100 to 2,435,500. Apparent magnitudes are indicated at the right and left. Determined by the American Association of Variable Star Observers. (*Diagram by Margaret W. Mayall*)

An example is RS Ophiuchi (Fig. 13·8), usually around the 12th magnitude, which rose abruptly to the 4th magnitude in 1898 and 1933, and to the 6th magnitude in 1958. There are also groups of hot subdwarf stars having characteristics resembling those of novae.

An example is SS Cygni (Fig. 13·22). Normally around apparent magnitude 12, this star brightens abruptly about 4 magnitudes at irregular intervals and declines in a few days. The spectra at the outbursts have wide emission lines.

There is some indication that the amount of brightening of stars resembling novae increases directly with the average interval between outbursts. If the relation includes normal novae, the intervals between their outbursts should be several thousand years, so that eruptive stars such as Nova Aquilae 1918 may be expected to flare out again. Because the novae before and after the outbursts are subdwarf stars, it seems improbable that a more stable main-sequence star such as the sun would become a nova within the next several billion years.

13·23. Flare Stars. Some red main-sequence stars are subject to repeated intense outbursts of very short duration remindful of the solar flares (10·14). At least 20 stars of this type have been listed.

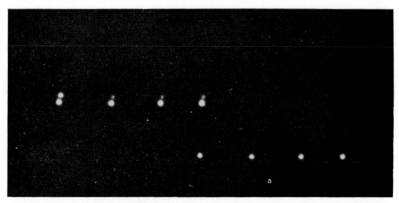

Fig. 13·23. Flare-Up of Krueger 60 B, July 26, 1939. The last of 4 successive exposures (left) on the binary and its distant optical companion, showing the brightening of the fainter star of the pair. Note also by comparison with Fig. 13·1 that the binary, having a period of 44½ years, had made nearly three quarters of a revolution since 1908. (*Photographed at Sproul Observatory*)

An example was the sudden brightening by 1½ magnitudes of the normally fainter component of the visual binary Krueger 60 (Fig. 13·23) observed by Peter van de Kamp and S. L. Lippincott at Sproul Observatory.

Flare stars are designated in the *General Catalogue* as UV Ceti-type variables after a typical representative first recorded by W. J. Luyten in 1948. This star is the fainter component of the binary Luyten 726-8. The main outbursts of UV Ceti occur at average intervals of 1½ days, when the rise in brightness of the star is generally from 1 to 2 magnitudes. On one occasion in 1952, however, an increase of 6 magnitudes was observed, the greatest flare on record for any star. Only a small fraction of the star's surface is affected, as in the case of a solar flare. Between the main outbursts the light of the flare star varies continuously and irregularly in smaller amplitude.

QUESTIONS ON CHAPTER 13

1. The majority of visual binary stars have shown no evidence of mutual revolution. How is it known that they are physically connected?

2. Describe the discovery of the companion of Sirius before it was observed.

3. Why do the lines in the spectrum of Mizar (Fig. 13·7) appear double at times and single at other times?

4. Where the spectrum lines of a star are always single, how is it possible to decide whether it is an ordinary single star, a pulsating star, or a spectroscopic binary where the fainter spectrum is not visible?

5. The diagram of the system of Algol shown in Fig. 13·12 is derived from the accompanying light curve and the spectroscopic data. What features of the light curve show that:

   (a) The eclipses are partial?
   (b) The companion is much less luminous than the brighter star?
   (c) The companion reflects some light of the brighter star?

6. Mention some differences between RR Lyrae stars, classical cepheids, and type II cepheids.

7. Explain the method of determining the distance of a classical cepheid variable star by means of the period-luminosity relation; the distance of an RR Lyrae variable star.

8. Show that the recent raising of the period-luminosity curve of the classical cepheids by 1½ magnitudes doubled the former values of their distances.

9. Mention 3 types of intrinsic variable stars which are not pulsating stars.

10. Describe the outburst of a nova according to the view we have given here.

11. In what respects do recurrent novae differ from ordinary novae?

12. Does it seem likely that Nova Aquilae 1918 will flare out again? that the sun may soon become a nova? Explain.

REFERENCES

Aitken, Robert G., *The Binary Stars.* Second edition. McGraw-Hill Book Company, New York, 1935.

Campbell, Leon, and Luigi Jacchia, *The Story of Variable Stars.* Harvard University Press, Cambridge, 1941.

Kukarkin, B. V., P. P. Parenago, and others, *General Catalogue of Variable Stars.* Second edition. Moscow, 1958.

Payne-Gaposchkin, Cecilia, *The Galactic Novae.* Interscience Publishers, New York, 1957.

"Horsehead" Nebula in Orion. A contrast of dark and bright nebulosity. *(Mount Wilson and Palomar Observatories photograph)*

14

COSMIC GAS AND DUST

DIFFUSE NEBULAE – PLANETARY NEBULAE – THE INTERSTELLAR MATERIAL

Nebulae in general are clouds of cosmic gas and dust. *Diffuse nebulae* are condensations of the interstellar material that is abundant in our Milky Way and in the arms of exterior spiral galaxies. Such nebulae are believed to supply the material from which stars are born. *Planetary nebulae* constitute a second category. These are glowing gaseous envelopes expanding around certain very hot stars; they are examples of the return of gas by stars to the interstellar clouds.

DIFFUSE NEBULAE

14·1. Diffuse Nebulae have irregular forms and often large angular dimensions. Some resemble the cumulus clouds of our atmosphere, while others have a filamentary structure that is remindful of our high cirrus clouds. Shocks and compressions of the colliding turbulent material and effects of magnetic fields can account for the complex structures and also for the light of nebulae in certain cases.

Some diffuse nebulae are made luminous by the radiations of stars in the vicinities. In the absence of involved or neighboring stars the nebulae are generally practically dark. This relation was first explained by Edwin Hubble, who also showed that the quality of the nebular light depends on the temperature of the associated stars. Where the star is as blue as type B1, the nebular spectrum differs from that of the star, being mainly a pattern of bright lines. Where the star is cooler than B1, the light is mainly reflected starlight, so that the spectrum resembles that of the star. Thus the bright diffuse nebulae are of two types with respect to the quality of their light; these are emission nebulae and reflection nebulae.

14·2. Emission Nebulae. The extreme ultraviolet radiations of very hot stars contain enough energy to remove electrons abundantly from atoms of certain elements in the gases of the surrounding nebulae. As the ionized atoms capture other electrons, the nebulae emit light differing from that of the stimulating stars. The spectrum of the emitted light is more conspicuous than that of the starlight reflected by the same nebula for two reasons: (1) The emitted light is concentrated in a few bright lines of the spectrum, whereas the reflected light is dispersed over the entire spectrum; (2) much of the reflecting dust may have been blown away from the vicinity of the star by the star's radiations. Because diffuse emission nebulae and the associated blue stars in our galaxy are features of the spiral arms, they have been useful in the optical tracing of the arms (17·7).

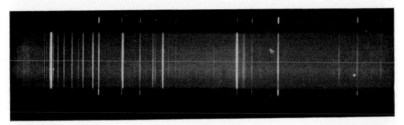

Fig. 14·2.   Spectrum of the Orion Nebula.   From ultraviolet to blue. The very strong line at the left is the double line of singly ionized oxygen at 3727 A.   Short comparison lines above and below are of hydrogen and helium.   (*Photograph by Donald E. Osterbrock*)

Prominent in the spectra of emission nebulae are "forbidden lines," so called because they are not likely to be observed in ordinary laboratory conditions. These bright lines of oxygen, nitrogen, and some other elements remained unidentified until they were explained theoretically by I. S. Bowen, in 1927. Despite their stronger showing in the spectra, oxygen and nitrogen are less abundant in these nebulae than are hydrogen and helium; in collisions with other atoms, however, they are able to utilize greater quantities of energy provided by the exciting starlight.

A strong pair of oxygen lines at wavelengths 4959 and 5007 in the green region of the spectrum impart the characteristic greenish hue to emission nebulae. In another oxygen pair at 3726 and 3729 in the ultraviolet, the strength of one line relative to the other depends on the density of the gas. This relation has been employed by D. E. Osterbrock and others to determine the densities of these nebulae.

14·3. The Great Nebula in Orion is the brightest diffuse emission nebula in the direct view with the telescope. Scarcely visible to the unaided eye, it surrounds the middle star of the three in Orion's sword. With the telescope the nebula appears as a greenish cloud around the star, which itself is resolved into the familiar Trapezium of type O stars. In the photographs the Orion nebula is spread over an area of the sky having twice the apparent diameter of the moon.

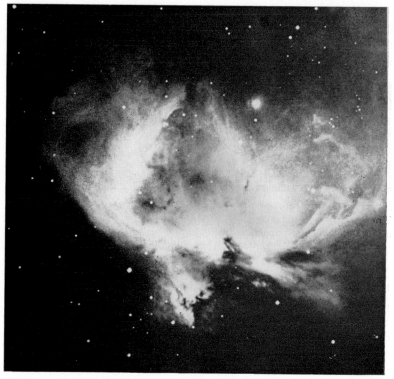

FIG. 14·3.   Great Nebula in Orion.   *(Photograph with a 12½-inch reflector by Clarence P. Custer, Stockton, California)*

At its distance of 1600 light years the corresponding linear diameter is 26 light years, or about the distance of Vega from the sun.

By the method mentioned in the previous section, Osterbrock finds that the gas of the Orion nebula has unusually high density, about 20,000 atoms per cubic centimeter, in one of the brightest central regions. The density is reduced to 300 atoms per cubic centimeter at a point halfway from the center to the edge.

Among other conspicuous diffuse emission nebulae are M 8 in Sagittarius and the nebula surrounding the star Eta Carinae.

14·4. Reflection Nebulae. Where stars involved in interstellar material are cooler than type B1, the nebulae around them reflect the starlight scattered by their dust. The bright nebulae surrounding stars of the Pleiades are examples of reflection nebulae. These have the same spectra as the associated stars.

The similarity in color of reflection nebulae and of the stars responsible for their shining is well shown in photographs with filters

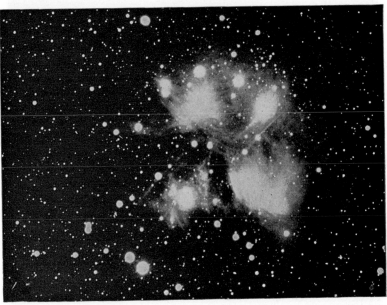

Fig. 14·4. Nebulae Surrounding Stars of the Pleiades. (*Photographed by E. E. Barnard*)

of a dusty region of Scorpius. Here the reflection nebulae surround stars like the glows around street lamps on a foggy night. The nebular light around the red star Antares is scarcely noticeable with blue filters and becomes conspicuous with red ones. The opposite is the case for the nebulae around blue stars in the vicinity.

14·5. Dark Nebulae are clouds of gas and dust that have no stars near enough to light them effectively. Their faint illumination by the general star fields can be detected only by measurements of high precision. Dark nebulae make their presence known optically by obscuring whatever lies behind them. The rifts they imprint on the bright background of the Milky Way are conspicuous in the photographs. Some rifts, such as the Coalsack near the Southern Cross, are easily visible to the naked eye and have accordingly been known for a long time; but their interpretation as dark clouds rather than as vacancies came in fairly recent times.

The darkest clouds in the Milky Way are relatively near us at distances of 300 to 1500 light years. At greater distances their con-

FIG. 14·5. Rifts in the Milky Way. Region of southern Ophiuchus and northern Scorpius. (*Photographed by F. E. Ross*)

trast with the bright background is diluted by increasing numbers of stars in front of them. Few dark nebulae are recognized optically in our galaxy at distances exceeding 5000 light years.

PLANETARY NEBULAE

14·6. Features of Planetary Nebulae. These nebulae are envelopes around blue stars at their centers. They are called *planetary nebulae* simply because some nearer ones appear with the telescope as greenish disks remindful of the disks of Uranus and Neptune. The disks may be amorphous or irregular, and some either have the appearance

of rings or are actually rings. A familiar example is the Ring
nebula in Lyra (Fig. 14·6).

Several hundred planetary nebulae are recognized. They range
in size from the ring-like NGC 7293 in Aquarius, having half the
moon's apparent diameter, to objects so reduced in the distance that

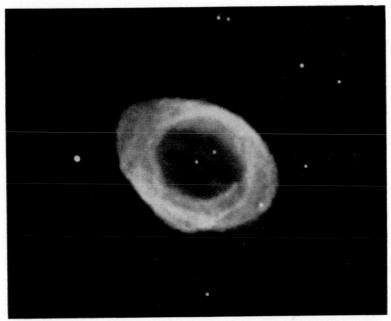

FIG. 14·6. Ring Nebula in Lyra. Photographed with the Hale telescope.
(*Mount Wilson and Palomar Observatories photograph*)

they are distinguished from ordinary stars only by their peculiar
bright-line spectra. Their linear diameters range from 20,000 to
more than 100,000 times the earth's distance from the sun.

The central stars of planetary nebulae are about as massive as
the sun, but are much smaller and denser than the sun. Having
surface temperatures of 50,000° K, or more, they furnish a rich
supply of ultraviolet radiation to cause the illumination of these
emission nebulae. Because their radiations are mainly in the ultraviolet, the central stars are less easy to see than are the nebulae themselves; but the stars come out as clearly in the photographs taken
in blue light.

14·7. Expansion of Planetary Nebulae. Planetary nebulae are expanding around their central stars, as Doppler effects in their spectra show. Although they resemble the envelopes around novae in this respect, the planetaries are expanding more slowly and their lifetimes are much longer. Their moderate speeds of expansion in radius range from 6 to 30 miles a second. After lifetimes as long as 20,000 years they begin to disintegrate by breaking into separate clouds of gas, whereas the envelopes of normal novae have disappeared only a few years after emerging from the stars.

There is also a pronounced difference in the amount of material involved. The mass of a planetary nebula is about one tenth the sun's mass; but the mass of a normal nova envelope does not exceed 1/10,000 the sun's mass.

THE INTERSTELLAR MATERIAL

In addition to the more obvious bright and dark nebulae, the spiral arms of our galaxy contain an abundance of tenuous gas and dust. The gas imprints dark lines in the spectra of stars beyond it. The presence of optically invisible neutral hydrogen in the gas is recorded with radio telescopes. The interstellar dust dims and reddens the light of more distant stars.

14·8. Interstellar Lines in the Spectra of Stars are abstracted from the starlight by the gas through which the light passes. These dark lines are generally narrower than the lines in the spectra of the stars themselves and have different Doppler displacements than

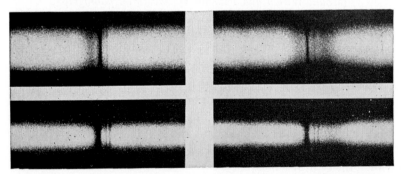

Fig. 14.8. Interstellar Lines in the Spectra of Two Stars. The Fraunhofer K line of calcium appears at the left and the H line at the right; both are separated into components. The broad calcium lines of the stars are shown as well. (*Mount Wilson Observatory photographs*)

those of corresponding star-lines. Among the chemical constituents of the interstellar gas indicated by these lines are atoms of sodium, potassium, calcium, iron, and titanium, and molecules of cyanogen and hydrocarbon. Hydrogen atoms are doubtless very abundant, but in these conditions their lines would appear only in the generally unobservable extreme ultraviolet region of the spectrum.

The division of interstellar lines into two or more components was recognized some time ago, particularly by W. S. Adams (Fig. 14·8). The division is given important interpretation by the more recent studies of Guido Münch; his photographs of stellar spectra with the 200-inch telescope show that the principal components of the interstellar lines are absorbed by gas in two intervening arms of our galaxy.

14·9. Ionized Interstellar Hydrogen. Where a cloud of interstellar gas surrounds a hot star, the gas is set glowing within a radius around the star that depends on the temperature of the star and

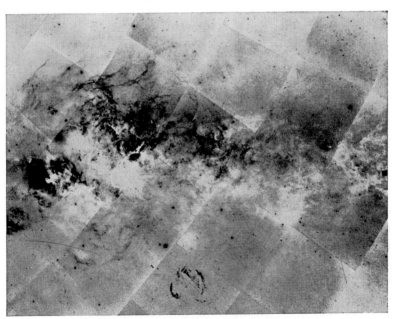

FIG. 14·9. Hydrogen Wreaths in Cygnus. A mosaic of negative photographs with the 48-inch Schmidt telescope. The loop of filamentary nebulosity at the bottom is the most conspicuous wreath in the region. (*Copyright by National Geographic Society–Palomar Observatory Sky Survey. Courtesy of J. L. Greenstein*)

the density of the gas. Outside this region the gas is normally dark. Because hydrogen is the most abundant chemical element, it has been the custom to speak of the two parts of the cloud as the H-II and H-I regions, respectively.

In the part of the cloud that is nearer the star, hydrogen atoms are ionized by the star's ultraviolet radiation. Because the atoms that have lost electrons soon capture others, the gas is thereby made luminous. In addition to the conspicuous emission nebulae, many faint H-II regions are detected in photographic surveys with wide-angle cameras and plates especially sensitive to the spectral region of the red line of hydrogen. Such surveys have been useful in tracing the spiral arms of our galaxy.

The bright material in the inner region of a cosmic cloud is likely to expand and to collide with the gas in the dark region outside. Such collisions may be vigorous enough to set the contact areas glowing conspicuously. This reason is assigned for the familiar loop of bright nebulosity near Epsilon Cygni (Fig. 14·9).

14·10. Neutral Interstellar Hydrogen. In the part of a gas cloud that is too remote from a hot star to be much stimulated by it, the hydrogen is generally dark and optically unobservable. Radiation by neutral atoms of cosmic hydrogen at a wavelength of 21 cm, previously predicted by H. C. van de Hulst, was first recorded with a radio telescope by H. I. Ewen and E. M. Purcell in 1951. This emission line, the only one so far detected in the radio spectrum, has been employed effectively in tracing the spiral arms of the galaxy (17·13).

The emission at 21 cm occurs when the single electron of the hydrogen atom at its lowest level passes from parallel to antiparallel direction of spin relative to that of the nucleus of the atom. Although the transition occurs very infrequently in any one atom, it supplies a continuous stream of radiation from the combined atoms of a gas cloud. The corresponding absorption line has also been recorded where a cloud of neutral hydrogen lies between us and a strong source of radio emission in continuous wavelengths.

14·11. Dimming of Starlight by Dust. Interstellar dust dims the light of stars behind it. The dust also reddens the light of those stars, because the dimming is greater in the shorter than in the longer wavelengths of the light. A corresponding effect is observed in the reddening of the light of the setting sun by particles of our atmosphere.

The *color excess* of a star is the difference of magnitude by which the observed color index, blue minus visual, exceeds the accepted value for a star of its spectral class; it is a measure of the reddening of the star by the dust. Where the color excess is multiplied by an appropriate factor, we have the *photographic absorption*, that is, how much in magnitudes the star is dimmed by the dust as photographed with a blue-sensitive plate.

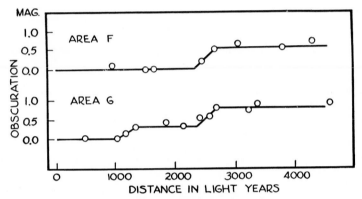

FIG. 14·11. Photographic Absorption by Dust in Two Areas of Auriga. The separate points represent the averages for many stars measured in blue and red light.

The distance of a reddened star determined by photometric means requires correction for absorption, which magnifies the actual distance. The corrected distance, r, is calculated by the formula: $5 \log r = m - M + 5 - K$, where m is the observed photographic magnitude, M is the corresponding absolute magnitude for a star of this particular spectral type, and K is the photographic absorption.

14·12. The Dust Grains. The dimming of stars by intervening cosmic dust is attributed to particles of the order of a hundred thousandth of an inch in diameter. Dust grains of this size would scatter the light in inverse proportion to the wavelength, which is not far from the observed relation for the reddened stars. Considerably larger particles would obstruct but not redden the starlight. The origin of the dust grains is not clearly understood; whether they build up from atoms of the interstellar gas or are particles transferred to the medium from the upper atmospheres of stars, or both, is conjectural.

Starlight becomes polarized in its passage through clouds of interstellar dust, as the photoelectric studies of J. S. Hall and W. A. Hiltner revealed independently. A possible explanation is that the polarization is produced by dust grains shaped like needles and rotating on their short axes, which give concerted effect by setting themselves along magnetic lines of force of the galaxy. This and other implications that our galaxy has a general magnetic field have added other items to the growing list of problems in celestial hydromagnetics.

QUESTIONS ON CHAPTER 14

1. Why are some nebulae luminous, whereas others are practically dark?
2. Distinguish between emission and reflection nebulae as to the cause and quality of their light.
3. In what respects do planetary nebulae differ from envelopes expanding around novae?
4. Name: (a) a diffuse emission nebula; (b) a reflection nebula; (c) a planetary nebula; (d) a dark nebula.
5. How may interstellar lines be distinguished from lines in the spectra of the stars themselves? Why may interstellar lines be split into two or more components?
6. How is it possible to decide by means of the spectrum whether the light of a star is reddened by interstellar dust? Define: color excess.
7. Distinguish between the H-II and H-I regions of a gas cloud surrounding a very hot star.
8. The nebulous loop and fainter hydrogen wreaths in Cygnus have been ascribed to collisions between the two hydrogen regions. Explain.

15

STAR CLUSTERS

GALACTIC CLUSTERS – GLOBULAR CLUSTERS

Star clusters are physically related groups of stars having their members less widely spaced than are the stars around them. The stars of a cluster had a common origin and are moving along together through the star fields, so that the cluster will maintain its identity for a very long time. Although the members of a cluster are of about the same age, the more massive stars have shorter lives and are further developed in their evolutions than the less massive ones. Together, they give important information about the course of stellar evolution. Star clusters are of two types: galactic clusters and globular clusters.

The brighter clusters are often called by special names, such as the Praesepe and Pleiades clusters. More generally, the clusters are designated by their running numbers in one of two catalogs where they are listed together with nebulae and exterior galaxies. Thus the great cluster in Hercules is known as M 13 or as NGC 6205. The first designation is by the number in the catalog of 103 bright objects, which Charles Messier published in 1784; a useful list of these objects and their positions in the sky is given in *Sky and Telescope* for March, 1954. The second designation of the Hercules cluster is by its number in Dreyer's *New General Catalogue* (1887), which with its extensions in the later *Index Catalogue* (**IC**) lists over 13,000 objects.

GALACTIC CLUSTERS

15·1. Features of Galactic Clusters. Galactic clusters are so named because those in our galaxy lie near its principal plane. They accordingly appear close to the Milky Way except a few of the nearest ones, notably the Coma Berenices cluster, which is near the north pole of the Milky Way. They are also known as *open clusters,* because they are loosely assembled and are not greatly concentrated toward their centers.

The Pleiades, or "Seven Sisters," in Taurus and the Hyades in the same constellation are familiar examples of galactic clusters. Their brighter stars are clearly visible to the unaided eye and those of the Coma cluster are faintly visible. The Praesepe cluster in Cancer, also known as the "Beehive," the double cluster in Perseus, and some others are hazy spots to the eye alone and are resolved into stars with binoculars. These are fine objects with small telescopes.

FIG. 15·1.   Galactic Cluster in Coma Berenices.   (*Yerkes Observatory photograph*)

About 500 galactic clusters are recognized in our region of the galaxy. Their memberships generally range from two dozen to a few hundred, and exceed 1000 stars in the rich Perseus clusters. The known galactic clusters are all within 20,000 light years from the sun. More remote ones are too faint to be noticed in bright areas of the Milky Way or are concealed by dust in the dark areas.

15·2. The Hyades Cluster is relatively so near us that the proper motions of its members offer a good example of the common motions of cluster stars. It comprises the stars of the V-shaped group itself, except the bright Aldebaran which has an independent motion not

shown in the diagram (Fig. 15·2), and also stars in the vicinity within
an area having a diameter of 20°. The cluster of at least 150 stars
has its center 130 light years from the sun. It is moving toward
the east and is also receding from us, so that the parallel paths of

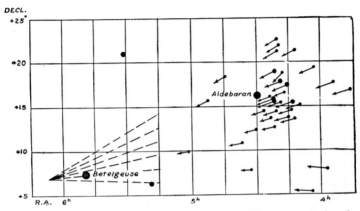

FIG. 15·2. Convergence of the Hyades Cluster. The stars of the cluster
are converging toward a point in the sky east of the present position of
Betelgeuse. The lengths of the arrows show the proper motions in 50,000
years.

its stars are converging toward a point in the sky east of the present
position of Betelgeuse in Orion. This cluster passed nearest the
sun 800,000 years ago at half its present distance.

15·3. The Color-Magnitude Diagram is an array of points representing the color indexes of stars plotted with respect to their magnitudes. In the diagram of the Praesepe cluster (Fig. 15·3) the stars
become redder from left to right—from blue stars such as Sirius at
the left to yellow stars like the sun near the middle and to red stars
at the right. Color index has a known relation to spectral type,
which also advances as the temperature diminishes; it is preferred
to the other in this and following diagrams, because color index
can be determined the more easily and precisely. The stars become
brighter from the bottom to the top of the diagram. In this case
the apparent, or observed, photographic magnitude is plotted.

The diagram of the Praesepe cluster can inform us of the distance
and relative age of the cluster, as follows:

(1) *Distance of the cluster.* Compare the Praesepe diagram with
the standard spectrum–absolute magnitude diagram (Fig. 12·22),

supposing that the latter is first redrawn to the same scales of color and brightness as the former. In the cluster diagram a main-sequence star having the same color index, +0.6, as the sun, has apparent photographic magnitude, m, about 11.3. The sun's absolute photographic magnitude, M, is $4.8 + 0.6 = 5.4$. The formula: log $r = (m - M + 5)/5 = 2.18$ gives r, the distance in parsecs. Without correction for the effect of intervening dust (14·11), the distance of the Praesepe cluster is accordingly about 150 parsecs.

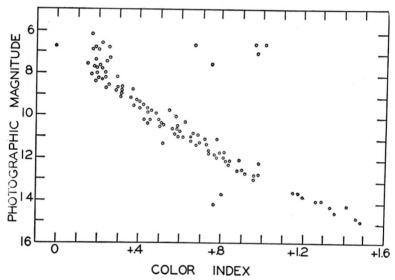

Fig. 15·3. Color-Magnitude Diagram of the Praesepe Cluster. (*Adapted from a diagram by Harold L. Johnson*)

(2) *Age of the cluster.* Note that the top of the main sequence of the Praesepe cluster bends to the right and that a few of the brightest stars have moved away still farther to the right. As the cluster grows older, the point at which the stars break from the sequence progresses down the sequence, as we see presently.

15·4. Distances of Galactic Clusters. The distances of 16 galactic clusters, given in Table 15·I, were derived by H. L. Johnson from his photoelectric measures of the brightness of the cluster stars in the ultraviolet, blue, and yellow. His method was to restore to their original apparent magnitudes on each cluster main sequence the stars that have broken away from this sequence. With allowance for the dimming and reddening of the cluster stars by intervening

TABLE 15·I   DISTANCES OF GALACTIC CLUSTERS *

Cluster	Constellation	Parsecs	Light Years
Hyades	Taurus	40	130
Coma	Coma Berenices	80	260
Pleiades	Taurus	126	410
Praesepe	Cancer	158	515
M 39	Cygnus	250	820
IC 4665	Ophiuchus	330	1080
M 34	Perseus	440	1440
M 25	Sagittarius	550	1790
M 67	Cancer	830	2710
NGC 2264	Monoceros	870	2840
M 36	Auriga	1260	4110
NGC 2362	Canis Major	1450	4730
NGC 6530	Sagittarius	1580	5150
NGC 2244	Monoceros	1660	5410
M 11	Scutum	1740	5670
Double	Perseus	2250	7340

* Determined photoelectrically by Harold L. Johnson, Lowell Observatory.

dust, the restored main sequence was then matched with that of a standard color–absolute magnitude diagram. The difference, apparent minus absolute magnitude, at corresponding points in the two scales at the left of the diagrams gave all the information needed for calculating the distance of the cluster by the formula we have already noted.

15·5. Star Clusters of Different Ages. The theory of stellar evolution described in the following chapter first traces the stars from their births in the nebulae to positions of temporary stability on the main sequence of the color-magnitude diagram. Here they are arrayed in order of color, from blue at the left to red at the right. In this order the stars of a cluster break from the sequence and move to the right to become giant stars. The greater the age of a cluster, the lower on the main sequence is the place where the stars begin to break from the sequence.

A composite color-magnitude diagram for ten galactic clusters and one globular cluster is shown in Fig. 15·5. The color indexes, blue minus visual, of the cluster stars were plotted against their absolute visual magnitudes, and the trends of the points so plotted are represented here by broad lines. The ages of the clusters in years are read from the scale at the right opposite the points where the curves begin to break from the main sequence. Above its point of departure a particular cluster has no stars remaining on the sequence.

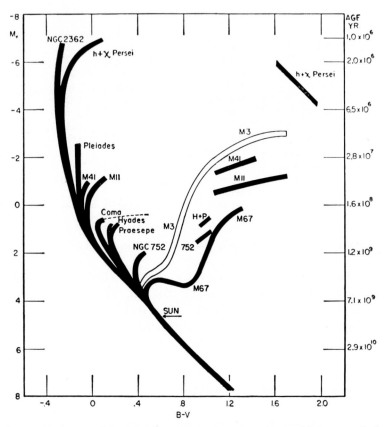

FIG. 15·5. Color-Magnitude Diagrams for 10 Galactic Clusters and the Globular Cluster M 3. Color indexes are plotted with respect to absolute visual magnitudes. (*Diagram by Allan Sandage*)

NGC 2362 is the youngest cluster represented in the figure. Although its bluest stars have already begun to move away, the yellow and red stars have not yet had time to reach the main sequence. The double cluster in Perseus is also in its youth. The Pleiades cluster is middle-aged, and the Hyades and Praesepe clusters are approaching old age. M 67, age 7 billion years, is the oldest cluster represented; it breaks from the sequence where the stars are not much bluer than the sun. The sun itself has moved only slightly from the sequence since its arrival there.

15·6. The Lives of Galactic Clusters. The common motions of the stars of a cluster indicate their common origin in a fragmented interstellar cloud. The persistence of the nearly parallel motions

FIG. 15·6. Praesepe Cluster in Cancer. *(Photographed by William Henry)*

shows how very slowly the cluster is loosened and dispersed by attractions of stars and collisions with cosmic clouds in the fields through which it passes. The more compact clusters and especially those farther removed from the central plane of the galaxy should have the longest lives.

The cluster M 67 may have the longest life of any galactic cluster; it breaks from the main sequence at about the same place as does the durable globular cluster M 3. Yet M 67 still contains at least 500 stars. This cluster in Cancer is about 10° from the Praesepe cluster. Both clusters are more than 50° from the central line of the Milky Way. M 67, however, is 5 times as far away from us as is Praesepe and is therefore at an unusually great distance from the principal plane of the Milky Way; there it is relatively immune to disturbances which tend to disrupt clusters.

15·7. The Brighter Globular Clusters. Globular clusters are spheroidal assemblages often of many tens of thousands of stars; they are much the larger and more compact of the two types. More than 100 are recognized in our galaxy and many more are likely to be hiding behind its dust clouds. Instead of crowding toward the Milky Way, as the galactic clusters do, they form a nearly spherical halo around the galaxy. Relatively scarce in space, not one of them has been seen within the distance of 20,000 light years from us, where all our galactic clusters are observed. Their high luminosity makes them visible afar in our galaxy and around nearer exterior galaxies.

The brightest globular clusters for us are Omega Centauri, near the northern edge of the Milky Way in the south polar region, and 47 Tucanae, also in that region. They appear to the unaided eye as slightly blurred stars of the 4th magnitude and were given designations as stars before their true character was recognized. These two are the nearest globular clusters, at the distance of 22,000 light years, and are among the richest in stars.

M 13 in Hercules is faintly visible to the unaided eye, as is M 22 in Sagittarius. M 5 in Serpens, M 55 in Sagittarius, and M 3 in Canes Venatici can be glimpsed without a telescope in favorable conditions.

15·8. The Hercules Cluster, M 13, at the distance of 30,000 light years, is well known to observers in middle northern latitudes, where it passes nearly overhead in the early evenings of summer. This cluster covers an area of the sky having two thirds the moon's apparent diameter. Its linear diameter is 160 light years, or the distance of Spica from the sun.

More than 50,000 stars of the Hercules cluster are bright enough to be observed with present telescopes, although the stars in the central region are too crowded to be counted separately. The total membership is estimated as half a million stars, including the yellow and red stars of the main sequence, which are too faint to be observed. The slightly elliptical outline of the cluster, less than that of Jupiter's disk, suggests flattening at the poles by slow rotation; but no other evidence of rotation has been detected.

The stars in the compact central region of the Hercules cluster have an average separation of 20,000 times the earth's distance from the sun, or about a twentieth of the spaces between the stars in the sun's vicinity. For anyone observing from there the night sky would have a splendor quite unfamiliar to us. Probably a hundred times

Fig. 15·8.   Globular Cluster M 13 in Hercules.   (*Mount Wilson and Palomar Observatories photograph*)

as many stars as we see in our skies would be visible to the unaided eye, and the brightest ones would shine as brightly as the moon does for us.

15·9. Variable Stars in Globular Clusters.   The presence in these clusters of many stars that are variable in brightness has been recognized for a long time.   The majority are RR Lyrae variables, having periods around half a day; originally called cluster variables, they are now known to be even more abundant outside the clusters. More than 1400 variable stars are listed by Helen Sawyer Hogg in the 72 clusters that have been searched for such objects.   M 3 and Omega Centauri are the richest in known variables, having 187 and 164, respectively.   Among the few variables of other kinds in such clusters are some type II cepheids.

15·10. The System of Globular Clusters.   Harlow Shapley, in 1917, made the first important step toward the present understanding of our galaxy by determining the arrangement of the globular clusters in space. His purpose was to answer a question of long standing: Do the stars go on out into space indefinitely, or do they form a system of limited extent? His idea was that the cluster system should have about the same dimensions and center as the system of stars.

Shapley measured the distances of the clusters by use of their RR Lyrae stars, which can serve as distance indicators, as we have seen (13·15). Having found the distances and of course knowing the directions from us, he then made a model of the cluster system, showing the sun's position in it. With later correction for the effect of intervening dust in magnifying the measured distances, the cluster system occupies mainly a spherical volume of space 100,000 light years in diameter surrounding the flat disk of the galaxy proper. The center of the system is 30,000 light years from the sun in the direction of Sagittarius and in the region of the sky where a third of the globular clusters are found.

This classical survey established the separate status of our galaxy and the eccentric position of the sun in it.

15·11. Two Stellar Populations. The diagram that arrays the spectral classes, or else the colors, of stars in the sun's vicinity with respect to the absolute magnitudes differs from the diagram for the globular clusters. Interest in this matter was increased by Walter Baade's discovery with the 100-inch telescope, in 1943, that a similar difference is shown in the galaxy M 31 in Andromeda between the spiral arms and the central region or the two elliptical companions of that galaxy. Baade called the two arrays populations I and II, respectively (Fig. 15·11).

The type I population is represented by our region of our galaxy and was accordingly the first to be recognized. It frequents regions where gas and dust are abundant. Its brightest stars are hot blue stars of the main sequence, which is intact. Its giants are mainly red stars around absolute visual magnitude zero. This is a young population.

The type II population, represented by the globular clusters, occurs in regions free from gas and dust. Its brightest stars are K-type red giants of absolute visual magnitude −2.4, where the giant sequence begins. On the downward slope in the diagram this sequence divides into two branches, one of which runs horizontally to the left at magnitude zero. The second branch continues in

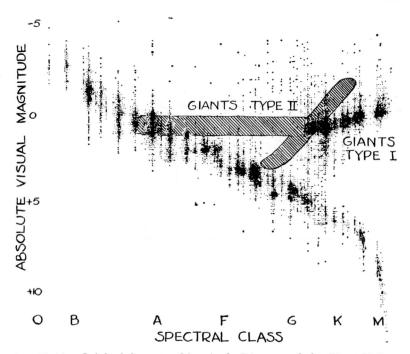

FIG. 15·11. Original Spectrum-Magnitude Diagram of the Type II Population. The points represent stars of type I, as in Fig. 12·22. The shaded strips represent type II giants. (*Adapted from a diagram by Walter Baade*)

about the original direction until it reaches the type I main sequence. To the left of the junction there are no main-sequence stars of the cluster. This is an old population.

15·12. Extension of the Type II Diagram. An extension of Baade's type II diagram from photographs of the globular cluster M 3 with the 200-inch telescope is shown in Fig. 15·12. RR Lyrae stars were not included in this survey; a gap in the horizontal branch where they would appear suggests that this may be exclusively the domain of these variable stars. From the lower end of the vertical giant branch the remnant of the cluster main sequence is shown extending down and to the right to yellow stars at the limit of faintness for the larger telescope.

Baade's types I and II represent extremes of young and old populations of stars. Intermediate types have seemed to be needed to indicate the relative ages of stars in different parts of our galaxy and

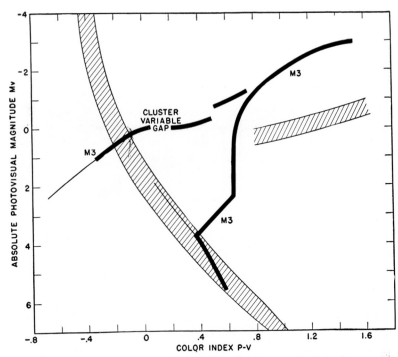

Fig. 15·12. Color-Magnitude Diagram of the Globular Cluster M 3. The type II array of the cluster stars is shown by the solid lines. The main sequence and red giants of the type I population are represented by the shaded areas. (*Diagram by H. C. Arp, W. A. Baum, and Allan Sandage*)

of exterior galaxies. Five types of stellar population have been proposed (17·8) instead of two.

Questions on Chapter 15

1. Distinguish between galactic and globular star clusters. Name an example of each type.

2. How may the distance of a galactic cluster be calculated when its color-magnitude diagram is determined?

3. Explain that the distance and linear diameter of a cluster may be magnified by the method of Question 2 if dust intervenes and is not allowed for.

4. Turning to the color-magnitude diagram of Fig. 15·5, explain that the Perseus double cluster may be considered youthful, the Pleiades in middle age, and M 67 in old age.

5. Describe the method of evaluating the distance of a globular cluster containing RR Lyrae variable stars.

6. How did Shapley demonstrate from the globular clusters the separate status of our galaxy and the sun's eccentric position in the galaxy?

7. Distinguish between the original types I and II of stellar population. Take as examples the stars around us and the stars in globular clusters.

8. Describe the later extension of the type II diagram (Fig. 15·12) and its significance.

The 100-inch Reflecting Telescope, Mount Wilson Observatory.

16

THE LIVES OF THE STARS

YOUTHFUL STARS – THE STARS IN MIDDLE AGE – THE
DECLINING STARS

The problem of stellar evolution is to understand how stars are
born and how they spend their lives until they cease to shine. The
idea that stars condense from nebulae was pioneered by Kant and
Laplace in the 18th century and has persisted to the present time.

New stars are continually forming from condensations in the
interstellar gas and dust, according to the presently favored theory
of stellar evolution. The primitive stars are heated by contraction
until they begin to shine. Thereafter, they go on shrinking until
their central temperatures are hot enough to permit the building
up of atoms of heavier chemical elements from lighter ones. Atomic
synthesis, as of hydrogen into helium, then replaces contraction as
the main source of stellar energy.

The stars stay on the main sequence as long as they remain practically homogeneous in composition. The energy released by the
fusing atoms keeps the stars shining steadily. As the building up
of helium in their cores continues, the stars eventually lose stability;
they then begin to expand and brighten, leaving the main sequence
to become giant stars. The bluer stars withdraw sooner than the
redder ones. When their available supplies of atomic fuel are exhausted, the stars collapse and finally approach the end of their
luminous careers as very dense white dwarf stars.

YOUTHFUL STARS

16·1. The Birth of Stars. The account of stellar evolution begins
conveniently with structureless interstellar gas. When a denser
cloud develops in the gas and is not considerably heated in the
process, the cloud is likely to condense further under its own gravity
and to break into smaller clouds. The fragmented cloud would be
the beginning of a cluster or an association (16·3) of stars.

Photographs of the Milky Way show small roundish "globules"

of dark material against backgrounds of star-rich regions and of bright nebulosities, such as M 8 (Fig. 16·1). These dark spots, which continue in a sequence of diminishing sizes to the limit of the 200-inch telescope, are viewed with interest as perhaps representing the first visible stages in the formation of stars from nebulae.

FIG. 16·1. Nebula M 8 in Sagittarius. *(Photograph by N. U. Mayall with the Crossley reflector, Lick Observatory)*

An objection to the idea that such protostars can be observed is that stars are likely to form in the interiors of cosmic clouds, where they would be concealed by dust in the clouds. Exceptions are considered possible, however, when the most massive stars of a very young group have already become hot blue stars. The intense radiations of these stars may have dispersed enough of the dust around the group so that the redder members can be seen still forming within the cloud. This seems to be the case with the T Tauri stars.

16·2. The T Tauri Stars were so named after the prototype by A. H. Joy, who in 1945 first recognized them in considerable numbers in a clouded area of Taurus. Now observed in other heavily obscured regions of the Milky Way as well, these yellow and red stars are irregularly variable in brightness. Their spectra are characterized by strong bright lines of various elements superposed on ordinary dark-line patterns. In some cases the stars illuminate portions of the surrounding clouds, producing fan-shaped reflection nebulae which may be variable in brightness and appearance.

Young stars very recently formed in the clouds, the T Tauri stars are believed to vary in brightness and to have bright lines in their spectra because of the instability of extreme youth rather more than by their interaction with the dust grains of the clouds. A few such stars appear in the photographs in places where no stars were previously observed; these may have been revealed lately by rapid thinning of the dust in front of them.

16·3. Associations of Young Stars. Several years ago, V. A. Ambartsumian called attention to groups of type O and B stars, which he called *associations,* in nebulous regions of the Milky Way. The stars of each group are not held together firmly enough by mutual gravitation to prevent their dispersal by separate motions in different directions. Evidently the groups are so young that they have not had time to disperse. Some associations, studied especially by Adriaan Blaauw and W. W. Morgan at Yerkes Observatory, are definitely spreading from centers where they must have originated.

Blaauw was first concerned with the proper motions and radial velocities of 17 stars of the Zeta Persei association, named after its brightest member. He found that stars of this group, at the distance of 520 light years from us, are moving at the rate of 14 km/sec away from the center where they were born only 1.3 million years ago. It came as a surprise that cosmic evolution could proceed so rapidly.

Blaauw and Morgan have reported a remarkable expansion of an association centered in Orion at the distance of 1300 light years. The stars here are withdrawing generally at the rate of about 8 km/sec, so that they must have started out 2.8 million years ago. Two of them, AE Aurigae and Mu Columbae, however, have speeds of 130 km/sec. These and possibly a third star, 53 Arietis, have already moved out of Orion into neighboring constellations.

The type O9 star AE Aurigae has reached the vicinity of the nebula IC 450, which it is now illuminating. An unusual feature, described by G. H. Herbig, is that part of the nebula gives an emission spectrum, as would be expected from the presence of the very hot star, whereas another part gives a reflection spectrum and has more nearly the color of the star itself. It would seem that there has not

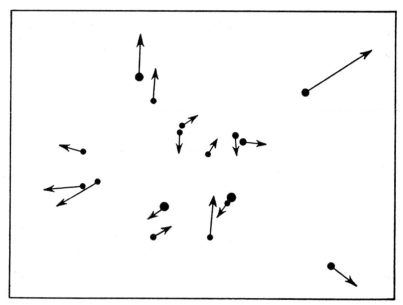

FIG. 16·3. Expansion of Zeta Persei Association. Arrows show directions and amounts of proper motions of the stars during the next 500,000 years. (*Diagram by Adriaan Blaauw*)

been time enough since the star came near the nebula for the radiations of the star to complete the dispersal of the nebular dust.

16·4. Arrival at the Main Sequence. When the contracting stars of a cluster or an association have begun to shine, they move to the left in the color-magnitude diagram until they reach the main sequence. The stars are brighter and attain higher surface temperatures as their masses are greater. Thus they array themselves along this diagonal band in order of mass, the most massive stars at the blue end and the least massive at the red end.

The time required for the development of the stars of a group also depends on the masses. The more massive blue stars may arrive at the main sequence only a few hundred thousand years after their births; these hot stars have presumably blown away enough dust from around the group so that we are able to look into the cloud and see how the other stars are progressing. The least massive stars may require many million years to arrive at the sequence. Thus in some very young clusters the blue stars are already settled in the sequence, while the other stars are still approaching it.

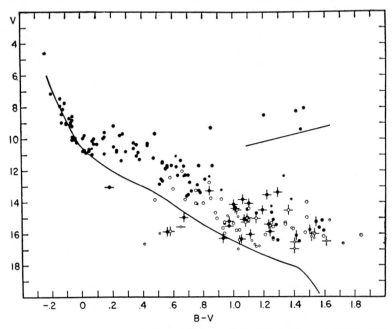

Fig. 16·4. Color-Apparent Magnitude Diagram of Cluster NGC 2264. The bluest stars have arrived before the others at the standard main sequence represented by the curve. (*Diagram by Merle F. Walker*)

This recently recognized effect is shown in Fig. 16·4 for the very young cluster NGC 2264 in Monoceros, near the central line of the Milky Way about 15° east of Betelgeuse and 2800 light years distant from us. The points representing the blue stars appear on the main sequence, whereas those for the yellow and red stars depart abruptly to the right from the standard sequence at type A0 and tend to lie about 2 magnitudes above the curve. Many of the latter are variable stars of the T Tauri type, according to Walker.

16·5. The Stable Main-Sequence Stars. Contraction is halted when the stars reach the main sequence. This process, which was regarded in earlier theories as the main source of stellar energy, is inadequate to supply the stars during their long lives. Contraction suffices in the present account to heat the stars to central temperatures that are high enough to initiate the fusion of lighter chemical elements into heavier ones. Atomic syntheses then become the source of stellar energy and continue to be until the stars' supplies of atomic — fuel are exhausted.

Main-sequence stars are stable for a time, neither contracting nor expanding. They accordingly vary little in size, temperature, and brightness. Consider the sun as an example.

At any level in its interior the sun is in mechanical equilibrium; the weight of overlying gas is just supported by the upward push of the gas pressure at that level. Because the gas pressure depends on the temperature of the gas, among other factors, the temperature becomes known when the other necessary information is available. Obtained in this way, the sun's present central temperature is 15 million degrees centigrade. Another form of balance in the sun concerns its shining. The rate of radiation of energy from the sun's surface is 5 followed by 23 ciphers horsepower. In order to preserve the mechanical balance, this must also be the rate at which energy is provided in the hot core of the sun. As soon as the sun reached the main sequence, the central temperature became high enough to promote the fusion of hydrogen into helium with the release of energy at the required constant rate.

THE STARS IN MIDDLE AGE

16·6. Fusion of Hydrogen into Helium. The relative weight of the nucleus of a hydrogen atom is 1.0076 and that of a helium atom is 4.003. The electrons normally associated with atoms need not be taken into account here, because these atoms are stripped of their electrons in the hot interiors of stars. When four hydrogen atoms unite to form one helium nucleus, seven tenths of one per cent of the original mass is left over. The excess mass is converted into energy. By the relativity theory, the amount of energy (in ergs) released equals the mass (in grams) of the excess material multiplied by the square of the speed of light (in centimeters a second). Calculation by this formula shows that enough energy is thereby made available to keep the sun shining at the present rate if 700 million tons of hydrogen gas are converted each second to

695 tons of helium in the sun's interior. This colossal consumption is trivial compared with the vast supply of hydrogen in the sun.

Two possible processes by which hydrogen may be fused into helium in the sun and stars were explained, in 1938, by the physicist H. A. Bethe. One of these, known as the *carbon cycle*, because carbon serves as a catalyst to promote it, becomes effective in stars hotter than the sun. The second process, known as the proton-proton reaction, is considered more appropriate at the central temperatures of the sun and the main-sequence stars redder than the sun.

In the *proton-proton reaction* in a form somewhat different than in the original proposal, six protons, or normal hydrogen nuclei, unite successively in the sun to form a helium nucleus, leaving the two unused protons to go back into circulation. The excess mass in the four protons employed is released as energy, which is carried up to the sun's surface to contribute to the sunshine.

16·7. Evolution from the Main Sequence. While the hydrogen in the hot core of a star is being converted more and more to helium, the core contracts and grows hotter, and a new balance requires that the outer layers of the star expand. The star becomes brighter and redder, moving away from the main sequence. The evolution is more rapid for the blue stars, which consume their fuel at a faster rate, than for the redder stars. We have noted this effect in the diagrams of galactic clusters and have seen how the main sequence disappears progressively from left to right as the clusters are older.

When the hydrogen in the core of the star is nearly exhausted, the interior has become hot enough so that its fusion extends to outer layers and goes on at a furious rate. Presently the star reaches the climax of its luminous career as a red giant. All its hydrogen fuel is then nearly consumed; and if it is not considerably more massive than the sun, the star with its maximum central temperature of 100 million degrees C has not become hot enough for the synthesis of helium to heavier elements. Its only recourse is to contract, which it continues to do until the white dwarf stage is reached.

The diagram of Fig. 16·7 shows the probable evolution tracks of stars of the globular cluster M 3 since they withdrew from the main sequence more than 5 billion years ago. Stars originally a little bluer than the sun are now red giants, and those that were still bluer are presumably moving to the left in the diagram or have already declined to become white dwarf stars in the lower left corner. Mean-

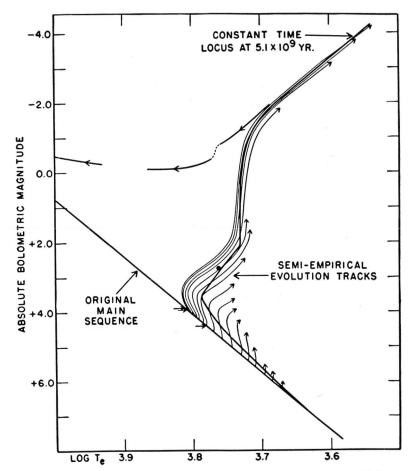

FIG. 16·7.   Semiempirical Evolution Tracks of Stars in the Globular
Cluster M 3.   Values of log T_e correspond to the following spectral types:
3.9 to A5, 3.8 to F5, 3.7 to K0 for the main sequence and G0 for giants,
3.6 to K5 for the main sequence and K0 for giants.   (*Diagram by Allan
Sandage*)

while, the cluster stars that were similar to or redder than the sun
have not yet risen far above the main sequence.

16·8. The Life of the Sun.   As an example of the evolution of a
star of moderate mass, Allan Sandage has predicted the future of the
sun and its effect on the earth.   He makes the reasonable assumption
that the sun's evolutionary track in the temperature-luminosity dia-

gram of Fig. 16·8 should closely resemble the color-magnitude diagram for the stars of comparable mass in the cluster M 67 (Fig. 15·5).

The sun today is approaching middle age; it has brightened only
slightly in the 5 or 6 billion years since it left the main sequence
and will continue to brighten moderately for 6 billion years more.
Life on the earth should go on in reasonable comfort to the end of

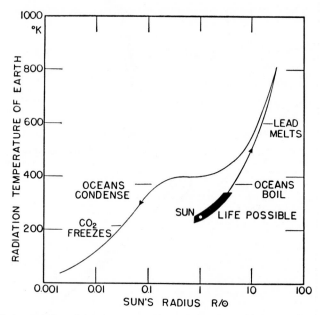

FIG. 16·8. Predicted Variation in the Earth's Radiation Temperature as
Evolution Alters the Sun's Radius. Temperature is on the absolute centigrade scale. (*Diagram by Allan Sandage*)

that period, as far as this effect is concerned. Thereafter, the sun
will begin to consume its remaining hydrogen so rapidly that in the
following 500 million years the temperature on the earth will rise
500° C. The oceans will boil away, lead will melt here, and "conditions will be miserable," as Sandage remarks. At its maximum the
sun will appear as a red globe in the sky 30 times its present diameter.

With little available fuel remaining, the sun will then decline
rapidly, moving to the left and down in the diagram. Water on
the earth will condense again to form oceans; these will soon freeze
and carbon dioxide will freeze as well. The sun will end its visible
life as a white dwarf star, according to this prediction, having a

higher surface temperature for a long time than that of the present sun but a diameter more nearly like that of the earth. The sunshine will be less than a thousandth as bright as it is now, and the temperature at the earth's surface will be more like the present low temperature at the surface of Neptune.

16·9. Evolution of More Massive Stars. All yellow and red main-sequence stars are expected to follow about the same track of evolution that we have traced for the sun. Stars considerably bluer and more massive than the sun will have shorter active lives. The most massive ones will exhaust their supplies of fuel in scarcely more than a million years. We have seen how they have already broken away from the main sequence in very young clusters such as the double cluster in Perseus.

The middle stages in the lives of blue main-sequence stars are likely to be more spectacular than in the case of the sun, because they attain higher temperatures. These stars at their hottest may continue the building of chemical elements beyond helium and may return much of their material to the cosmic clouds by powerful explosions and by other less violent means.

16·10. Synthesis of Heavier Elements. Two recent theories of how the chemical elements originated have been of special interest. In the first theory, George Gamow and associates suppose that before the stars were born the elements were built up from neutrons in the course of half an hour in the very hot and dense early stages of the expanding universe. The second theory, as described by W. A. Fowler and associates, supposes that helium is synthesized from hydrogen in evolving stars and that the process is extended to the forming of heavier elements in the more massive stars.

The later theory supposes that the fusion of helium atoms into those of heavier elements begins in the core of the more massive star when it attains a temperature of 150 million degrees centigrade. At this temperature three helium nuclei can be forced together to form a carbon nucleus, which in turn may capture helium nuclei to produce successively oxygen, neon, and perhaps magnesium.

When the supply of helium in the core of the star is nearly exhausted, the core contracts and grows hotter, extending the combustion of helium into the mantle. The outer layers expand and the star brightens until it becomes a supergiant. At a central temperature of 5 billion degrees the building of elements should go as far as iron, the final synthesis that can release energy for the star's radiation. The synthesis of elements heavier than iron might then be accomplished, as in the Gamow theory, by successive captures of neutrons that were released abundantly in the preceding processes; it could possibly be extended to the heaviest known elements by use of the great energy provided by the explosions of supernovae. Explosions of great violence are known to produce the heaviest elements. As an example, traces of the very heavy element californium were identified in the residue of a thermonuclear explosion in the Bikini tests of 1952.

Thus, according to the theory, atoms of heavier chemical elements have been and will continue to be formed from lighter atoms in the evolving stars.

16·11. Return of Material to Cosmic Clouds. In the course of their lifetimes the stars return to the interstellar clouds much of the material they originally acquired from the clouds. As examples, the supernovae may blow out more than the sun's mass of gas at a single explosion. The normal novae eject much less material on each occasion, but they explode much more frequently. The expanding planetary nebulae and the red supergiants are important contributors. In the average a star jettisons half its original mass during its lifetime. The other half remains when the white dwarf stage is reached.

In the exchange of material between the clouds and stars, the clouds are becoming more complex chemically as the galaxy grows older. The stars of successive generations formed in the clouds contain a greater percentage of metallic gases compared with those of the lightest elements. All in all, as J. L. Greenstein remarks, a good case can be made for systematic change in the relative abundances of the elements.

It is convenient to suppose the first-generation stars were originally of pure hydrogen. A second-generation star might also contain helium, carbon, oxygen, and nitrogen, but no metals; however, no relic of either type is known. The sun would be at least a third-generation star, having all the elements heavier than hydrogen and helium as impurities. Although its age may be as much as 6 billion years, the sun is younger than the stars formed near the beginning of the metal-building process.

THE DECLINING STARS

16·12. Collapse of Old Stars. When a star has nearly exhausted all its available fuel, the cooling gas in its interior no longer has enough outward pressure to support the weight of the gas above. The star accordingly begins to contract. For a time the additional heat produced by contraction raises the temperature of its diminishing radiating surface. From its place as a red giant in the color-magnitude diagram the star moves rapidly to the left, becoming yellow and then blue until it arrives in the vicinity of the main sequence.

The account of the declining period of the evolution is incomplete. It seems probable, however, that the star would then quickly collapse with repeated explosions until it reaches the white dwarf stage. This part of the decline may be illustrated by the recent behavior of the star WZ Sagittae, which flared out as a nova-like star in 1913 and again in 1946. It is now a white dwarf, having about a hundredth of the luminosity of the sun.

16·13. White Dwarf Stars have diameters comparable with that of the earth, and masses averaging half the mass of the sun. They are globes of highly compressed gas that may be a million times as dense as the sun, aside from a less dense 65-mile envelope and a

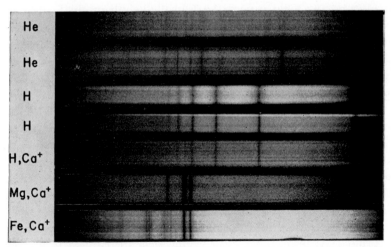

Fig. 16·13. Spectra of White Dwarf Stars. From the ultraviolet at the left to Hβ at the right. Chemical elements prominently represented in the spectra are denoted at the left. (*Photographs by Jesse L. Greenstein*)

surrounding atmosphere. Although they comprise 3 per cent of the stars in the galaxy, they are so faint that only a few hundred have been identified, many of these in the searches of W. J. Luyten.

Examples of white dwarfs are the faint companions of Sirius and Procyon. Another is a companion of the star 40 Eridani; D. M. Popper has observed that the lines in the spectrum of this star are shifted to the red by an amount that agrees well with the shift predicted by the theory of relativity for this very dense star.

The spectra of 50 white dwarfs have been photographed with the Hale telescope by J. L. Greenstein. Some spectra show only helium, others only hydrogen, others only a few metallic lines, and still others no visible lines at all. There is no relation between the spectrum patterns and the colors, as with normal stars.

The white dwarf stars, which are also yellow and even reddish, form a sequence below the main sequence in the color-magnitude diagram. They move very slowly to the right along their sequence as they cool, without any reduction in their diameters. Martin Schwarzschild has said that a white dwarf requires 8 billion years to cool from the initial blue stage to the red stage and from there a longer interval before it ceases to shine. It may be that our galaxy is not yet old enough to possess a single "black dwarf."

16·14. The Present Theory of stellar evolution resembles earlier ones in tracing a star from its birth in the nebulae to its final luminous stage as one of the densest known stars. Contraction remains the principal process in youthful stars; it is further introduced at critical periods in the star's middle age, when the supply of available fuel runs low, and it becomes the principal process again during the initial stages of the star's old age.

Novel features of the present theory are noted particularly in the intermediate stages of the star's career. The spectacular evolution from the main sequence to the giant stage was made reasonable by the discovery of the vast amounts of energy released in atomic transformations. This part of the account receives strong support from the observed evolution in star clusters. Another novelty appears in the very extended duration of the white dwarf stage.

The picture of a universe of stars that emerges from hydrogen gas and ends in a cinder heap would seem incomplete to anyone who may prefer the idea of an eternally active universe. If the universe can somehow wind itself periodically, however, the remark that "in the beginning was hydrogen" would refer simply to a convenient starting place in an unending process.

16·15. Origin of a Planetary System. The problem of how a planetary system may evolve around a star relates specifically to the solar system as the only known system of its kind. Theories offered as possible solutions of the problem have appeared in the course of the past two centuries. Prominent among the early theories was the *nebular hypothesis* proposed by the French mathematician and astronomer P. S. Laplace in 1796. An example of the recent theories is the *protoplanet hypothesis* offered by the American astronomer Gerard P. Kuiper in 1951. In both accounts the solar system evolved from a nebula surrounding a primitive sun.

The nebular hypothesis described how the planetary system might have resulted from the contraction of the solar nebula. The process was intended to produce a system having the regularities we have noted (7·21) and to which only a few important exceptions were then detected. The protoplanet hypothesis involves the fracturing of the nebula; it undertakes to reproduce the more complex system known today and to explain the many departures from the regularities, particularly among the less massive members of the system.

A dozen satellites in the solar system are "irregular." Their orbits are more inclined to the ecliptic or are more eccentric, or both, than the others. Half of these have direct and half have retrograde revolutions around their primaries. The theory supposes that these satellites escaped from their planets and were subsequently recaptured or else returned close enough to be diverted into orbits very different from their original ones. Kuiper believes that Hidalgo and the Trojan asteroids were formerly satellites of Jupiter and that Pluto belonged to Neptune.

Many scientists suppose that the process which produced the planetary system around the sun could operate frequently throughout the universe.

QUESTIONS ON CHAPTER 16

1. State the possible observational evidence that stars are condensing from the cosmic clouds.

2. Define: T Tauri stars. What seems to be their place in stellar evolution?

3. How may the age of an association of stars be determined? Describe two examples of such associations.

4. Why do youthful stars array themselves on the main sequence in order of their masses?

5. State the evidence that the more massive stars of a youthful group arrive on the main sequence in advance of the less massive stars.

6. Explain that fusion of hydrogen into helium in the interior of a star can supply its energy for a very long time.

7. Trace the evolution from the main sequence of a star of moderate mass, such as the sun, according to the present theory.

8. Trace the more extensive synthesis of chemical elements suggested for more massive stars.

9. Explain how repeated interaction between stars and cosmic clouds may enrich the chemical constitution of successive generations of stars.

10. In what respects do white dwarf stars differ from other types of stars? Give reasons for supposing that they represent final stages in the lives of stars.

REFERENCES

Rush, J. H., *The Dawn of Life.* Hanover House, Garden City, N. Y., 1957.
Schwarzschild, Martin, *Structure and Evolution of the Stars.* Princeton University Press, Princeton, 1958.

17

THE GALAXY

THE MILKY WAY — STRUCTURE OF THE GALAXY — RADIO
RECEPTION FROM THE GALAXY

The *galactic system,* or system of the Milky Way, is so named because the luminous band of the Milky Way around the heavens is an impressive feature of the system in our view from inside it. This spiral stellar system, of which the sun is a member, is commonly known as *the galaxy* as distinguished from the multitudes of exterior galaxies.

THE MILKY WAY

17·1. The Milky Way of Summer. The full splendor of the Milky Way is reserved for one who observes on a clear moonless night from a place removed from artificial lights. The view with the unaided eye or with a very wide-angle camera is best for the general features. Photographs show the details more clearly than the eye alone can detect them. An excellent collection of photographs with a 5-inch Ross camera is available in the *Atlas of the Northern Milky Way,* prepared by F. E. Ross and Mary R. Calvert. More recent and more penetrating photographs north of declination −27° are those of the National Geographic Society—Palomar Observatory Sky Survey. These are pairs of negative prints in blue and red light made with the 48-inch Schmidt telescope (5·9).

The Milky Way is produced by the combined light of great numbers of stars that are not separately visible without the telescope. Its central line is nearly a great circle of the celestial sphere, so highly inclined to the celestial equator that it takes quite different positions in our skies in the early evenings of the different seasons.

At nightfall in the late summer in middle northern latitudes the Milky Way arches overhead from the northeast to the southwest horizon. It extends upward through Perseus, Cassiopeia, and Cepheus to the region of the Northern Cross (Fig. 11·12). Here in Cygnus the Great Rift formed by cosmic dust clouds divides the Milky Way apparently into two parallel streams, which go on southward through Aquila into Sagittarius and Scorpius. This spectacu-

Fig. 17·1. The Milky Way from Scutum to Scorpius. The Scutum star cloud is near the upper left corner, and the Sagittarius star cloud is near the center. (*Mount Wilson Observatory photograph*)

lar part of the Milky Way (Fig. 17·1) contains the bright star clouds of Scutum and Sagittarius; the latter is near the direction of the center of the galaxy.

17·2. The Milky Way of Winter. In the early evenings of late winter in our latitudes the Milky Way again arches overhead, now from northwest to southeast. It passes through Cepheus, Cassiopeia, Perseus, and Auriga, which is near the zenith in the early evenings of February. Here it is narrowed by a succession of relatively nearby dust clouds, which angle from northern Cassiopeia through Auriga to southern Taurus. The Milky Way then continues on past Gemini, Orion, and Canis Major, where it becomes broader and less noticeably obscured by dust.

FIG. 17·2. Region of the Southern Cross. The Cross and the Coalsack are near the center. The bright stars at the extreme left are Alpha and Beta Centauri. (*Photographed by Margaret Harwood*)

The part of the Milky Way in the vicinity of the south celestial pole is either out of sight or else never rises high enough for favorable view in the United States. This region from Centaurus to Carina (Fig. 17·2) contains some fine star clouds and the dark Coalsack near the Southern Cross.

17·3. Galactic Longitude and Latitude. In descriptions of the galaxy it is convenient to denote positions in the heavens with reference to the Milky Way. For this purpose an additional system of circles of the celestial sphere is defined as follows.

The north and south *galactic poles* are the two opposite points that are farthest from the central line of the Milky Way. By international agreement they are respectively in right ascension $12^h 49^m$, declination +27°.4 (1950), in Coma Berenices, and 0ʰ 49ᵐ. −27°.4, south of Beta Ceti. Halfway between these poles, the *galactic equator* is a great circle inclined 63° to the celestial equator; it crosses the equator northward in Aquila and southward at the opposite point east of Orion. The galactic equator passes nearest the north celestial pole in Cassiopeia and nearest the south celestial pole in the region of the Southern Cross. Thus the earth's equator is inclined 63° to the principal plane of the flattened galaxy.

Galactic longitude was formerly measured in degrees along the galactic equator from its intersection with the celestial equator in Aquila, near R.A. 18ʰ 40ᵐ. By decision of the International Astronomical Union in 1958, the zero of galactic longitude is now changed to the direction of the galactic center (17·5), on the revised galactic equator in R.A. 17ʰ 42ᵐ.4, Decl. −28° 55′ (1950), in Sagittarius. As before, the longitude is measured through 360° in the counterclockwise direction as viewed from the north galactic pole; the new value equals the former one plus about 32°.

Galactic latitude is measured from 0° at the galactic equator to 90° at its poles and is positive toward the north galactic pole. Its present reckoning differs from the former one because of recent slight revision of the position assigned to the galactic equator. Possible confusion will be avoided in the following sections by specifying in each case whether the galactic coordinates are given in the old or the new systems.

STRUCTURE OF THE GALAXY

The galaxy is an assemblage of the order of 100,000 million stars together with much gas and dust. Its spheroidal central region is surrounded by a flat disk of stars at least 80,000 light years in diameter, in which spiral arms of stars, gas, and dust are embedded. The center of the galaxy is about 30,000 light years from the sun in the direction of Sagittarius. The disk of the galaxy is rotating around an axis joining the galactic poles with speeds that diminish as the distance from the center is greater. Surrounding the disk is a more slowly rotating and more nearly spherical halo containing scattered stars and the globular clusters.

17·4. The Disk of the Galaxy. The stars are concentrated toward the Milky Way. Stars visible to the unaided eye are 3 or 4 times as numerous around the galactic equator as they are in similar areas near its poles; and the corresponding increase for large telescopes exceeds 40-fold, despite the greater obscuration by cosmic dust in the lower latitudes. This shows that the majority of the stars of our galaxy are assembled in a relatively thin disk along the

FIG. 17·4. The Southern Milky Way from Sagittarius to Crux. The total field is 140° in diameter and is centered on the star Antares. (*Photographed by Arthur D. Code at Bloemfontein, South Africa, with a Greenstein-Henyey wide-angle camera*)

plane of the galactic equator. When we look in the direction of this equator, we are looking the longest way out through the disk and therefore at many more stars.

The flat disk is estimated as 80,000 light years in diameter; its thickness is at least 10,000 light years at the center and 5000 light years at the sun's distance from the center. Present values of these and other dimensions in the galaxy are subject to considerable uncertainty. The view from our place inside the galaxy is less favorable for precise measurements than would be possible from outside.

Part of the available data is still inferred from studies of exterior galaxies, particularly the great spiral in Andromeda, which seems to resemble our own galaxy in structure.

17·5. The Galactic Center. The position of the center of the galaxy was first announced by Harlow Shapley in 1917. He had determined the position of the center of the system of globular clusters that form a nearly spherical halo around the disk of the galaxy, and had reasoned correctly that this must be the position of the galactic center itself. The direction originally assigned to the center in the former coordinate system was in galactic longitude 325°, latitude 0°, in Sagittarius. Shapley pointed out that the correctness of the position is indicated by the greater brightness and complexity of the Milky Way in this region.

As defined by international agreement in 1958, the direction of the galactic center is remarkably close to the original one. It is situated in Sagittarius in R.A. $17^h 42^m.4$, Decl. $-28°$ 55′ (1950), or in former galactic longitude 327°.7, latitude $-1°.4$, and is taken as the new zero of galactic longitude (17·3). The position of the galactic center in space is about 30,000 light years from the sun. Thus the sun is situated in the disk of the galaxy more than halfway from the center to the edge in the direction of the constellation Auriga.

17·6. The Central Region is a spheroidal concentration of stars and gas, having a diameter of 10,000 light years or more in the principal plane of the galaxy. Here the stars are spaced rather uniformly and considerably closer than in the surrounding disk. This area of the heavens near the borders of Sagittarius, Scorpius, and Ophiuchus would be remarkably bright if most of the central region were not concealed from ordinary observation by the heavy dust clouds of the Great Rift. The Sagittarius star cloud is an exposed portion.

Radiation from the central region was recorded through the dust by Joel Stebbins and A. E. Whitford, who scanned this part of the heavens with a photoelectric cell and infrared filter at the focus of the 60-inch Mount Wilson telescope. They found the area of the most intense radiation extending 8° in galactic longitude and rather more than half as far in latitude. Infrared photographs (Fig. 17·6) show the brightest region in general agreement with the photoelectric sweeps.

FIG. 17·6. Central Region of the Galaxy in Infrared Light. (*Photograph by Jean Dufay, Haute Provence Observatory, France*)

17·7. The Spiral Structure Traced by Photography. After the existence of exterior spiral and associated galaxies had been demonstrated by Hubble, in 1924, the frequent opinion that our own galaxy might be a spiral remained without firm observational support for more than a quarter of a century. The first definite evidence of spiral structure in the galaxy was announced in 1951 by W. W. Morgan, Stewart Sharpless, and D. E. Osterbrock at Yerkes Observatory. They employed as indicators of such structure the emission nebulae, which had proved to be abundant in the arms of the Andromeda spiral.

The photographs for locating emission nebulae in the Milky Way were taken with a Greenstein-Henyey wide-angle camera having a filter for transmitting the red light of hydrogen from the nebulae. The positions of the nebulae in the sky and their distances from us permitted the tracing in space of two lengths of arms and the suggestion of a third. The three with the names originally assigned them are as follows.

The *Orion arm* passes near the sun. It contains the Orion nebula, the North America nebula in Cygnus, and the dust clouds of the Great Rift and the Coalsack. Some radio astronomers have renamed this long length of arm the Carina-Cygnus arm and have regarded the Orion portion as one of its spurs. Outside the first arm, the *Perseus arm* passes about 7000 light years from the sun; it contains the double cluster in Perseus. The *Sagittarius arm* is nearer the center than the sun's distance. Not well placed for ob-

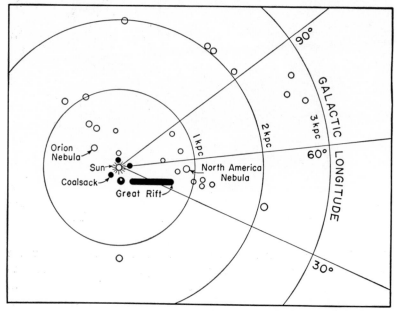

Fig. 17·7. Parts of Spiral Arms of the Galaxy. Traced by directions and distances of emission nebulae. The galactic longitudes may be corrected to the present system by adding 32° to each value. (*Adapted from a model by W. W. Morgan, Stewart Sharpless, and D. E. Osterbrock, Yerkes Observatory*)

servation in northern latitudes, its tracing was extended photographically and later with the radio telescope by observers in the southern hemisphere.

Optical tracing of the arms of the galaxy is made difficult by the obscuring dust of the Milky Way. The tracing of the spiral pattern has since been extended by radio reception (17·13), which is not hampered by intervening dust.

17·8. Stellar Populations in the Galaxy. The stellar populations I and II originally proposed by Baade (15·11) comprised the younger and older stars, respectively. Meanwhile, the theory of stellar evolution has developed far enough to suggest the choice of a greater number of gradations, the precise number being a matter of convenience. The following sequence of five types of population in the galaxy with respect to increasing age of the stars was offered for consideration by a conference of astronomers at Rome in 1957.

1. *Extreme population I.* This very young population is contained in the spiral arms, and around the galactic center as well, where much gas and dust is still uncondensed into stars. Its brightest members are blue supergiant stars, such as Rigel, only a few million years old.

2. *Intermediate population I* comprises somewhat older stars, such as Sirius, situated near the principal plane of the galaxy but not confined to the arms.

3. *Disk population.* The majority of the stars between the arms and many in the central region of the galaxy belong to this type; they range from 3 to 5 billion years in age. The sun is believed to be a member.

4. *Intermediate population II* comprises many older stars in the halo and central region of the galaxy.

5. *Extreme population II,* the oldest population, is represented by the globular clusters of the halo and separate stars there that may have escaped from the clusters. An age of at least 7 or 8 billion years is assigned to this group.

17·9. Differential Effect of the Galactic Rotation. The flattened form of the galaxy suggests its rotation around a line joining the galactic poles. The manner of rotation must be somewhere between the following extremes: (1) If its material were distributed uniformly, the galaxy would rotate like a rigid body. All parts would go around in the same period, and the linear speed of the rotation would increase in direct proportion to the distance from the center. (2) If the material were concentrated mainly near the center, the rotation would resemble the revolution of the planetary system around the sun. By Kepler's third law, the speed of the rotation would be inversely proportional to the square root of the distance from the center. Thus the speed would diminish as the distance from the center is greater.

In the planetary type of rotation, stars nearer the center than the sun's distance are overtaking the sun and passing on ahead, whereas stars farther from the center than the sun's distance keep falling behind us. As is seen in Fig. 17·9, stars around galactic longitude 45° and 225°, reckoned from the direction of the center, would have the greatest observed velocities of recession, and those around longitudes 135° and 315° would have the greatest observed velocities of approach.

This effect was first reported by J. H. Oort, in 1927, from his analysis of radial velocities of stars in the Milky Way within a few thousand light years from the sun. The result established the

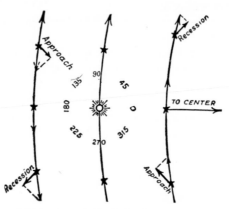

FIG. 17·9. Effect of Rotation of the Galactic System on the Radial Velocities of Stars. Stars nearer the center than the sun's distance are going around faster and are passing by the sun. Stars farther from the center are moving more slowly and are falling behind the sun. Thus stars around longitudes 45° and 225° greater than that of the center are receding from the sun, and stars around 135° and 315° are approaching the sun.

planetary type of rotation in our vicinity in the galaxy, and later provided the means of determining the distances in radio tracing of the spiral arms (17·13).

17·10. Rotation of the Galaxy. The direction of the galactic rotation is clockwise as viewed from the north galactic pole. As we look toward the center in Sagittarius, the direction of the rotation between us and the center is toward the left. The period of the rotation is believed to be about the same throughout the central region of the galaxy and to become greater with increasing distance out through the disk. The period at the sun's distance is of the order of 200 million years.

The sun's velocity in the rotation is generally taken to be 134 miles a second toward galactic longitude 90° in Cygnus. This is the velocity determined by Leiden radio astronomers in 1954, based

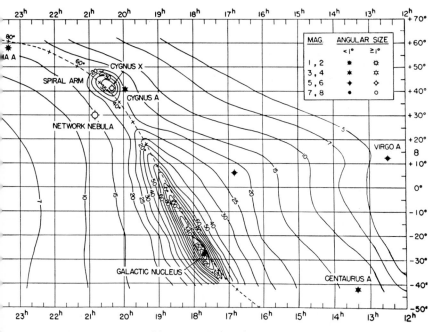

(H. C. Ko and J. D. Kraus, Ohio State University)

available as radio indicators of the arms after the detection of emission from neutral hydrogen at the wavelength of 21 cm. Two extensive surveys with radio telescopes around this wavelength have between them scanned the entire course of the Milky Way. The first of these was reported by H. C. van de Hulst, C. A. Muller, and J. H. Oort, in Holland in 1954, from their records with the 25-foot radio telescope at Kootwijk. The second survey was made by the Radiophysics Laboratory in Australia.

The tracing of the arms in space requires the direction and distance from us of each indicator that is observed. As an example of how it is done, consider a particular pointing of the radio telescope toward the galactic equator in longitude 80° by the former reckoning, or 112° from the galactic center, in Cassiopeia. The hydrogen clouds here are relatively approaching the sun in the rotation of the galaxy (Fig. 17·9). As the distances of the clouds are greater, their speeds of approach are greater, and accordingly the Doppler shift of their 21-cm radiation toward shorter wavelengths increases. Thus by tuning the radio telescope first to 21 cm and then to shorter wavelengths successively, the survey reaches

farther and farther in this direction. Where the signal becomes
most intense, there is one point in a hydrogen lane of a spiral arm.

The line profile of Fig. 17·13 recorded by the radio telescope in
this direction has three maxima at increasing negative radial velocities, toward the left in the diagram, corresponding to distances from
the sun of about 1600, 10,000, and 25,000 light years, respectively.

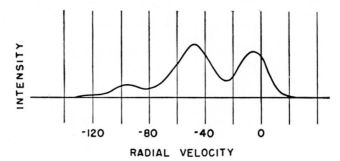

FIG. 17·13. Line Profile of Radio Emission by Neutral Hydrogen at 21 cm
in Galactic Longitude 80° by the Former Reckoning. The maxima represent, from right to left, three hydrogen lanes at increasing distances from
us. (*Diagram by C. A. Muller and G. Westerhout, Leiden Observatory*)

These determine a point in space in each of three lanes. Other directions of the telescope locate other points, until the hydrogen
lanes defined by the points may be plotted as they are in Fig. 17·14.

17·14. The Spiral Structure. The hydrogen lanes of the galactic
arms, as traced in Holland and Australia, are shown in the composite diagram of Fig. 17·14. The center of the galaxy is marked
by a cross and the sun's position by a circle above the cross. Our
view in this diagram is from the north galactic pole from which the
galactic rotation is clockwise. The numbers are galactic longitudes
by the former reckoning.

Of the three hydrogen lanes recorded by the maxima in the line
profile of Fig. 17·13 in the direction of longitude 80°, the first is
the Carina-Cygnus arm, which includes the sun, the second is the
Perseus arm, and the third suggests a more remote arm. The lane
tangent to the 18° direction from the sun is the Sagittarius arm.
Both the Carina-Cygnus and the Sagittarius arms are nearer the
center at the right than at the left, suggesting that these are spiral
arms and are trailing in the rotation. The Perseus arm, however,
seems more nearly circular at the present stage of the tracing.

A significant addition to the radio picture of the galaxy is recorded by the observers in Holland with their newer 82-foot paraboloid at Dwingeloo.   The radio source Sagittarius A around the galactic

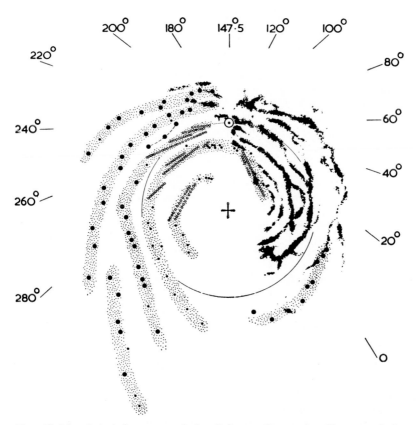

FIG. 17·14.   Spiral Structure of the Galaxy.   Composite diagram of the radio pattern of hydrogen lanes traced at Leiden (right) and at Sydney (left).   The numbers are the former galactic longitudes; these may be converted to longitudes from the galactic center by adding 32° to each. (*Diagram by J. L. Pawsey, Radiophysics Laboratory, Sydney, Australia*)

center is a region of neutral hydrogen 2° in diameter enclosing a few clouds of ionized hydrogen.   Gas streams are moving outward from here with speeds of from 50 to 200 km/sec and are also turning in the general rotation of the galaxy.   At 12,000 light years from the center, many youthful stars are ionizing the gas into a bright ring around the center.   How this gas originates and is being replenished is unknown, unless it keeps falling in from the rare gaseous medium of the galactic halo.

QUESTIONS ON CHAPTER 17

1. Why does the Milky Way have different positions in the sky at the same hour through the year? At what seasons does it pass near the zenith in the early evening in middle northern latitudes?

2. Define the terms: galactic longitude and latitude. Explain the recent change in the reckoning of these coordinates.

3. The appearance of the Milky Way suggests that the galaxy is generally much flattened and that the sun is far from its center. Explain.

4. Describe the following features of the galaxy: (a) the disk; (b) the central region; (c) the spiral arms; (d) the halo.

5. Describe the sun's place in the galaxy and its share in the galactic rotation.

6. State evidence from the radial velocities of stars in the Milky Way that the outer parts of the galaxy rotate more slowly with increasing distance from the center.

7. Explain that stars of the Milky Way having galactic longitudes around 112° greater than that of the center are approaching us in the galactic rotation, and faster as their distances are greater.

8. Describe the optical method of tracing the spiral arms of the galaxy.

9. Describe the radio method of tracing the arms. Why is it more effective than the optical method?

10. Contrast the optical and radio pictures of the heavens.

REFERENCES

Bok, Bart J., and Priscilla F. Bok, *The Milky Way*. Third edition. Harvard University Press, Cambridge, 1957.

Davies, R. D., and H. P. Palmer, *Radio Studies of the Universe*. D. Van Nostrand Company, Princeton, N. J., 1959.

Pawsey, J. L., and R. N. Bracewell, *Radio Astronomy*. Oxford University Press, New York, 1955.

Pfeiffer, John, *The Changing Universe*. Random House, New York, 1956.

18

THE EXTERIOR GALAXIES

STRUCTURAL FEATURES OF GALAXIES — DISTRIBUTION
OF GALAXIES — SPECTRA OF GALAXIES

Our galaxy is one of the many stellar systems that constitute major building blocks of the physical universe. The galaxies are structurally of three main types: spiral, elliptical, and irregular galaxies. They are assembled in large clusters and also in smaller groups, such as the local group. The redshifts of their spectrum lines, which increase as the galaxies are more remote, are the basis of theories of the expanding universe.

STRUCTURAL FEATURES OF GALAXIES

18·1. The Spiral Galaxy M 31 in Andromeda is the brightest exterior spiral system and is one of the two that are nearest us. Marked in Map 4 with its original designation as the "Great Nebula" in Andromeda, it is visible to the unaided eye as a hazy spot about as long and half as wide as the moon's apparent diameter. Only the central region appears to the eye alone and, for the most part, to the eye at the telescope. Fainter surrounding features come out in the photographs, where the object is shown in its true character as a flat, double-armed spiral inclined 13° from the edgewise presentation.

In the photograph in Fig. 18·1 the tilted nearly circular spiral appears as an oval 3° long. Separate stars in the arms were first observed, in 1924, by Edwin Hubble in his photographs with the 100-inch Mount Wilson telescope. The cepheid variable stars among them served to determine the distance of the spiral and to show it as another galaxy far beyond our own Milky Way.

The lens-shaped central region of the Andromeda spiral is surrounded by a flat disk of stars. Embedded in the disk are the spiral arms, which contain all the features observed in the Milky Way right around us. Young stars, gas, and dust are localized in the arms. Patches of the gas appear as emission nebulae, made luminous

FIG. 18·1. Spiral Galaxy M 31 in Andromeda. One elliptical companion, M 32, appears directly above the central region; the other companion, NGC 205, is at the left. Photographed with the 48-inch Schmidt telescope. (*Mount Wilson and Palomar Observatories photograph*)

by the radiations of blue stars in the vicinities. By their aid Walter Baade with the Hale telescope extended the tracing of the arms beyond their more conspicuous parts, increasing the diameter of the disk to $4\frac{1}{2}°$. At a distance of $1\frac{1}{2}$ million light years from us, the diameter of the Andromeda spiral is 120,000 light years, or half again the diameter often assigned to the disk of our own galaxy. Several hundred globular clusters of stars surround the disk, as they do in the halo around the disk of our galaxy.

18·2. Spiral Galaxies are structurally of two types: normal and barred spirals. *Normal spirals* have lens-shaped central regions, from opposite sides of which the two arms emerge and at once begin to

M 81 in Ursa Major   M 51 in Canes Venatici

Fig. 18·2.   Spiral Galaxies.   (*Mount Wilson Observatory photographs*)

coil around the centers in the same sense and the same plane. They are divided into three classes. *Class Sa* spirals have large central regions and thin, closely coiled arms; an example is NGC 4594 in Virgo (Fig. 18·3). In *class Sb* the centers are smaller, and the arms are larger and wider open; examples are M 31 and our own galaxy. In *class Sc* the centers are smallest, and the arms are largest and most loosely coiled; an example is M 33 in Triangulum (Fig. 18·9).

Barred spirals have their two coils starting abruptly from the ends of a bright bar, which projects from opposite sides of the central region. They are classified in the series *SBa, SBb,* and *SBc,* paralleling the series of normal spirals. Through this series the central region diminishes while the arms build up and unwind. A third and less familiar type of spiral galaxy has its arms beginning tangentially from opposite sides of a bright ring around the center.

Fig. 18·2A. Barred Spiral NGC 1300 in Eridanus. Photographed with the Hale telescope. (*Mount Wilson and Palomar Observatories photograph*)

18·3. Spirals at Different Angles. Spiral galaxies are presented to us in a variety of ways. In the flatwise view they appear nearly circular. M 51 (Fig. 18·2) is an example; it has an irregular companion projected near the end of one arm. When they are moderately inclined to the plane of the sky, as in the cases of M 31 and M 81, another giant, these galaxies appear elliptical. In the edge-

Fig. 18·3. Spiral Galaxy Viewed Nearly Edgewise. NGC 4594 in Virgo. (*Mount Wilson Observatory photograph*)

wise view they are reduced to bright streaks around thicker central regions. Characteristic of the spirals seen on edge is a dark band that sometimes seems to cut them in two; an example is NGC 4594. The dust in their arms obscures their equatorial regions, just as the dust clouds of the Milky Way obstruct our view of what lies beyond.

18·4. Elliptical Galaxies are so named because they appear with the telescope as elliptical disks having various degrees of flattening. They are designated by the letter E followed by a number that is

FIG. 18·4. Elliptical Galaxy NGC 185. Giant red stars are visible in the outer parts. (*Photograph by Walter Baade, Mount Wilson Observatory*)

10 times the value of the ellipticity of the disk. The series runs from the circular *class E0* to the most flattened *E7*, where the object resembles a convex lens viewed on edge. Examples are M 32, the nearly circular class E2 companion of the Andromeda spiral, and the second companion, NGC 205, of class E5.

These are systems of stars, generally dust-free. Almost all the gas and dust available for star-building seems to have been exhausted. Individual red giants, the brightest stars of this older population, are visible in photographs of the nearer elliptical galaxies when they are taken through red filters and with the largest telescopes.

18·5. Structural Sequence of Regular Galaxies. The separate series of elliptical and spiral galaxies are joined in Hubble's diagram (Fig. 18·5) into a structural sequence of all regular systems.

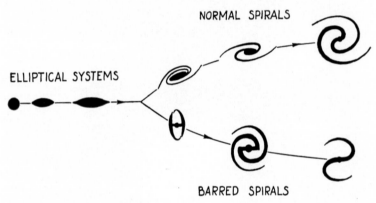

NORMAL SPIRALS

ELLIPTICAL SYSTEMS

BARRED SPIRALS

Fig. 18·5. Structural Sequence of Regular Galaxies. (*Adapted from a diagram by Edwin Hubble*)

Regular galaxies are those having rotational symmetry. The sequence begins at the left with the spherical forms. These become more and more extended around their equators, until thin disks containing spiral patterns begin to appear around them. Here the sequence divides into the two branches of normal and barred spirals. Toward the right the spiral coils gradually unwind, while the central regions become less prominent.

Two additional stages, *classes S0* and *SB0*, not shown in the original diagram, were added later near the point of division of the sequence. They resemble the central regions of spiral galaxies and are now believed to have originated by a catastrophic (18·11) rather than an evolutionary process.

The structural sequence serves as one basis for thinking about the evolution of galaxies. A progression from left to right in the sequence might imply the emergence of the disks and spiral arms from elliptical galaxies. On the other hand, a progression in the opposite direction, suggested by the trend of the stellar compositions of the galaxies (18·14), might imply a gradual collapse of the spirals into the elliptical forms.   As an example of another approach, W. A. Baum's studies suggest that the evolutionary history of a stellar system may be predetermined by its mass and angular momentum. Star formation in smaller systems, such as dwarf elliptical galaxies and globular clusters, came to an early end when its present old stars were born.   It went on in larger ellipticals to include stars now of intermediate age.   It continues in the still larger spiral galaxies to supply young stars in the spiral arms.

18·6. The Magellanic Clouds, named in honor of the navigator Ferdinand Magellan, are the two satellites of our galaxy.   Plainly visible to the unaided eye, they are too close to the south celestial

Fig. 18·6.   Large Magellanic Cloud.   (*Photograph by K. G. Henize*)

pole (Map 6) to be viewed north of the tropical zone.   As they generally appear in the photographs the Clouds have apparent diameters of 12° and 8°.   At nearly the same distance of 150,000 light years, their linear diameters would be 30,000 and 20,000 light

years. However, the neutral hydrogen of both Clouds extends out
much farther than do the stars, and almost runs together, as Australian radio astronomers have reported.

The Clouds have been classed usually with the *irregular galaxies,*
the ragged exterior stellar systems that lack rotational symmetry.
Yet their rotations have been observed with radio telescopes, and in
G. de Vaucouleurs' photographs with a small camera at Mount
Stromlo Observatory they might seem to resemble one-armed barred
spirals. The Large Cloud is presented nearly flatwise to us and the
Small Cloud is inclined 30° from the edgewise presentation, accord-
ing to this observer.

DISTRIBUTION OF GALAXIES

18·7. Their Arrangement in the Sky. The apparent distribution
of the nearer galaxies over the face of the sky is shown in Fig. 18·7.
This diagram resulted from a survey of the brighter galaxies by

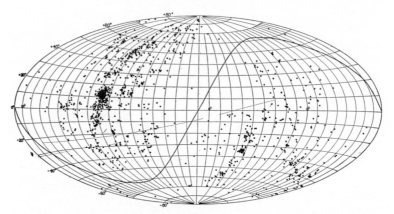

Fɪɢ. 18·7. Distribution of the Brighter Exterior Galaxies. The entire
celestial sphere is represented with the north celestial pole at the top.
The heavy curved line is the galactic equator. (*Harvard Observatory
diagram*)

Harlow Shapley and Adelaide Ames at Harvard Observatory. Few
such objects are visible within 10° from the galactic equator, which
is represented by the heavy curve in the figure; here they are concealed generally behind the dust of the Milky Way. Their numbers
increase toward the galactic poles, where the least amount of dust
intervenes; and the increase would be fairly symmetrical in the two

celestial hemispheres except for the conspicuous Virgo cluster at the left. It was because of the seeming avoidance of the Milky Way that the galaxies were called "extragalactic nebulae" before their true significance was recognized.

The more remote galaxies are similarly arranged in the sky, as was shown by Hubble's more penetrating survey with the Mount Wilson telescopes. If the obscuring dust were not present, the galaxies would be about equally numerous in all regions of the celestial sphere.

18·8. Distance Indicators of Galaxies. The distribution of galaxies in space can be considered when their distances as well as their directions from us are known. The distances were derived in Hubble's pioneer studies in three successive steps: (1) By use of cepheid variable stars that he found in M 31, M 33, and five other relatively nearby galaxies; (2) by observing the apparent magnitudes of what seemed to be the most luminous stars in more remote galaxies, where the cepheids were too faint to be seen; (3) by measuring the apparent brightness of still more distant galaxies, assuming that galaxies of the same class have the same absolute brightness. Later investigations with the 200-inch telescope showed the need for revising the early scale of distances.

One reason for revision was Baade's discovery, in 1952, that the classical cepheids average 1.5 magnitudes more luminous than they were previously supposed to be. On this account and with the availability of the more precise photoelectric standards for the apparent magnitudes, the former values of the distances of most galaxies required multiplication by the factor 3. The distances given in this book contain this revision.

More recently, Sandage pointed out that what seemed with the smaller telescopes to be the brightest stars in intermediate galaxies are in fact frequently small patches of emission nebulae. He estimated that these may appear 1.8 magnitudes brighter than the brightest stars in a particular galaxy. All together, the distances originally assigned to most galaxies may need to be multiplied by a factor as great as 10.

18·9. The Local Group. Our galaxy is a member of a group of at least 17 galaxies that occupy an ellipsoidal volume of space 2 million light years in its longest dimension. Our galaxy is near one end of this diameter and the Andromeda spiral is near the other end.

FIG. 18·9. Spiral Galaxy M 33 in Triangulum. A member of the local group. (*Mount Wilson Observatory photograph*)

These and M 33 in Triangulum are the normal spiral members. The less regular members are the Magellanic Clouds and two smaller ones. The remaining 10 are elliptical galaxies, of which 6 are less populous and fainter than the others. The first known examples of these dwarf ellipticals were discovered at Harvard Observatory in the constellations Sculptor and Fornax; the other four, two in Leo and one apiece in Draco and Ursa Minor, were found more recently in photographs with the Palomar 48-inch Schmidt telescope. The members of the local group are listed in Table 18·I. The Andromeda spiral is the largest of these and our galaxy is second in size. The distances and linear diameters are provisional, subject to possible revisions of the distance scale and of the obscuring effects of intervening dust.

18·10. Clusters of Galaxies are believed to be the rule rather than the exception. They range in population from a very few to several thousand galaxies. As many as 10,000 rich clusters will be listed in Zwicky's new catalog of clusters north of declination −30°, which

TABLE 18·I   THE LOCAL GROUP

Designation	Type	Distance (light years)	Apparent Diameter	Linear Diameter (light years)
Galactic system	Sb	. . . .	. . . . .	80,000
Large Mag. Cloud	I	150,000	12°	30,000
Small Mag. Cloud	I	150,000	8°	20,000
Draco system	E	200,000	31′	2,000
Ursa Minor system	E	200,000	55′	3,000
Sculptor system	E	230,000	45′	3,000
Fornax system	E	460,000	50′	7,000
Leo II system	E	800,000	10′	2,000
NGC 6822	I	950,000	20′	6,000
NGC 185	E	1,100,000	14′.5	5,000
NGC 147	E	1,100,000	14′.1	5,000
Leo I system	E	1,200,000	10′	3,000
IC 1613	I	1,500,000	17′	7,000
M 31	Sb	1,500,000	4°.5	120,000
M 32	E2	1,500,000	12′	5,000
NGC 205	E5	1,500,000	15′.8	7,000
M 33	Sc	1,500,000	62′	30,000

are recognized in yellow-sensitive photographs with the 48-inch Schmidt telescope of Palomar Observatory. A *rich cluster* is here defined as containing more than 50 members having photographic brightness within 3 magnitudes of the brightest galaxy in the cluster.

Individual clusters are often designated by the equatorial coordinates of their centers; an example is Cl 1215.6 +3025, where the first number is the right ascension in hours and minutes, and the second is the declination in degrees and minutes. Some of the more prominent clusters, such as the Virgo cluster, are also designated by the names of the constellations in which they appear.

A *compact cluster* in the catalog has a single concentration of galaxies that appear close together in the photographs. An example is the Coma Berenices cluster; it has a membership of 9000 galaxies and a preponderance of S0 galaxies, especially in its densest central region. A *medium compact cluster* has either a single concentration where the galaxies are separated by several of their diameters, or else a number of pronounced concentrations. The Virgo cluster

FIG. 18·10. Part of Cluster of Galaxies in Coma Berenices. (*Mount Wilson and Palomar Observatories photograph*)

is an example; it has many spiral and giant elliptical galaxies. An *open cluster* has no outstanding concentration. An example is the Ursa Major cluster, which includes the great spirals M 81 and M 101.

18·11. S0 Galaxies in the Clusters. The more compact clusters, especially near their centers, contain many S0 galaxies. These differ from the lenses of the E7 ellipticals in distribution of the brightness in their disks and in their greater flattening. The frequency of such objects in the crowded regions is taken to mean that they were formerly spirals, from which the arms were removed by collisions with other galaxies. The gas and dust of the arms were swept away in the collisions, and in the turmoil the spiral structure was disrupted.

Calculation shows that a galaxy moving radially near the center of the dense Coma cluster may collide with other members from 5 to 30 times during the possible lifetime of the cluster. Large quantities of hydrogen gas dispersed through this cluster are recorded with the radio telescope. This explanation of the S0 galaxies is strengthened by the observation of galaxies in actual collision.

18·12. Colliding Galaxies. Two interpenetrating galaxies are revealed in a photograph with the 200-inch telescope close to the strong double source of radio emission, Cygnus A (17·12). Although

Fig. 18·12. Colliding Galaxies, NGC 5128. (*Mount Wilson and Palomar Observatories photograph*)

the connection is not clearly explained, the finding of this counterpart of a discrete radio source promoted the optical search for and the discovery of other examples. NGC 1275, the brightest member of a cluster of galaxies in Perseus, consists of a loose spiral that has sliced through a more tightly wound spiral with a relative speed of 750 miles a second. NGC 5128 (Fig. 18·12) appears to be a central collision between an edgewise spiral and a large S0 galaxy.

Another remarkable feature is presented by the colliding galaxies NGC 4038 and 4039; this, however, is not a strong radio source. Long tidal filaments, evidently debris of the encounter, appear above and below the combined central regions. F. Zwicky has found many long luminous "bridges" between double and multiple galaxies in photographs with the 48-inch Schmidt telescope. E. F. Carpenter has observed several shorter intergalactic bridges in his photographs and has noted nebular emission in the spectra of some of them.

18·13. Novae in Exterior Galaxies. Novae flare out in the exterior galaxies, as they do in our own (13·19). They are of two general types, normal novae and supernovae, with respect to the order of luminosity they attain.

FIG. 18·13. Supernova in the Spiral NGC 4725. (*Mount Wilson Observatory photographs*)

Normal novae resemble the usual ones of our galaxy in their greater abundance and their lower luminosities at maxima. Surveys of many of these novae in the spiral M 31, reported by Hubble in 1929 and by H. C. Arp in 1956, reveal their characteristics more clearly with the elimination of the distance factor. Arp concludes that about 26 normal novae flare out annually in the Andromeda spiral; one fourth of these are likely to be concealed by the dust clouds of this galaxy or in its brighter regions. The absolute magnitudes at the maxima ranged from −6.2 to −8.5.

Supernovae attain much higher luminosities and are less frequent. These spectacular outbursts of the more massive stars occur in a

single galaxy only once in several centuries. They are most likely
to be detected in repeated photographs of clusters of galaxies.
Minkowski has divided supernovae into two groups. In his *group I*
they rise to absolute magnitude −15.5, or 200 million times as
luminous as the sun. The extreme width of the lines in their spectra
indicate the violence of the explosions. These supernovae are deficient in hydrogen. Examples are the supernova of 1940 in the
spiral galaxy NGC 4725 (Fig. 18·13) and the outburst associated
with the Crab nebula in our own galaxy. Supernovae of *group II*
attain maximum brightness equal to 20 million suns. They probably constitute the more numerous group, but being fainter are less
readily detected.

SPECTRA OF GALAXIES

The spectra are composites, as would be expected for assemblages
of stars of various spectral types. The lines are also widened and
weakened by the different radial velocities of the individual stars.
Doppler effects in the spectrum lines show the rotations of galaxies,
and redshifts of the lines increase as the distances of the galaxies
from us are greater.

18·14. New Classification of Galaxies. A reclassification, devised
by W. W. Morgan and explained by him in 1958, results from his
studies of composite spectra as well as direct photographs of many
galaxies. The principal feature of the new system is the idea that
the stellar populations are older as the galaxies are more highly
concentrated toward their centers. At one extreme are the slightly
concentrated irregular and Sc galaxies; their spectra contain strong
hydrogen lines characteristic of young blue stars of Baade's population I, and are designated as group a. At the other extreme are the
highly concentrated spirals and giant ellipticals; their spectra show
molecular bands characteristic of old yellow and red stars of population II, and are designated as group k.

Increasing central concentration of the galaxies is represented in
Morgan's system by a succession of groups: a, af, f, fg, g, gk, and k,
the lettering being in the same order as in the sequence of types of
stellar spectra. The particular population group for a galaxy is
followed by a capital letter denoting the form: S for normal spiral,
B for barred spiral, E for elliptical, and so on. Finally, a number

from 1 to 7 denotes the inclination to the plane of the sky, from flatwise, or nearly spherical, galaxies to edgewise presentation of flat objects. Thus the barred spiral NGC 1300, having rather small central concentration and young stellar population, is classified by Morgan as fB2. The normal spiral M 31, having high central concentration and an old population, is classed as kS5.

The population group assigned in each case is determined entirely by inspection of the central concentration of luminosity of the galaxy, but an equivalence with the spectral type is expected in the average. Such correspondence may provide significant data in studies of the evolution of galaxies.

18·15. Rotations Shown by the Spectra. The flattened forms of regular galaxies suggest that these galaxies are rotating. The character of the rotations may be determined from the spectra of spiral

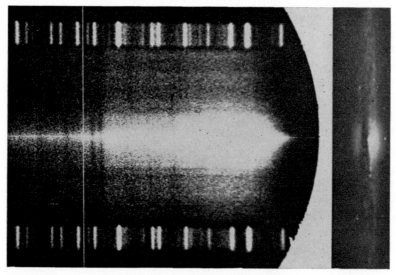

Fɪɢ. 18·15. Spectrum of Edgewise Spiral NGC 4565. The violet end of the spectrum is at the left. The slanting dark lines show that the upper part of the spiral is approaching and the lower part receding from us in the rotation. (*Photographed by N. U. Mayall, Lick Observatory*)

galaxies having their equators considerably inclined to the plane of the sky. When the slit of the spectroscope is placed along the major axis of the projected oval image of the spiral, the spectrum lines show Doppler displacements that depend on the direction of the rotation and its speed at different distances from the center of the spiral.

As an example of such spectroscopic studies, Mayall and Aller observed that the rotation period of the spiral M 33 is the same within 18′ from its center. In the outer parts, between 18′ and 30′ from the center, the period increases with increasing distance, as it does in the outer regions of our own galaxy (17·10). Hubble's conclusion that the arms of all spiral galaxies are trailing in the rotations has been verified wherever the evidence is available. Thus the spiral M 33 would be expected to rotate in the clockwise direction.

18·16. The Redshifts in the Spectra. A remarkable relation between the shifts of the spectrum lines and the distances of galaxies was announced in 1929 by Edwin Hubble. Having corrected the observed shifts of the lines for Doppler effects of the sun's motion in the rotation of our galaxy, Hubble found that the shifts are toward the red end of the spectrum and that they increase about linearly as the distances of the galaxies are greater. More extended investigations of the relation were reported in 1956 by Humason, Mayall, and Sandage. By this time the effect had been observed in the spectra of galaxies in 26 clusters and in hundreds of other galaxies.

From the relatively nearby Virgo cluster to the Hydra cluster at about the spectroscopic limit for the 200-inch telescope, the velocities of recession of the galaxies corresponding to the redshifts increase from 700 to 38,000 miles a second, or to one fifth the speed of light. With the distance scale then adopted, the increase is about 35 miles a second per 1 million light years. Although the redshifts for the most distant galaxies seem to be slightly greater than a linear relation would require, a definite conclusion is deferred until the spectra of still more remote galaxies can be photographed.

Another means of observing the relation between the redshifts and distances is by the resulting reddening of the galaxies. W. A. Baum's six-color measures of the energy curves of galaxies with a photon counter on the 200-inch telescope permit the calculation of the redshifts and the corresponding velocities of recession. His preliminary investigation of six clusters of galaxies ranges from the Virgo cluster to the cluster 1448, for which the velocity of recession is found to be 75,000 miles a second, or two fifths the speed of light. The points (Fig. 18·16A), representing the mean for the galaxies observed in each cluster, fall on a straight line.

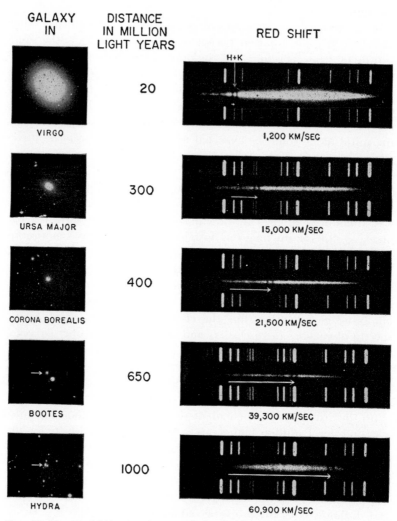

FIG. 18·16. Redshifts in the Spectra of Exterior Galaxies. The arrows
show the shifts of the H and K lines of calcium. The distances of the
galaxies are as assigned after the 1952 revision of the scale. (*Mount Wilson
and Palomar Observatories photographs*)

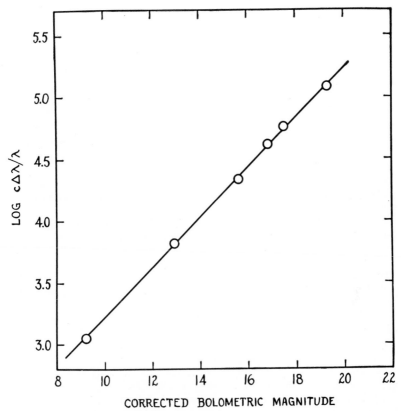

FIG. 18·16A. Velocity-Distance Relation for Six Clusters of Galaxies. From the relatively nearby Virgo cluster to the very remote cluster 1448. For the mean of the galaxies observed in each cluster the logarithm of the velocity of recession in kilometers is plotted against the bolometric magnitude, which is a function of the distance of the cluster. (*Diagram by William A. Baum, Mount Wilson and Palomar Observatories*)

18·17. The Expanding Universe. Regarded as Doppler effects, the redshifts in the spectra show that the galaxies are receding from us at a rate that increases in about a direct proportion to their distances from us. Presumably they are receding similarly from any other point in our region of space. The galaxies are separating; but the expansion does not operate within the individual galaxies or in the groups and clusters of galaxies.

A simple interpretation of the observed effect is that all the material in the visible universe was originally concentrated in a small volume of space from which the expansion began. When the character of the expansion is reliably determined, it should be possible to calculate the "age of the universe," that in the context would refer to the length of time in which the expansion has been in progress. This "age of the universe" refers to its duration from as far in the past as anything has been known about it.

QUESTIONS ON CHAPTER 18

1. Describe the three main types of galaxies, naming an example of each.

2. Distinguish between normal and barred spiral galaxies. Describe the division of each type into three classes.

3. Interpret the sequence of regular galaxies (Fig. 18·5) as a possible progression of evolution either from left to right or in the opposite direction.

4. State the reasons: (a) for multiplying original values of distances and dimensions of most galaxies by the factor 3; (b) for possible increase of this factor.

5. What is the significance of dark bands across spiral galaxies presented edgewise to us?

6. How could knowledge of our own galaxy be promoted by investigations of the great spiral in Andromeda?

7. Give reasons for supposing the S0 galaxies are formed by collisions of spiral galaxies.

8. Distinguish between normal novae and supernovae in exterior galaxies. Why are clusters of galaxies promising hunting grounds for supernovae?

9. The dark lines in the spectra of spiral galaxies are rather wide and are often slanting. Bright lines appear as well. Explain.

10. Describe the idea of the expanding universe. What is meant by the "age of the universe"?

REFERENCES

Gamow, George, *The Creation of the Universe*. The Viking Press, New York, 1952.

Hubble, Edwin P., *The Realm of the Nebulae*. Yale University Press, New Haven, 1936.

Shapley, Harlow, *Galaxies*. Harvard University Press, Cambridge, 1943.

Shapley, Harlow, *The Inner Metagalaxy*. Yale University Press, New Haven, 1957.

Current contributions to the literature of astronomy appear in periodicals, such as:

The Astronomical Journal. Published 10 times a year for the American Astronomical Society by the American Institute of Physics, 335 East 45th Street, New York 17.

The Astrophysical Journal. An International Review of Spectroscopy and Astronomical Physics. Published bimonthly. The University of Chicago Press, Chicago 37.

The Journal of the British Astronomical Association. Published 10 times a year. 303 Bath Road, Hounsley West, Middlesex, England.

The Journal of the Royal Astronomical Society of Canada. Published bimonthly. 252 College Street, Toronto, Ontario. The Society also publishes for each year *The Observer's Handbook,* a useful reference for astronomical data and events of the ensuing year.

Monthly Notices of the Royal Astronomical Society. Published monthly. Burlington House, London, W. 1.

The Observatory. A Review of Astronomy. Published monthly. The Editors, Royal Greenwich Observatory, Herstmonceux Castle, Hailsham, Sussex, England.

Publications of the Astronomical Society of the Pacific. Published bimonthly by the Society. Natural History Museum, Golden Gate Park, San Francisco 18. The Society also publishes monthly *Leaflets* written in popular style by various astronomers.

Scientific American. Contains frequent articles on astronomy and allied sciences. Published monthly by Scientific American, Inc., 2 West 45th Street, New York 36.

Sky and Telescope. Published monthly. Sky Publishing Corporation, Harvard Observatory, Cambridge 38, Massachusetts.

INDEX